INTRODUCTION
TO
PROJECTIVE GEOMETRY
AND
MODERN ALGEBRA

BY ROBERT A. ROSENBAUM, *Wesleyan University*

ADDISON-WESLEY PUBLISHING COMPANY, INC.
READING, MASSACHUSETTS · PALO ALTO · LONDON

This book is in the
ADDISON-WESLEY SERIES IN MATHEMATICS

PREFACE

The late nineteenth-century development of algebra and geometry was marked by continual interplay between the two subjects. Algebraic methods were applied to the study of geometry, and geometry was helpful in interpreting algebraic results. Indeed, many concepts now regarded as of primarily algebraic interest had their genesis in geometric problems, and today's "n-dimensional geometry" is a branch of algebra couched in geometric language solely for reasons of analogy. This book returns to the spirit of the historical development as providing a natural and effective approach to these topics, exploiting their relationships whenever possible.

This course is designed for undergraduates at a stage when it may bridge the gap between the usual intuitive introduction to calculus and the more rigorous and abstract treatment of advanced mathematics courses. For some students an abrupt change from "intuition" to "rigor" may be a traumatic experience, accentuated by instructions to *prove* theorems when it is not clear what one is permitted to *assume*. We attempt to effect a smooth transition from plausibility to proof, indicating at every stage our presuppositions and level of rigor. This is not, then, intended as a tightly organized presentation of projective geometry and linear algebra; other related topics of interest (e.g., groups) are included. Highly structured presentations have greater significance to a student already somewhat familiar with their subject matter. An acquaintance with the main concepts and methods of modern algebra and geometry is needed both by students who will go on to more specialized courses in these subjects and by those in other fields.

The starred exercises in the problem sets are not necessarily difficult. The star is used to indicate that the problem is especially significant, or that the result is likely to be encountered again later in the book. Hence all the starred problems should at least be read, if not worked.

There are many gaps in the textual exposition which are left to the reader to fill. Attention is called to such gaps by the reference, "See Problem 00 at the end of this section." The student is invited to attempt to fill the gap before turning to the cited problem at the end of the section. If he is unsuccessful, he may find a hint as to how to proceed by reading the

iii

cited problem, for such hints are given in the case of a number of nonroutine problems.

Serious use of this device can, we believe, encourage initiative in the student and give him both a firmer grasp of the material and greater enjoyment than would come from reading a presentation complete in every detail. Because of these features, the amount of material covered is some-what greater than the number of pages in the book may indicate.

Chapters 1, 2, and 3 may be covered as quickly or as slowly as the background and interests of the students dictate. For students with a substantial background in algebra, the main topics in the book can be covered in one semester. Most classes with little college experience in algebra and geometry (beyond analytic geometry) will find ample material for a full year course.

The idea for this book originated when I was a visiting professor at Swarthmore, many years ago. The initial drafts were written at Reed, during tenure of a fellowship of the Fund for the Advancement of Education. A Cottrell Grant from The Research Corporation and grants from the research funds of Wesleyan University were helpful in developing the manuscript. Colleagues at several colleges have made useful suggestions, have caught errors, and have offered interesting exercises; T. H. M. Cramp-ton, R. G. Long, A. P. Mattuck, G. M. Merriman, and Hing Tong should be especially mentioned. I owe thanks to all these individuals and institu-tions. But it transcends my power to express my indebtedness to my principal colleague—Louise Johnson Rosenbaum.

Middletown, Conn.   R. A. R.
January 1963

CONTENTS

v

CHAPTER 1

Geometrical Introduction (I)

Mathematics has been traditionally divided into three categories: geometry, algebra, and analysis. There are no clear-cut dividing lines separating these disciplines, and each is useful in, and in some instances essential to, the solving of problems in the other two fields. Some analysis (i.e., material concerned with limits and limiting processes) will appear in this book, but its role will be a subordinate one. Geometry and algebra will be presented as closely related subjects, each interesting in itself, each helpful in obtaining results and clarifying concepts in the other field, and both furnishing methods which can fruitfully be applied in the physical sciences, in engineering, and in some of the social sciences.

Of these three branches of mathematics, geometry has the longest history as a formal discipline. This first chapter will be devoted to reviewing some familiar subject matter and methods of geometry, and to introducing some new types of problems and new methods.

1–1 CLASSIFICATION OF GEOMETRIES

There are many sorts of geometries, with two principal modes of classification: by subject matter and by method. One division on the basis of subject matter, for example, is that between plane and solid geometry. More significant subject-matter divisions, giving rise to a "hierarchy" of geometries, will receive considerable attention in later chapters.

A classification on the basis of method, namely, the synthetic and the analytic, is familiar to all students, at least in fact if not by name. In the synthetic approach, the proof proceeds by logical argument to the desired conclusion from geometrical hypotheses and already proven theorems. In the analytic method, the geometrical data of the problem are translated into algebraic terms through the medium of a coordinate system, laws of algebra are utilized to transform the data and to draw (algebraic) conclusions from them, and finally the results are translated back into geometrical language, presumably as the desired result.

Two remarks should be made about the foregoing characterizations of the synthetic and analytic methods. (i) The analytic method has no necessary connection with "analysis," one of the three branches of mathematics mentioned in the introduction to this chapter. (ii) Deductive reasoning from hypothesis to conclusion is not restricted to synthetic geometry. A rigorous approach to analytic geometry would also start with axioms (synonyms: postulates, assumptions), permitting the translation from geometrical language to algebraic and back again, and justifying the algebraic manipulations which we perform. Indeed, the current view of mathematicians is that *every* mathematical system is one in which each conclusion is obtained by a chain of logical argument from certain axioms assumed at the start. The characteristic feature of "pure" synthetic geometry is that almost all axioms refer to geometrical entities, and that a coordinate system (with its attendant arithmetic and algebra) does not enter. More will be said about axiomatized systems in Section 2–1.

As an exercise in comparison of methods, we will sketch analytic and synthetic proofs that the altitudes of a triangle are concurrent. A set of lines is *concurrent* if all the lines of the set pass through one point. The point of concurrency of the altitudes is called the *orthocenter* of the triangle.

It will be especially instructive if you close the book before reading the outlines of proofs given below, and try to work out the analytic and synthetic proofs yourself.

Analytic. Let the vertices of the triangle be $A(a, 0)$, $B(b, 0)$, $C(0, c)$. Then the line BC has slope $-c/b$, and AC has slope $-c/a$. Hence the altitudes through A and B have slopes b/c and a/c, respectively. Therefore, the altitude through A has the equation $bx - cy = ab$, while the altitude through B has the equation $ax - cy = ab$. Solving these equations simultaneously gives $x = 0$ as the abscissa of the point of intersection of the altitudes through A and B. But the altitude through C clearly lies along the y-axis, i.e., the third altitude is the line $x = 0$. ☐

Synthetic. Through each of the vertices A, B, C of the given triangle, draw a line parallel to the opposite side of the triangle. In this way we construct a triangle, $A'B'C'$, say. The altitudes of ABC are the perpendicular bisectors of the sides of $A'B'C'$. But the perpendicular bisectors of the sides of a triangle are known to meet in a point (the center of the circumscribed circle, or *circumcenter*, of the triangle). ☐

Comments. (i) The position of the coordinate axes relative to the triangle is virtually standard; any student, after only a brief introduction to analytic geometry, would make the choice suggested above, or another equally convenient. After the axes have been chosen, the rest of the analytic procedure is also standard.

But there is a trick to the synthetic proof. An individual might be quite experienced, ingenious, and perceptive, and still not hit upon the easy approach.

This is a common situation; the synthetic method often requires considerable ingenuity and power of visualization on the part of the student, while the analytic method, once a convenient position has been chosen for the coordinate axes, usually proceeds in fairly routine fashion. The synthetic method often provides a short and elegant proof if essential features are noted and correctly interpreted, or if appropriate construction lines are drawn. The analytic method has the advantage of being "sure," albeit sometimes "slow."

(ii) Note that both proofs involve much background material. To consider only one item of the analytic proof, we observe that the formula for the slope of a line comes from the concept of similar triangles. Likewise, one step of the synthetic proof is based on the concurrency of the perpendicular bisectors of the sides of a triangle, an easily obtained result, usually proved early in a geometry course.

PROBLEM SET 1–1

Try each of the following problems by both the synthetic and the analytic methods. In some cases one of the methods will prove to be decidedly simpler than the other.

1. Prove that the diagonals of a parallelogram bisect each other, and the converse.

2. Prove that the medians of a triangle meet in a point (called the *centroid* of the triangle) which is two-thirds the distance from each vertex to the midpoint of the opposite side.

*3. Prove that the bisectors of the angles of a triangle are concurrent. (The point of concurrency is the center of the inscribed circle, abbreviated "incenter.")

*4. Let A_1, A_2, A_3, A_4, P, Q be 6 distinct points on a circle. Show that

$$\frac{\sin \angle A_3 P A_1}{\sin \angle A_3 P A_2} \cdot \frac{\sin \angle A_4 P A_2}{\sin \angle A_4 P A_1} = \frac{\sin \angle A_3 Q A_1}{\sin \angle A_3 Q A_2} \cdot \frac{\sin \angle A_4 Q A_2}{\sin \angle A_4 Q A_1}.$$

5. Let A, B, C, D be any four points, not all on one line and not necessarily all lying in a plane. Let P, Q, R, S be the midpoints of the segments AB, BC, CD, DA, respectively. What can be said about the figure $PQRS$?

6. (a) Suppose that a variable line through a fixed point P meets a fixed circle in A and B. The point P may be inside, on, or outside the circle. Show that the product $PA \cdot PB$ is constant.

(b) If P is outside the circle, with a tangent from P touching the circle at T, show that $PA \cdot PB = PT^2$.

7. Given a fixed line l and a fixed point A not on l. Point P moves so that its distance from l always equals the distance AQ, where Q is the foot of the perpendicular dropped from P to l. What is the locus of P?

8. (a) In a plane, what is the locus of a point, the sum of the squares of whose distances from two fixed points is constant?

(b) Same as (a), in three dimensions.

9. What is the locus of the midpoint of a line segment of constant length whose end points move on two fixed intersecting perpendicular lines?

10. (a) Show that the locus of the midpoint of a line segment of constant length whose end points move on two fixed intersecting nonperpendicular lines is an ellipse.

(b) What is the locus of a point which divides a line segment of length l in the ratio $r: (l - r)$ if the ends of the line segment move on two fixed, intersecting lines?

(c) Show that in 9(b), the locus is a circle if and only if the lines are perpendicular and $r = l/2$.

11. What is the locus of the midpoint of a line segment of constant length whose endpoints move on two fixed, perpendicular, nonintersecting lines?

12. Show that in a plane, the locus of the center of a circle tangent to two fixed unequal circles which are external to each other consists of both branches of two hyperbolas whose foci are the centers of the fixed circles.

13. Let A, B, C, D be consecutive vertices of a parallelogram and let X, Y be arbitrary points on AB, CD, respectively.

(a) Let AY and DX meet at P, and BY and CX meet at Q. Show that the line PQ bisects the area of the parallelogram.

(b) Let AY and CX meet at R; BY and DX meet at S. What can be said about the line RS?

14. Let D be an arbitrary point of the altitude AH of triangle ABC. Let BD meet AC at E, and CD meet AB at F. Show that angle AHE equals angle AHF. Are there any cases which need special treatment? (From a Putnam Prize Exam.)

15. Prove that, if two medians of a triangle are equal in length, then the triangle is isosceles.

16. In triangle ABC (Fig. 1–1), AD and BE meet on the bisector of angle C, and $AD = BE$. Show that the triangle is isosceles.

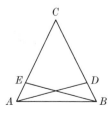

FIGURE 1–1

17. In triangle ABC with $AC = AB$, let D be the midpoint of BC, let E be the foot of the perpendicular from D to AC, and let F be the midpoint of DE. Show that AF is perpendicular to BE. (From *The American Mathematical Monthly*.)

18. In triangle ABC, D lies on BC and E on AC. $AC = BC$, the measure of angle C is 20°, that of angle DAB is 50°, and that of angle EBA is 60°. Prove that the measure of angle DEB is 30°.

*19. The points P, Q, R, S lie on the sides AB, BC, CD, DA of the quadrilateral $ABCD$. Show that if PQ and RS meet on AC, then PS and QR meet on BD.

20. Given a triangle ABC and a point P not on any side of the triangle. Let M_1, M_2, M_3 be the centroids of triangles PAB, PBC, PCA. Prove that for a fixed triangle ABC and for the position of P arbitrary, the triangle $M_1M_2M_3$ has a fixed size and shape. Does P have to be in the plane of triangle ABC? Can you describe the size and location of triangle $M_1M_2M_3$ relative to the size and location of triangle ABC?

21. (a) In triangle ABC, let P, Q, R be points on AB, BC, CA such that $AP/AB = \frac{1}{3} = BQ/BC = CR/CA$. Show that the area of the triangle whose sides are CP, AQ, BR is $\frac{1}{7}$ the area of triangle ABC.

(b) If the fraction $\frac{1}{3}$ in part (a) is changed to $1/n$, what does the fraction $\frac{1}{7}$ become?

22. (a) Suppose that a secant l meets a circle in A and B, the midpoint of the chord AB being M. Let P_1Q_1 and P_2Q_2 be chords of the circle through M. Suppose that P_1Q_2 and P_2Q_1 meet l in G and H, respectively, and that P_1P_2 and Q_1Q_2 meet l in R and S, respectively. Show that $MG = MH$ and that $MR = MS$. (Brooks)

(b) With reference to part (a), let the tangents at P_1 and Q_1 meet l in U and V. Show that $MU = MV$. (Morgan)

23. Given a parallelogram $ABCD$ with a circle passing through A. Let the circle meet AB, AC, AD in P, Q, R, respectively. Prove that $AB \cdot AP + AD \cdot AR = AC \cdot AQ$. (Morgan)

24. In Fig. 1–2, PX and PY are the tangents to the circle from the arbitrary point P; XY is also tangent to the circle (at A), and AB is a diameter of the circle. Show that $XC = YA$. Is your proof valid for all positions of P outside the circle? (Morgan)

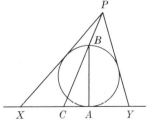

FIGURE 1–2

*25. In a plane, l, l', m are three concurrent lines, and O, P are two points not lying on any of the lines. To each point X of l we make correspond the point X' of l' such that OX and PX' meet on m. Show that all the lines XX' are concurrent at a point Q. What can be said about the location of Q?

*26. Let the circles $\mathfrak{C}_1$, $\mathfrak{C}_2$ intersect in P, P'; circles $\mathfrak{C}_2$, $\mathfrak{C}_3$ intersect in Q, Q'; and circles $\mathfrak{C}_3$, $\mathfrak{C}_1$ intersect in R, R'. Show that the lines PP', QQ', RR' are concurrent. Must the circles all lie in one plane?

27. *Definition.* Two lines are *skew* if they do not lie in a plane.

(a) Let l, m be skew lines, with P, Q any points on l, and P', Q' any points on m. Show that the lines PP', QQ' are skew.

(b) Let each pair of lines: l, m; m, n; n, l be skew. Are there lines which intersect all three lines l, m, n? Describe fully.

1–2 "MODERN" GEOMETRY

The theorems used in the foregoing set of problems are all standard results of Euclidean geometry, the sort of propositions known to the Greeks over 2000 years ago and proved by them by the synthetic method. Virtually no advance over the geometry of the Greeks was made until the introduction of the analytic method (Descartes, 1637).

The preceding sentences represent an oversimplification of the situation. Some of the Greek geometers used a sort of coordinate system, but not in a systematic fashion, probably because of their poorly developed algebraic notation.

"Descartes' merits," writes Struik in his book, *A Concise History of Mathematics*, "lie above all in his consistent application of the well developed algebra of the early Seventeenth Century to the geometrical analysis of the Ancients, and, by this, in an enormous widening of its applicability . . . the first analytic geometry of conic sections which is fully emancipated from Apollonios appeared only with Euler's *Introductio* (1748)."

Analytic geometry permitted easy and systematic study of the conic sections (which had already been investigated by the Greeks by what we now consider laborious methods) and also of some higher plane curves, such as the cycloid, the cissoid, the conchoid, and the limaçon, some of which likewise had been studied by the Greeks.

After the introduction of analytic geometry, its methods became standard for certain work in astronomy, but enthusiasm for geometry as a subject for study again subsided until the 18th and 19th centuries. The revival took several forms: the development of new geometries (i.e., of new subject matter) some of which will be treated in this book; a marked extension of analytic geometry with the introduction of algebraic methods different from and supplementary to those of Descartes (this will be an important concern for us); and a renewal of interest in the methods and general subject matter of Euclid, leading to the discovery of many beautiful theorems (principally relating to simple figures like the triangle and the circle) which had not been suspected by the Greeks or by any mathematicians in the intervening 2000 years.

Listed below are a few of the many theorems discovered in the 18th and 19th centuries. (Some of them had also been known to the Greeks.) These particular theorems have been selected because of their relationship to each other and to other theorems of more general nature, which will appear later in our work. It is suggested that you attempt to prove them, by synthetic or analytic means. If you are unsuccessful, look up a proof in one of the texts listed after the problems. (It will be surprising if you succeed in proving more than a few of these theorems, but you should at least understand their statements.)

PROBLEM SET 1–2

1. The circumcenter, the orthocenter, and the centroid of a triangle are collinear. (A set of points is *collinear* if all the points of the set lie on a straight line.) The distance from the centroid to the orthocenter is equal to twice the distance from the centroid to the circumcenter. (Euler line, 18th century)

2. Let R be the radius of the circumscribed circle of a triangle, r the radius of the inscribed circle, and d the distance between the circumcenter and the incenter. Then (Euler, 18th century)

$$\frac{1}{R+d} + \frac{1}{R-d} = \frac{1}{r}.$$

*3. The lines joining the vertices of a triangle (Fig. 1–3) to a given point not on the sides of the triangle determine on the sides of the triangle six segments such that the product of three nonconsecutive segments is equal to the product of the remaining three (Ceva, 17th century):

$$AC' \cdot BA' \cdot CB' = C'B \cdot A'C \cdot B'A \qquad \text{or} \qquad \frac{AC'}{C'B} \cdot \frac{BA'}{A'C} \cdot \frac{CB'}{B'A} = 1.$$

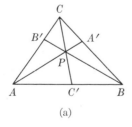

(a)

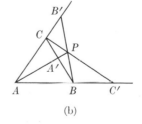

(b)

FIGURE 1–3

*4. *Discussion of directed distances.* It is often convenient to choose one of the two "senses" on a line as *positive*, in which case the opposite sense is *negative*. Thus, if the arrowhead denotes the positive sense in Fig. 1–4, AB is positive and CB is negative. Whichever is the choice of positive sense on the line, if B is the midpoint of the segment AC, then $CA/AB = -2$. With this convention for directed distances, it is possible to state the following converse of Ceva's theorem.

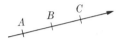

FIGURE 1–4

Given a triangle ABC with A', B', C' on BC, CA, AB, respectively, such that $AC' \cdot BA' \cdot CB' = C'B \cdot A'C \cdot B'A$, where the equality is valid both in magnitude and in sign. Then AA', BB', CC' are concurrent.

*5. Let a transversal t meet the sides BC, CA, AB of triangle ABC in A', B', C'. Then, considering directed distances (Menelaus, 1st century, A.D.)

$$AC' \cdot BA' \cdot CB' = -C'B \cdot A'C \cdot B'A, \qquad \text{or} \qquad \frac{AC'}{C'B} \cdot \frac{BA'}{A'C} \cdot \frac{CB'}{B'A} = -1.$$

*6. Given a triangle ABC with A', B', C' on BC, CA, AB, respectively, such that $AC' \cdot BA' \cdot CB' = -C'B \cdot A'C \cdot B'A$. Then A', B', C' are collinear. (Converse of Menelaus' theorem)

Each of the theorems of Problems 7 through 11 can be treated as a corollary of the converse of Ceva's theorem.

7. The medians of a triangle are concurrent.

8. The internal angle bisectors of a triangle are concurrent.

9. The altitudes of a triangle are concurrent.

10. The lines joining each of the vertices of a triangle to the point of contact on the opposite side of the inscribed circle are concurrent. (Gergonne, 19th century)

11. (a) *Definition.* An *escribed circle* (or, *excircle*) of a triangle is a circle tangent to one side of the triangle between the vertices and to the other two sides produced. (There are, then, three escribed circles of a given triangle.)

The lines joining the vertices of a triangle to the points of contact of the opposite sides, with the excircles relative to those sides, are concurrent. (Nagel, 19th century)

(b) Show that the Nagel point can also be described as the point of intersection of lines joining each vertex of a triangle to the point "halfway around the perimeter" of the triangle.

Each of the theorems of Problems 12 through 15 can be treated as a corollary of the converse of Menelaus' theorem.

12. The external angle bisectors of a triangle meet the opposite sides in three collinear points.

13. Two interior angle bisectors and the bisector of the exterior angle at the third vertex meet their respective opposite sides in collinear points.

14. The tangents to the circumcircle of a triangle at its vertices meet the opposite sides of the triangle in three collinear points. What can be said concerning the special cases involving parallelism?

15. (a) Let A, B, C be three points of a line l, and X, Y, Z three points on another line m, coplanar with l. Then the points of intersection of AY and XB, of AZ and XC, and of BZ and YC are collinear. (Theorem of Pappus, 4th century, or Pascal, 17th century)

(b) Can you use the result of (a) to solve easily Problem 13 (a), Section 1-1?

16. (a) In a given plane, let A, B, C be fixed collinear points, and l, m fixed lines. Let x, y, z be lines through A, B, C, respectively, with x and y meeting on l, and y and z meeting on m. Show that the locus of the intersection of z and x is a line. (Euclid)

(b) Same as part (a), except that A, B, C are *not* collinear. Then the locus of the intersection of z and x is a conic. (Maclaurin, 18th century)

(c) Generalization of part (a): In a given plane, let A_1, A_2, ..., A_n be fixed collinear points, and l_1, l_2, ..., l_{n-1} be fixed lines. Let x_1, x_2, ..., x_n be lines through A_1, A_2, ..., A_n, respectively, with x_1 and x_2 meeting on l_1, x_2, and x_3 meeting on l_2, ..., x_{n-1}, and x_n meeting on l_{n-1}. Show that the locus of the intersection of each pair not already mentioned is a line. (Pappus)

(d) Obtain a result related to part (c) as part (b) is related to part (a).

The following references may be helpful.

N. A. Court, *College Geometry.* New York: Barnes and Noble, Inc., 1952.

R. A. Johnson, *Advanced Euclidean Geometry.* New York: Dover Publications, 1929.

D. J. Struik, *A Concise History of Mathematics.* New York: Dover Publications, 1948.

Drawings of the figures associated with the foregoing theorems will impress a reader with the simplicity and beauty of the results, and a study of the proofs of the theorems will probably impress him with their difficulty and diversity. The traditional methods of elementary geometry are not sufficient for easy handling of such material. More than that, the traditional methods do not lay bare certain *essential relationships* of configurations, of which the results of the foregoing theorems are merely special cases.

This book is devoted to the elucidation of methods which are powerful in bringing to the fore some of the basic features of geometry and algebra, and in obtaining and proving results economically. This presentation begins in Chapter 4; the remainder of Chapter 1 and Chapter 2 involve an informal discussion of various topics to be included in the subsequent systematic development, and Chapter 3 sets forth material, mainly of an algebraic nature, which is required as background for our later work and which is highly significant in its own right.

1–3 THE NOTION OF PROJECTION

Consider the situation pictured in Fig. 1–5: one ellipse E_1 outside another E_2. If we should start with an arbitrary point P on E_1, draw a tangent to E_2 meeting E_1 in Q, from Q draw another tangent to E_2 meeting E_1 in R, and then join R and P by a straight line, we would consider it unlikely that RP would be tangent to E_2. Or, to put it another way, for two ellipses, one within the other, there is usually no triangle inscribed in one of the ellipses and circumscribed about the other.

Now consider Fig. 1–6, consisting of the equilateral triangle ABC, its circumcircle K_1, and its incircle K_2. If we think of this figure as lying

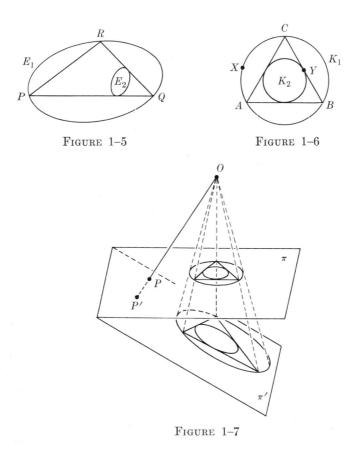

FIGURE 1–5   FIGURE 1–6

FIGURE 1–7

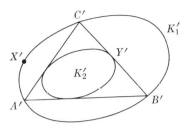

FIGURE 1–8

in a plane π, and "projected" onto the plane π' from the "center of projection," O (Fig. 1–7), we obtain the configuration shown in Fig. 1–8. A *projection* from a plane π onto a plane π' from a *center of projection*, O, not on π or π', is a transformation whereby a point P of π is carried into the point P' in which the line OP pierces π'. An arbitrary point, such as X, of K_1 is taken by the projection into a point X' of π', so that K_1 as a whole is projected into an oval curve K_1', which can be shown to be an ellipse. Likewise K_2 is projected into an ellipse K_2'. The vertices A, B, C of the equilateral triangle are projected into A', B', C' in plane π'; since A, B, C lie on K_1, A', B', C' lie on the ellipse K_1', but triangle $A'B'C'$ is generally not equilateral. Any point of the straight line AB is carried into a point of the straight line $A'B'$ (why?); i.e., straight lines are projected into straight lines. Moreover, since the line BC, for example, is tangent to K_2, the line $B'C'$ is tangent to the ellipse K_2'. To demonstrate this, we may argue as follows: The point of tangency, Y, of BC with K_2 is projected into the point Y' which lies on both $B'C'$ and K_2'. Suppose that $B'C'$ had another point, say Z', in common with K_2'. This point would be the projection of a point, Z say, which would lie on both BC and K_2. But BC, being tangent to K_2, has no point other than Y in common with it. Hence $B'C'$ has no point other than Y' in common with K_2'.

We are appealing here to an intuitive characteristic of tangents to circles and ellipses. For some other curves we cannot say that a tangent is a line which meets the curve in just one point, so that this type of argument will be inadequate in our subsequent more rigorous presentation. But it will suffice for the present informal discussion.

By the process of projection from the center O, we have transformed the configuration of Fig. 1–6 into that of Fig. 1–8, thus obtaining two (particular) ellipses such that a triangle *can* be inscribed in the one and circumscribed about the other. We can say more than this. By the symmetry of Fig. 1–6, it is clear that any point of K_1 could have been chosen as a vertex of an equilateral triangle inscribed in K_1 and circumscribed about K_2. Hence, by the same projection, we conclude that *any* point on the ellipse K_1' can be taken as one vertex of a triangle inscribed in K_1' and circumscribed about K_2'; i.e., if we start with any point P on K_1' in Fig. 1–8, draw a tangent to K_2' meeting K_1' again in Q; from Q draw another tangent to K_2' meeting K_1' again in R; from R draw another tangent to K_2', then this last tangent will meet K_1' in the starting point P.

Had we started with a regular n-gon (polygon of n sides), its circumcircle, and its incircle, the same process of projection would have led us to a special case of a theorem due to J. V. Poncelet (1788–1867).

Theorem. If two conics C_1 and C_2 are such that an n-gon can be inscribed in C_1 and circumscribed about C_2, then there are infinitely many n-gons in the same relationship to the conics, with any point on C_1 serving as a vertex of an n-gon.

Our foregoing development does not prove Poncelet's theorem in general, for the incircle and the circumcircle of a regular n-gon are concentric, and not all pairs of conics of the theorem are obtainable by projection from two concentric circles. Nevertheless, by projection, we do obtain quite easily at least a limited result, and from this example we can get a feeling for the subject matter of *projective geometry*. Those properties of a configuration which are preserved by all projections are known as projective properties, and theorems involving only projective properties form the body of projective geometry.

From this definition it follows that a projective theorem about a certain configuration remains a true theorem relative to a projection of that configuration.

For example, in Fig. 1–6, the following are projective properties: X lies on curve K_1; C is the point of intersection of the lines AC and BC; AB is a straight line; and BC is the tangent line to curve K_2 at point Y. The following is *not* a projective property: "K_1 is a circle," for we know that K_1 can be carried by projection into an ellipse. Likewise, the following are not projective properties (referring again to Fig. 1–6): ABC is equilateral; angle CAB equals 60°; Y is the midpoint of BC. Note that all the items of this list of nonprojective properties involve magnitudes of lengths and angles. Such "metric" properties are the concern of traditional elementary geometry.

The situation may be loosely described by stating that metric geometry treats of more highly restricted properties than those of projective geometry. Indeed, as will be seen later there are many geometries "between" metric geometry and projective geometry, i.e., there are geometries which deal with properties less restrictive than metric, but more restrictive than projective properties.

1–4 CRITIQUE OF SECTION 1–3

Fundamentally, the arguments advanced in Section 1–3 require a projection to be a "one-to-one correspondence." That is, to each point U of plane π (Fig. 1–9) there corresponds exactly one point U' of plane π', viz., the point in which the line OU meets π'; and, to each point V' of plane π', there corresponds the unique point V in which the line OV' meets plane π. Note that the "forward correspondence" (from π to π') was used, for example, in arguing that the projection of C lies on both the projection of K_1 and the projection of AC; while the "backward correspondence" (from π' to π) was used in arguing that $B'C'$ is tangent to K_2'. But things really are not so simple. If there is a point X on the circle K_1 such that OX is parallel to π' (Fig. 1–10), then there will be no point of π' corresponding to X of π. (If there is one such point X of K_1, it can be shown that the projection of K_1 is a parabola. If there are two points X, Y of K_1, such that OX and OY are both parallel to π' (Fig. 1–11), then it can be shown that the projection of K_1 is an hyperbola.)

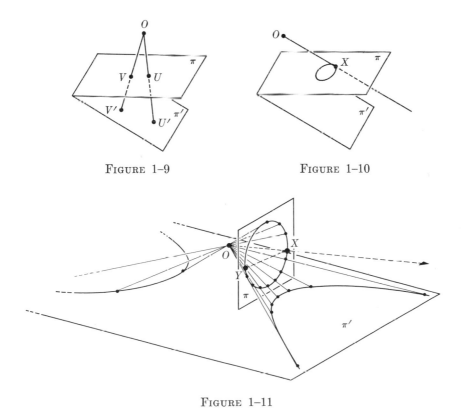

FIGURE 1–9   FIGURE 1–10

FIGURE 1–11

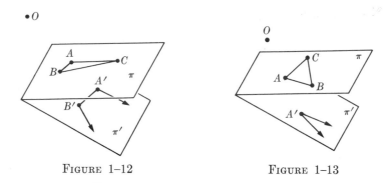

FIGURE 1–12   FIGURE 1–13

If the vertex C of the triangle were in such a position that OC was parallel to π', then the projection of triangle ABC would appear as in Fig. 1–12. If both B and C were in such position that OB and OC were parallel to π', then the projection of triangle ABC would appear as in Fig. 1–13.

These illustrations indicate that in ordinary geometry our definition of a projective property is not very useful. Recalling that the definition on p. 12 called for properties preserved under *all* projections, we see that in truth, "X lies on K_1" is *not* a projective property in our ordinary space. For, if we consider the projection pictured in Fig. 1–10, X does not even have a correspondent X' in plane π'.

In all the illustrated cases, and in some more as well (see the problems below), we do not have the basic "one-to-one correspondence" which we would like, as things stand.

Indeed, there is only one situation in which a projection does establish a one-to-one correspondence between *all* the points of one plane of ordinary space and all the points of another: that in which the two planes are parallel. For all other relative positions of π and π', a projection does not establish a one-to-one correspondence. This deficiency would constitute a serious blow to the usefulness of the notion of projection if a remedy could not be found. There *is* a remedy, as will be described in the next section.

PROBLEM SET 1–4

*1. The two-dimensional analogue of the projections described in Sections 1–3 and 1–4 is as follows: Given two coplanar lines l, l' and a center of projection O in the plane of the lines but not on either line (Fig. 1–14), the projection of a point P on l is the point P' in which OP meets l'. The point, M, common to l and l', corresponds to itself in the projection and is known as the *self-corresponding point* of the projection.

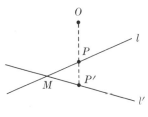

FIGURE 1–14

(a) The correspondence is not "one to one without exception." For what points does it fail?

(b) In what situation does a projection of one line onto another fail to have a self-corresponding point?

(c) What are the self-corresponding points of a projection of one plane onto another?

2. Suppose that in projecting a triangle ABC of plane π to plane π' it happens that there is a point X on the segment AB and a point Y on the segment AC such that OX and OY are parallel to π'. Draw the projection of ABC on π' in this case.

1–5 IDEAL ELEMENTS

The difficulty described in Section 1–4 stems from the fact that, in the space of ordinary Euclidean geometry, parallel lines have no common point. For this reason we add "ideal points," or "points at infinity" to the set of "ordinary points." How many ideal points should we add? The answer to this question is determined by our basic purpose: to eliminate exceptional cases whenever possible. Since two nonparallel lines in a plane have precisely one common point, we make the convention that two parallel lines also have one common point, which we call an ideal point. Moreover, we assume that parallel lines all intersect in the same ideal point. Thus we make the convention that there is *one ideal point for each direction*. [This convention is rendered schematically in Fig. 1–15. It should be observed that on each line (in each direction) there is just *one* ideal point. We do *not* say that there is an ideal point at each "end" of

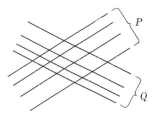

FIGURE 1–15

a line (for each "sense" of a given direction)]. Indeed, we make the same assumption for three dimensions as for two: every line in space contains one ideal point, and all lines in a given direction have the same ideal point in common.

With this agreement, we can replace the statement: (a) "Two distinct lines in a plane either have one and only one point in common or are parallel," by (b) "Two distinct lines in a plane have one and only one point in common."

Two nonparallel lines intersect in an "ordinary" point; two parallel lines, in an "ideal" point.

Questions probably arise immediately in your mind: "What right have we arbitrarily to add points to space? And, even if we may be permitted to do so, must we not differentiate between the "ordinary" points, which we can see as dots on the paper, and the "ideal" points, which are constructs of our imagination?"

To answer these questions, we must analyze the nature of geometry as a mathematical system. Although it is true that the subject grew out of our experience with physically perceived objects (table tops, stretched strings, dots of various sorts, etc.), geometry is not a study of these objects. Rather it deals with planes, straight lines, and points. These are entities about which certain assumptions (axioms, postulates) are made but which are otherwise undefined. Hence, we can give the name "point" to anything which conforms to our postulates about points and which suits our convenience to designate as "point." In short, *all* our geometry (indeed, *all* our mathematics) deals with constructs of our imagination; and an "ideal" point is on precisely the same footing, from this point of view, as an "ordinary" point.

This, however, is not the whole story. Our mathematical systems should be *self-consistent*. In particular, if we have an apparently consistent system (like the geometry of "ordinary" points), we should check, when we extend the system (by adding "ideal" points), that the extended system is also consistent. It turns out that the postulates embodied in our convention in Section 1–5, and also in the second and third conventions, which are about to be introduced, are consistent with the postulates of "ordinary" geometry, to which they are appended; but no attempt will be made to justify this assertion now. The study of consistency, important as it is, would take us too far afield.

The creation of ideal points and the convention that there is one ideal point corresponding to each direction in space are not sufficient to obtain the desired one-to-one correspondence in a projection. We stated, in Section 1–3, that a projection carries a straight line into a straight line; but we saw in the case illustrated by Fig. 1–13 that the straight line *BC* of plane π has no correspondent in plane π'. According to the convention we have made, the *points* of *BC* correspond to the ideal points of π'; hence we make a second convention: that the ideal points of a plane constitute a straight line called *the ideal line of the plane*.

It turns out to be useful to make a third convention: the ideal points of three-dimensional space constitute a plane, called *the ideal plane*.

In three-space, the points common to the ideal plane and an ordinary plane π constitute the ideal line of π.

With these conventions, we may now make the following statements.

(1) Under central projection from one plane π to a second plane π' there is a one-to-one correspondence between points and a one-to-one correspondence between lines.

(2) In a plane, under central projection from one line l to a second line l', there is a one-to-one correspondence between points.

(3) In three-dimensional space, any two distinct planes intersect in a unique line.

(4) In a plane, any two distinct lines intersect in a unique point.

Each of statements (1) through (4) represents a consolidation of cases which would have to be considered separately without the agreements about ideal points. There is still another consolidation possible.

In "parallel projection" from π to π' (Fig. 1–16), P', Q', R', ... are obtained as the points in which lines parallel to some fixed direction and passing through P, Q, R, ... of π meet π'. "Orthogonal projection" is the parallel projection in which the fixed direction is perpendicular to π'. We can readily see that parallel (including orthogonal) projection is a case of central projection in which the center of projection is an ideal point.

The space of ordinary points, lines, and planes is called ordinary space; that of the ordinary *and* ideal points, lines, and planes is called "extended space." Analogously, in two dimensions, we speak of the "ordinary plane" and the "extended plane."

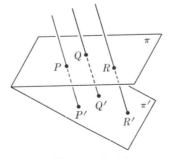

FIGURE 1–16

PROBLEM SET 1–5

1. Describe any particular features of statement (1) in each of the following cases:

(a) when π' is the ideal plane,

(b) when π is the ideal plane,

(c) when π and π' are parallel, and O is an ordinary point,

(d) when π and π' are parallel, and O is an ideal point,

(e) when π and π' are parallel, and O is the ideal point in the direction perpendicular to that of π and π'.

2. Give the analogue of statement (2) for each of parts (a) through (e) of Problem 1.

3. What particular feature is involved in statement (3) when the planes are parallel?

4. What points or lines may be common to three distinct planes? Describe carefully and completely the different cases which can occur.

5. Which of the following are projective properties of the figure described?

(a) $ABCD$ is a parallelogram; a rhombus; a quadrilateral.

(b) The points A, B, C are distinct; collinear.

(c) The point B lies on the line segment AC.

(d) For the collinear points A, B, C, the length of segment AB equals the length of segment BC.

(e) The curve E is an ellipse.

6. For those nonprojective cases in Problem 5, state which of the properties are preserved under parallel projection.

7. Why is it appropriate for our purposes to assume that a family of parallel lines in a plane has a single common point, rather than that each pair of lines of the family has a different common point from every other pair? [*Hint:* Consider the projection of a family of lines through a single "ordinary" point.]

CHAPTER 2

Geometrical Introduction (II)

We continue our study of geometric concepts basic to our further work, turning now to the analytic method. This method will itself be extended over that which is familiar in elementary geometry in order to deal effectively with the "extended space" of Chapter 1, and this space will be still further extended. You will note that the underlying motive for these various extensions is the removal of exceptional cases. To illustrate this point, the circle is discussed in considerable detail, although the corresponding treatment of the conics in general is left to our later systematic development.

2–1 HOMOGENEOUS COORDINATES

In the familiar analytic geometry of the plane, we deal with ordered pairs of real numbers (x, y), which correspond only to ordinary points of the plane. If we wish to use comparable algebraic methods to work with the extended plane, we must invent a new algebraic representation for the purpose. This we may do as follows. Let us consider a line through the origin and the point (x, y) (Fig. 2–1). The points $(2x, 2y)$, $(5x, 5y)$, $(100x, 100y)$, ... all lie on this line and may be represented by $(x/\alpha, y/\alpha)$ for $\alpha = \frac{1}{2}, \frac{1}{5}, \frac{1}{100}, \ldots$. In accordance with our vague intuitive notion that the ideal point on the line is "infinitely far out," we might think of the

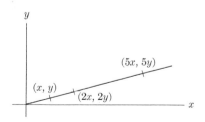

FIGURE 2–1

19

ideal point, in the direction determined by this line, as having the coordinates $(x/\alpha, y/\alpha)$ for $\alpha = 0$. But division by zero is undefined in arithmetic and algebra. An alternative approach is to use *three* coordinates, (x_0, x_1, x_2). For $x_0 \neq 0$, we have an ordinary point, with nonhomogeneous coordinates (x, y), where $x = x_1/x_0,\ y = x_2/x_0$. For $x_0 = 0$, we have the ideal point in the direction under discussion. For any given point, these so-called "homogeneous coordinates" are not uniquely determined; (x_0, x_1, x_2) and (kx_0, kx_1, kx_2) are coordinates of the same point for all $k \neq 0$. But every triad (x_0, x_1, x_2) except $(0, 0, 0)$ corresponds to a unique point; it is ordinary if $x_0 \neq 0$, and ideal if $x_0 = 0$.

EXAMPLE 1.   (a) The point given in rectangular coordinates as $(3, -5)$ may be represented in homogeneous coordinates by $(1, 3, -5)$ or by $(\frac{1}{10}, \frac{3}{10}, -\frac{5}{10})$, or by $(-2, -6, 10)$, etc.

(b) The point given in homogeneous coordinates by $(0, 1, 2)$ is the ideal point of the plane in the direction of lines of slope 2.

This point cannot be represented in nonhomogeneous coordinates. In general, the ideal point in the direction of lines with slope m has homogeneous coordinates $(0, 1, m)$.

(c) The point given in homogeneous coordinates by $(0, k, 0)$, for any $k \neq 0$, is the ideal point in the direction of lines parallel to the x-axis. It cannot be represented in nonhomogeneous coordinates.

(d) To find homogeneous coordinates of the ideal point on the line $2x + 5y + 6 = 0$, we may proceed as follows. The given line has slope $-\frac{2}{5}$. Homogeneous coordinates of the ideal point in the direction of lines of slope $-\frac{2}{5}$ are $(0, 5, -2)$.

In analogous fashion we define homogeneous coordinates for points in space of three dimensions as quadruples of real numbers, not all zero. Then, for $k \neq 0$, (x_0, x_1, x_2, x_3) and (kx_0, kx_1, kx_2, kx_3) are homogeneous coordinates of the same point. If the first coordinate x_0 is zero, the point is ideal; otherwise the point is ordinary, having rectangular coordinates (x, y, z), with $x = x_1/x_0$, $y = x_2/x_0$, $z = x_3/x_0$.

In order to specify conveniently the direction of a line in space of three dimensions, we use direction numbers of the line. (A summary of basic material of solid analytic geometry will be found in Appendix 1.) You are reminded that one set of direction numbers of the line joining the points with rectangular coordinates (x, y, z) and (x', y', z') is $x' - x$, $y' - y$, $z' - z$.

The ideal point in the direction determined by the direction numbers n_1, n_2, n_3 has coordinates $(0, n_1, n_2, n_3)$.

EXAMPLE 2.   Let points P and Q have rectangular coordinates $(1, 4, -3)$ and $(3, 2, 0)$, respectively. Then direction numbers of the line PQ are

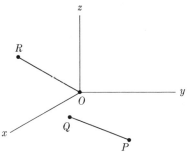

FIGURE 2–2

2, −2, 3. Hence the line PQ is parallel to the line joining the origin $(0, 0, 0)$ to the point $R(2, -2, 3)$ (Fig. 2–2).

EXAMPLE 3. Let us consider the problem of finding points common to the three planes:

$$\text{(i)} \qquad 2x + 3y - z - 1 = 0,$$

$$\text{(ii)} \qquad x + 3y - 2z - 4 = 0,$$

$$\text{(iii)} \qquad 3x + 2y + z - 5 = 0.$$

We may try to solve these three equations simultaneously by a process of elimination. If we subtract (ii) from (i), we obtain

$$\text{(iv)} \qquad x + z + 3 = 0.$$

If we subtract two times (i) from three times (iii), we obtain

$$\text{(v)} \qquad 5x + 5z - 13 = 0.$$

But (iv) and (v) clearly have no common solution, so there are no ordinary points common to the three planes.

We may write equations of the line of intersection of planes (ii) and (iii) as

$$\text{(vi)} \qquad \frac{x - 0}{-1} = \frac{y - 2}{1} = \frac{z - 1}{1} .$$

Direction numbers of this line are −1, 1, 1; and direction numbers of the normal to plane (i) are 2, 3, −1. Since $(-1)(2) + (1)(3) + (1)(-1) = 0$, the line (vi) is parallel to plane (i). Hence, in extended space, there *is* a point common to the three given planes. It is the ideal point in the direction of line (vi). Homogeneous coordinates of this point are $(0, -1, 1, 1)$.

PROBLEM SET 2–1

1. Plot the points in the plane whose homogeneous coordinates are $A(1, 2, 3)$; $B(2, 0, 0)$; $C(-1, 1, 0)$; $D(\frac{1}{10}, 1, 2)$; $E(-\frac{1}{10}, 1, 2)$.

2. Obtain homogeneous coordinates, subject to the indicated conditions, for each of the following points given in terms of nonhomogeneous coordinates.

(a) $P(1, 2)$, with $x_1 = -1$ (b) $Q(0, 0)$, with $x_0 = 3$
(c) $R(-2, 1)$, with $x_2 = 2$ (d) $S(0, 1, -3)$, with $x_2 = -2$
(e) $T(1, 0, 0)$, with $x_3 = 0$ (f) $U(0, 4, -1)$, with $x_0 = -1$

3. What are coordinates of the ideal point on lines parallel to the y-axis, if we consider (a) only the extended xy-plane; (b) extended three-dimensional space?

4. What are the coordinates of the "center" of an orthogonal projection of (a) a line l onto the line l', whose equation is $x - 3y + 7 = 0$; (b) a line l onto the line l', whose equation is $x_0 + x_1 = 0$; (c) a plane π onto the plane π', whose equation is $2x + y - z + 4 = 0$?

5. Express in homogeneous coordinates the point of intersection of the following lines.
(a) $2x + 3y - 4 = 0$ and $x - y + 3 = 0$
(b) $2x + 3y - 4 = 0$ and $4x + 6y - 9 = 0$

6. Find an equation of the line joining the points whose homogeneous coordinates are as follows.

(a) $(1, 3, -2)$ and $(2, -1, 4)$
(b) $(1, 3, 0)$ and $(0, 5, -1)$
(c) $(1, 0, 1)$ and $(2, 3, 1)$
(d) $(2, 1, 0)$ and $(-1, 1, 0)$

7. What are coordinates of the ideal point on the line of intersection of the planes $3x + 3y + z - 2 = 0$ and $3x - 2z + 13 = 0$?

8. What are coordinates of the ideal point on the common secant of the circles whose equations are $2x^2 + 2y^2 = 19$ and $x^2 - 4x + y^2 + 2y = 0$?

9. Find equations of the line joining the points whose homogeneous coordinates are as follows.

(a) $(1, 1, 0, 2)$ and $(3, 6, -1, 0)$ (b) $(1, 1, 0, 2)$ and $(0, 1, -1, 2)$

10. Consider the points with homogeneous coordinates $A(1, 4, 3, 0)$, $B(2, 0, 1, -1)$, $C(0, 1, -2, 1)$. Find equations of the line AB; of the line AC.

11. In the following, refer to Example 3 of Section 2–1.
(a) Explain how the fact that equations (iv) and (v) have no common solution implies that there are no ordinary points common to planes (i), (ii), and (iii).
(b) Fill in the steps leading to (vi) as the line of intersection of (ii) and (iii).
(c) Explain how to arrive at the conclusion that line (vi) is parallel to plane (i).

*12. Discuss nonhomogeneous and homogeneous coordinates of points in one-dimensional space. Find homogeneous coordinates for the origin on the line; for the ideal point on the line.

2–2 EQUATIONS IN HOMOGENEOUS COORDINATES

To say that, in a given two-dimensional coordinate system, the equation of a certain line l is

$$a_1x + a_2y + a_0 = 0 \tag{1}$$

means that if $P(p_1, p_2)$ is a point on l, then $a_1p_1 + a_2p_2 + a_0 = 0$, and also that if $x = r$, $y = s$ is a solution of Eq. (1), then the point $U(r, s)$ lies on l. Equation (1) expresses the relation between abscissa and ordinate of *ordinary* points only; we clearly cannot use the equation to check whether a certain ideal point lies on l.

A modification of Eq. (1) will make it applicable to both ordinary and ideal points. If we replace x by x_1/x_0 and y by x_2/x_0 with $x_0 \neq 0$, Eq. (1) becomes

$$a_0x_0 + a_1x_1 + a_2x_2 = 0. \tag{2}$$

Equation (2) is obviously satisfied by the homogeneous coordinates of those and only those ordinary points which lie on l; it is satisfied by the homogeneous coordinates of an ideal point if and only if the ideal point lies on l. (Problem 1 below.) We say, then, that Eq. (2) is the equation of l in homogeneous coordinates.

A polynomial function in several variables is called *homogeneous of degree n* if every term is of the nth degree in the variables jointly. Thus, $Ax^3 + Bx^2y + Cy^3$ is homogeneous of degree 3 in x and y, and

$$a_{00}x_0^2 + a_{11}x_1^2 + a_{22}x_2^2 + 2a_{01}x_0x_1 + 2a_{02}x_0x_2 + 2a_{12}x_1x_2$$

is homogeneous of degree 2 in x_0, x_1, x_2.

If the polynomial function $f(x_0, x_1, \ldots, x_{r-1})$ is homogeneous in the r variables, then the equation, $f(x_0, \ldots, x_{r-1}) = 0$ is called homogeneous. Thus, Eq. (1) *is not* homogeneous in x and y, but Eq. (2) *is* homogeneous of degree 1 in x_0, x_1, x_2. We will discover that some theorems about functions and equations are true whether they are homogeneous or not, while in other theorems there is a great difference between the homogeneous and nonhomogeneous cases.

Some of the problems at the end of Section 2–1 can be solved more neatly by using equations in homogeneous coordinates. It would be worthwhile for you to work through Problem 5 of Section 2–1 in this way.

EXAMPLE 1.   The point of intersection of the two straight lines whose equations are

$$5x_0 + 4x_1 + x_2 = 0 \quad \text{and} \quad 4x_0 - x_1 - 2x_2 = 0$$

can be found by solving the equations simultaneously. Think of x_1 and

x_2 as variables to be expressed in terms of x_0. The result is $x_1 = -2x_0$, $x_2 = 3x_0$; hence, the required point of intersection has homogeneous coordinates $(x_0, -2x_0, 3x_0)$, or $(1, -2, 3)$.

The result for the same problem, worked through in nonhomogeneous coordinates, would read, in algebraic terminology, "The simultaneous solution of the pair of linear equations

$$4x + y + 5 = 0 \quad \text{and} \quad -x - 2y + 4 = 0$$

is

$$x = -2, \quad y = 3."$$

EXAMPLE 2.   Suppose that we try to find the point of intersection of the two straight lines whose equations are

$$5x_0 + 4x_1 + x_2 = 0 \quad \text{and} \quad 7x_0 + 12x_1 + 3x_2 = 0.$$

If we subtract the second equation from three times the first, we obtain $8x_0 = 0$, or $x_0 = 0$. Hence $x_2 = -4x_1$, and we have $(0, x_1, -4x_1)$ or, more simply, $(0, 1, -4)$ as homogeneous coordinates of the point of intersection of the two lines. This is the ideal point in the direction of lines with slope -4.

If the equations of the lines had been written in nonhomogeneous coordinates, we would have had

$$4x + y + 5 = 0 \quad \text{and} \quad 12x + 3y + 7 = 0,$$

a pair of equations that we would quickly recognize as representing two parallel lines of slope -4, hence having no simultaneous solution.

EXAMPLE 3.   We can now solve problems like Problem 6 of Section 2–1 without distinguishing between ordinary and ideal points. We illustrate by working Problem 6(b). The general equation of a line is

$$a_0x_0 + a_1x_1 + a_2x_2 = 0.$$

If $(1, 3, 0)$ lies on this line, then $a_0 + 3a_1 = 0$. If $(0, 5, -1)$ lies on this line, then $5a_1 - a_2 = 0$. Hence $a_0 = -3a_1$, and $a_2 = 5a_1$. Therefore the line has the equation $-3a_1x_0 + a_1x_1 + 5a_1x_2 = 0$ or, dividing both sides by a_1, $-3x_0 + x_1 + 5x_2 = 0$. (Since $a_1 = 0$ leads to $0 = 0$, we may take $a_1 \neq 0$). In nonhomogeneous coordinates, this is the line $x + 5y - 3 = 0$.

EXAMPLE 4.   There are certain lines whose equations are particularly simple. If we turn the equation of the x-axis, $y = 0$, into homogeneous coordinates by replacing y by x_2/x_0, we obtain $x_2 = 0$. Alternatively, we might note that a point with coordinates (x_0, x_1, x_2) lies on the x-axis if and only if $x_2 = 0$. It is instructive to consider the problem in still a third way. The general straight line, $a_0x_0 + a_1x_1 + a_2x_2 = 0$, with not all the a's equal to zero, is the x-axis if the line passes through the points with coordinates $(1, 0, 0)$ and $(0, 1, 0)$. Hence $a_0 = 0 = a_1$, and the equation of the x-axis is $a_2x_2 = 0$; thus, $x_2 = 0$ is the desired equation.

A similar method leads to the following results:

$$y\text{-axis:}\quad x_1 = 0,$$

$$\text{ideal line:}\quad x_0 = 0,$$

$$\text{general } line \text{ } through \text{ } the \text{ } origin: \quad a_1x_1 + a_2x_2 = 0.$$

The analogous situation in three dimensions involves replacing x by x_1/x_0, y by x_2/x_0, and z by x_3/x_0, when $x_0 \neq 0$. Thus the plane π whose equation in nonhomogeneous coordinates is

$$a_1x + a_2y + a_3z + a_0 = 0 \tag{3}$$

becomes

$$a_0x_0 + a_1x_1 + a_2x_2 + a_3x_3 = 0; \tag{4}$$

and the line l with nonhomogeneous equations

$$\frac{x - r}{n_1} = \frac{y - s}{n_2} = \frac{z - t}{n_3} \tag{5}$$

becomes

$$\frac{x_1 - rx_0}{n_1} = \frac{x_2 - sx_0}{n_2} = \frac{x_3 - tx_0}{n_3}. \tag{6}$$

It is clear that an ordinary point P lies in plane π (or on line l) if and only if homogeneous coordinates of P satisfy Eq. (4) [or Eq. (6)]. It can be shown that the same statement holds if P is an ideal point.

We say, then, that in three dimensions, Eq. (4) is the equation of a plane, and Eqs. (6) are the equations of a line in homogeneous coordinates.

REMARK. Equations (5) represent the line with direction numbers n_1, n_2, n_3, none of the n's zero, passing through the point A with nonhomogeneous coordinates (r, s, t). Equations (6) represent the line in homogeneous coordinates. However, we can get a more symmetrical result by using homogeneous coordinates for A also, say (r_0, r_1, r_2, r_3) where

$$r = \frac{r_1}{r_0}, \qquad s = \frac{r_2}{r_0}, \qquad t = \frac{r_3}{r_0}.$$

Then we have

$$\frac{r_0x_1 - x_0r_1}{n_1} = \frac{r_0x_2 - x_0r_2}{n_2} = \frac{r_0x_3 - x_0r_3}{n_3}. \tag{7}$$

EXAMPLE 5.   We illustrate by working Example 3 of Section 2–1 in homogeneous coordinates: In homogeneous coordinates, the planes of this example have the equations

$$\text{(i')} \qquad x_0 - 2x_1 - 3x_2 + x_3 = 0,$$

$$\text{(ii')} \qquad 4x_0 - x_1 - 3x_2 + 2x_3 = 0,$$

$$\text{(iii')} \qquad 5x_0 - 3x_1 - 2x_2 - x_3 = 0.$$

A process of elimination similar to that attempted in Section 2–1 leads to $28x_0 = 0$, or $x_0 = 0$.   Hence, $x_3 = -x_1$, and $x_2 = -x_1$. Therefore, the point common to the three given planes is $(0, x_1, -x_1, -x_1)$ or $(0, 1, -1, -1)$ or $(0, -1, 1, 1)$.   This is the ideal point in the direction of lines with direction numbers $-1, 1, 1$.

EXAMPLE 6.   It may happen that three distinct planes have an entire line in common, not just one point.   Consider the case of planes with the following equations in homogeneous coordinates:

$$\text{(vii)} \qquad 2x_0 - x_1 + 3x_2 - x_3 = 0,$$

$$\text{(viii)} \qquad x_0 + 4x_1 - x_2 + 2x_3 = 0,$$

$$\text{(ix)} \qquad 7x_0 + 10x_1 + 3x_2 + 4x_3 = 0.$$

If we eliminate x_3 between (vii) and (viii) we obtain

$$\text{(x)} \qquad 5x_0 + 2x_1 + 5x_2 = 0,$$

and if we eliminate x_3 between (vii) and (ix) we get

$$\text{(xi)} \qquad 15x_0 + 6x_1 + 15x_2 = 0.$$

But dividing both sides of (xi) by 3 gives (x), so that we have only one equation among x_0, x_1, x_2, and we have used all the data.   Thus, we cannot solve for x_1, x_2, and x_3 in terms of x_0, but we must leave *two* of the variables undetermined.   Solving Eq. (x) for x_2 gives

$$x_2 = -\tfrac{2}{5}x_1 - x_0,$$

and substituting this expression for x_2 in (vii) gives

$$x_3 = -\tfrac{11}{5}x_1 - x_0.$$

Thus

$$x_1 = \frac{x_2 + x_0}{-\tfrac{2}{5}} = \frac{x_3 + x_0}{-\tfrac{11}{5}}.$$

Comparing these equations with Eqs. (6), we recognize that the three given planes intersect in the line with direction numbers $5, -2, -11$ passing through the point with nonhomogeneous coordinates $(0, -1, -1)$, or with homogeneous coordinates $(1, 0, -1, -1)$.

Our procedure in solving sets of linear simultaneous equations, involving somewhat haphazard "elimination," is distressingly unsystematic. Moreover, different cases arise. In Example 5 there is a single solution, while Example 6 has a whole "line of solutions," and at this stage, we have no criterion to determine neatly how many solutions a given set of equations will have. In Chapter 6 we will develop a general "theory" of sets of linear equations.

Curves other than straight lines and surfaces other than planes can also be studied efficiently through the use of equations expressed in homogeneous coordinates. For example, in the xy-plane, the circle $x^2 + y^2 = r^2$ becomes

$$x_1^2 + x_2^2 - r^2 x_0^2 = 0,$$

and the hyperbola $(x^2/a^2) - (y^2/b^2) = 1$ becomes

$$b^2 x_1^2 - a^2 x_2^2 - a^2 b^2 x_0^2 = 0.$$

(Note that, in terms of homogeneous coordinates, both these curves have equations which are homogeneous of degree two.)

We may ask whether there are any ideal points on these curves. An ideal point, (x_0, x_1, x_2), has $x_0 = 0$; hence, for an ideal point on the circle, we must have $x_1^2 + x_2^2 = 0$. But the only real solution of this equation is $x_1 = 0 = x_2$; and, since the triad $(0, 0, 0)$ does not represent a point in two-dimensional homogeneous coordinates, we conclude that the circle has no ideal points on it—a result in accord with our intuition that a circle is bounded in all directions, and does not "extend to infinity." (But another point of view will appear in Example 2 of Section 2-3.) In the case of the hyperbola, if $x_0 = 0$, then $x_2 = (b/a)x_1$; hence, we have the two ideal points on the hyperbola, $P_1(0, 1, b/a)$ and $P_2(0, 1, -b/a)$, which are the ideal points of the plane in the directions of lines of slopes b/a and $-b/a$. But the asymptotes of this hyperbola are lines of slopes $\pm b/a$; therefore, each of the ideal points P_1, P_2 is common to the hyperbola and one of its asymptotes.

PROBLEM SET 2-2

1. If P is an ideal point, show that P lies on the line l with nonhomogeneous equation $a_1 x + a_2 y + a_0 = 0$ if and only if the homogeneous coordinates of P satisfy the homogeneous equation $a_0 x_0 + a_1 x_1 + a_2 x_2 = 0$.

2. Fill in the omitted algebraic details in Example 1.

3. A generalization of the definition of homogeneity, not restricted to polynomial functions, is as follows: $f(x_0, x_1, \ldots, x_{r-1})$ is homogeneous of degree n in the variables if

$$f(kx_0, kx_1, \ldots, kx_{r-1}) = k^n f(x_0, x_1, \ldots, x_{r-1}),$$

for all $k \neq 0$.

Which of the following functions are homogeneous? For those which are homogeneous, state the degree of homogeneity.

(a) $x^2 - 4yz$

(b) $x \log y - x \log z + 3y \sin x/z$

(c) $a_1 x_1^3 + a_2 x_1^2 x_2 + a_3 x_1 x_2^2 + a_4 x_2^3 + a_5$, where a's are constants

(d) $u^2 w - 3uvw + 2v^3$

(e) $\dfrac{2}{x} + \dfrac{1}{y} - \dfrac{3}{z}$

(f) $x^{2/3} + y^{2/3} - c^{2/3}$, where c is constant

(g) $x_1^2 + x_2^2 + x_3^2 + \cdots + x_n^2 + 2x_1 x_2 + 2x_1 x_3 + \cdots + 2x_1 x_n + 2x_2 x_3 + \cdots + 2x_2 x_n + \cdots + 2x_{n-1} x_n$

4. Write out the details of the steps leading to the results of Example 4.

5. Use an analogue of the third method of Example 4 to obtain the equations of the following planes in three dimensions: xy-plane, xz-plane, yz-plane, ideal plane.

6. Fill in the omitted algebraic details of Example 5.

7. Find any points common to all three lines of each of the following sets.

(a) $5x_0 + 2x_1 + 4x_2 = 0$, $5x_0 - 2x_1 + x_2 = 0$, $15x_0 + 2x_1 + 9x_2 = 0$

(b) $4x_0 + 2x_1 - 3x_2 = 0$, $6x_0 - 2x_1 + 3x_2 = 0$, $x_0 + 4x_1 - 6x_2 = 0$

(c) $3x_0 + x_1 - 2x_2 = 0$, $8x_0 - 3x_1 + 4x_2 = 0$, $5x_0 - 2x_1 + 6x_2 = 0$

(d) $9x_0 + 12x_1 - 8x_2 = 0$, $5x_0 + 3x_1 - 2x_2 = 0$, $10x_0 + 4x_1 - 3x_2 = 0$

(e) $4x_0 + 2x_1 - x_2 = 0$, $x_0 - 2x_1 + x_2 = 0$, $x_0 + 4x_1 - 2x_2 = 0$

(f) $4x_0 + 2x_1 - x_2 = 0$, $x_0 - 2x_1 + x_2 = 0$, $x_0 + 2x_1 + x_2 = 0$

8. Find any points common to all three planes of each of the following sets.

(a) $5x_0 + x_1 - x_2 + 3x_3 = 0$, $3x_0 + x_1 - 2x_2 - x_3 = 0$,
$9x_0 + 8x_1 - 2x_2 + 5x_3 = 0$

(b) $3x_0 - x_1 + 2x_2 - x_3 = 0$, $2x_0 + 3x_1 - 6x_2 - 6x_3 = 0$,
$4x_0 - 4x_1 + 8x_2 - 3x_3 = 0$

(c) $5x_0 + x_1 - x_2 + 3x_3 = 0$, $3x_0 + x_1 - 2x_2 - x_3 = 0$,
$2x_0 + 3x_2 + 4x_3 = 0$

(d) $2x_0 - x_1 + 5x_2 - 3x_3 = 0$, $3x_0 - 2x_1 + 10x_2 - 6x_3 = 0$,
$4x_0 - 3x_1 + 15x_2 - 9x_3 = 0$

(e) $x_0 - x_1 + x_2 + x_3 = 0$, $x_0 + x_1 + 2x_2 + x_3 = 0$,
$2x_0 + 3x_2 + 2x_3 = 0$

(f) $x_0 - x_1 + x_2 + x_3 = 0$, $x_0 + x_1 + x_2 + x_3 = 0$,
$x_0 + x_2 + x_3 = 0$

9. Let $E_1 = 9x^2 + 16y^2 - 25$, $E_2 = 16x^2 + 9y^2 - 25$.

(a) What are the loci of $E_1 = 0$, $E_2 = 0$?

(b) Prove that the locus of $E_1 - E_2 = 0$ passes through all the points of intersection of $E_1 = 0$ and $E_2 = 0$.

(c) What is the locus of $E_1 - E_2 = 0$?

(d) Sketch the configuration.

10. (a) Show that the following lines are concurrent: $a_0x_0 + a_1x_1 + a_2x_2 = 0$, $b_0x_0 + b_1x_1 + b_2x_2 = 0$, $(k_1a_0 + k_2b_0)x_0 + (k_1a_1 + k_2b_1)x_1 + (k_1a_2 + k_2b_2)x_2 = 0$, where k_1, k_2 are any real numbers not both zero. [*Hint:* Write the third line as $k_1(a_0x_0 + a_1x_1 + a_2x_2) + k_2(b_0x_0 + b_1x_1 + b_2x_2) = 0$.]

(b) Draw the lines whose equations are $4x_0 - x_1 - 2x_2 = 0$, $9x_0 + 3x_1 - x_2 = 0$, and $3(4x_0 - x_1 - 2x_2) - 2(9x_0 + 3x_1 - x_2) = 0$.

(c) If $f(x_0, x_1, x_2) = 4x_0 - x_1 - 2x_2$, and $g(x_0, x_1, x_2) = 4x_0 + x_1 + 2x_2$, describe the loci of $f = 0$, $g = 0$, $f - g = 0$, and $f + g = 0$.

(d) If $f(x_0, x_1, x_2) = 0$, $g(x_0, x_1, x_2) = 0$ are the equations of two curves in two-dimensional space, expressed in homogeneous coordinates, show that $k_1f(x_0, x_1, x_2) + k_2g(x_0, x_1, x_2) = 0$, where k_1, k_2 are any real numbers not both zero, is the equation of a curve passing through all the points, ordinary and ideal, common to the curves $f = 0$ and $g = 0$.

(e) Let $\mathcal{C}$ be the curve with equation $k_1f + k_2g = 0$, $\mathcal{C}'$ the curve with equation $f = 0$, and $\mathcal{C}''$ the curve with equation $g = 0$. Show that, if there is a point P common to $\mathcal{C}$ and $\mathcal{C}'$, but not on $\mathcal{C}''$, then $\mathcal{C}$ and $\mathcal{C}'$ coincide.

11. Fill in the omitted algebraic details of Example 6.

12. Show that if P is an ideal point in three-dimensional space, then P lies on the line l with Eqs. (6) if and only if the homogeneous coordinates of P satisfy Eqs. (6).

2–3 THE IMAGINARY

Consider the relationship of each of the lines l_1, l_2, l_3 to the circle C in Fig. 2–3. We customarily say that l_1 meets C in two distinct points P, P'; that l_2 is tangent to C at Q; and that l_3 does not meet C. These

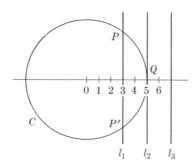

Figure 2–3

facts are presented in algebraic terms as follows.

(i) The simultaneous solutions of

$$l_1: \quad x = 3 \qquad \text{and} \qquad C: \quad x^2 + y^2 = 25$$

are $P(3, 4)$ and $P'(3, -4)$.

(ii) Solving $l_2: x = 5$ simultaneously with $C: x^2 + y^2 = 25$ leads to $y^2 = 0$, or $y = \pm 0 = 0$. Hence, $Q(5, 0)$ is the only point common to l_2 and C.

(iii) Solving $l_3: x = 7$ and $C: x^2 + y^2 = 25$ simultaneously leads to $y^2 = -24$, or $y = \pm 2\sqrt{6}\, i$, where $i = \sqrt{-1}$. Hence there are no points common to l_3 and C.

Thus we have three cases for the intersection of the line and the circle: two common points, one common point, or no common points. By creating the ideal points and adopting certain conventions, we were able to subsume a number of different cases involved in projection under one general statement. Likewise, in the situation under discussion, the invention of new points and the adoption of certain conventions permit us to combine the three different cases mentioned above into a single general description.

First of all, we introduce the convention, in (ii) above, of calling Q a "doubly counting" intersection, motivated by the notion that as l_1 moves to the right in the figure to approach l_2, each of the two distinct points P and P' approaches Q.

We extend the xy-plane to include imaginary points as well as real points by adopting the following definition. In two dimensions, a point shall be any ordered pair of numbers (x, y), where x and y are complex; that is, $x = u + iv$, $y = s + it$, u, v, s, t real.

Note that the complex number $u + iv$ is *real* if $v = 0$. If $v \neq 0$, the number is *imaginary*. Complex numbers, then, are divided into two classes, the reals and the imaginaries. In the complex domain, a point of the plane will be called *real* if both its coordinates are real; if either or both of its coordinates are imaginary, the point will be termed *imaginary*. In our ordinary graphical representation, only real points are represented as dots on the paper. Imaginary elements cannot be pictured in this system.

The plane in the complex domain, as described here, is not to be confused with the so-called "complex plane" whereby the single complex number $3 + 4i$, say, is represented as the point with coordinates $(3, 4)$ in the real plane—the representation associated with the names Gauss, Argand, and Wessel. A comparable representation of a point of the plane in the complex domain would require four real coordinates, and might be thought of as a point in "real space of four dimensions."

The set of points whose coordinates satisfy a first degree equation $a_1x + a_2y + a_0 = 0$, where a_1, a_2, a_0 are complex numbers, is called a *straight* line in the plane of the complex domain. Similarly, the set of points whose coordinates satisfy a second degree equation with complex numbers as coefficients is called a *conic*. If the ratios of the coefficients are all real, the conic is called real and is designated ellipse, parabola, or hyperbola according to the same criteria used to distinguish among these conics in the plane of the real domain. It is customary to call the conic with equation $ax^2 + bxy + cy^2 + dx + ey + f = 0$ a circle if $a = c$ and $b = 0$, even if not all the coefficients are real.

EXAMPLE 1.   (a) To find the points of intersection in the plane of the complex domain of the ellipse $x^2/9 + y^2/4 = 1$ and the line $x + y - 7 = 0$, we solve the equations simultaneously, which results in the two imaginary points of intersection, $(\frac{63}{13} + \frac{36}{13}i, \frac{28}{13} - \frac{36}{13}i)$, and $(\frac{63}{13} - \frac{36}{13}i, \frac{28}{13} + \frac{36}{13}i)$.

(b) To find the points of intersection of the circles with equations

$$x^2 + y^2 = r^2 \qquad \text{and} \qquad (x - a)^2 + y^2 = r^2, \tag{1}$$

we solve these equations (1) simultaneously. This is most easily done by subtracting the second of the equations from the first, which gives

$$x = \frac{a}{2}. \tag{2}$$

If we substitute this value for x in the equation of either circle, we obtain

$$y = \pm\sqrt{r^2 - (a^2/4)}.$$

We have, then, three cases to consider, $a < 2r$, $a = 2r$, $a > 2r$. As examples, we shall consider $a = r$, $a = 2r$, $a = 3r$.

(i) If $a = r$, we have the two (real and distinct) points of intersection:

$$\left(\frac{r}{2}, \frac{r}{2}\sqrt{3}\right) \qquad \text{and} \qquad \left(\frac{r}{2}, \frac{-r}{2}\sqrt{3}\right).$$

(ii) If $a = 2r$, we have the two (real and coincident) points of intersection: $(r, 0)$, counted twice.

(iii) If $a = 3r$, we have the two (imaginary and distinct) points of intersection:

$$\left(\frac{3r}{2}, \frac{r}{2}\sqrt{5}\, i\right) \qquad \text{and} \qquad \left(\frac{3r}{2}, -\frac{r}{2}\sqrt{5}\, i\right).$$

Homogeneous coordinates can be used in the plane of the complex domain to deal with ideal points, just as in the real domain. There is only one change necessary in the previous discussion — in that part relating to real and imaginary points. Since homogeneous coordinates are not uniquely determined, the (real) point with homogeneous coordinates $(2, 3, 7)$, say, also has homogeneous coordinates $(2(1 + i), 3(1 + i), 7(1 + i))$. Thus, it will not do to call a point "imaginary" if at least one of its homogeneous coordinates is imaginary, and otherwise, "real." Instead, we use the following definition: In the extended plane of the complex domain, a point is real if it *can* be written in terms of three homogeneous coordinates all of which are real; otherwise the point is imaginary. Alternatively, we may put this definition in the following terms. A point is real if the ratios of coordinates to each other are *all* real. (Obviously, we are here speaking only of those ratios which are defined. If $x_1 = 0$, we consider neither the ratio of x_0 to x_1 nor the ratio of x_2 to x_1.)

A similar definition is applied to lines. A straight line is called real if its equation *can* be written with all real coefficients; otherwise the line is imaginary. Note that a real point lies on imaginary, as well as on real, lines; and that a real line passes through imaginary, as well as through real, points (see Problem 6(h) below).

EXAMPLE 2. On p. 27 we concluded that in the extended plane of the real domain, the circle $x_1^2 + x_2^2 - r^2x_0^2 = 0$ contains no ideal points, i.e., that it has no intersections with the ideal line, $x_0 = 0$. But in the extended plane of the complex domain, the equations

$$x_1^2 + x_2^2 - r^2x_0^2 = 0 \qquad \text{and} \qquad x_0 = 0$$

do have simultaneous solutions:

$$x_0 = 0 \qquad \text{and} \qquad x_2 = \pm x_1 i.$$

Hence there are two (imaginary) ideal points on the circle: $I(0, 1, i)$ and $J(0, 1, -i)$. We can readily verify (Problem 3(a) below) that these same two points lie on *every* circle in the plane; they are called the *circular points at infinity* or *isotropic points*.

EXAMPLE 3. It is instructive to reconsider Example 1(b) when we use homogeneous coordinates. Let us review what we did in that example. We replaced the two quadratic equations (1) by a pair consisting of one of these equations and the linear equation (2), arguing, essentially, that the points of intersection (real and imaginary) of the two circles are precisely the points of intersection of either of the circles and the common secant of the two circles. This is true if we wish to ignore ideal points. But, in homogeneous coordinates, Eqs. (1) become

$$x_1^2 + x_2^2 - r^2x_0^2 = 0,$$

and

$$x_1^2 - 2a_1x_1x_0 + a^2x_0^2 + x_2^2 - r^2x_0^2 = 0. \tag{3}$$

Subtracting the second of these equations from the first gives

$$2ax_1x_0 - a^2x_0^2 = 0, \qquad \text{or} \qquad ax_0(2x_1 - ax_0) = 0.$$

Hence we have not only the possibility that $x_1 = \frac{1}{2}ax_0$, which is the case considered in Example 1(b), but also $x_0 = 0$, which was not then considered. The latter possibility leads to the ideal points I and J of Example 2. For the circles with Eqs. (3), we have, then, *four* points of intersection in the extended plane of the complex domain: I, J, and the two points of Example 1(b).

PROBLEM SET 2–3

1. Carry through the omitted algebraic details of Example 1(a).

2. In the ordinary plane of the complex domain, find the points of intersection of the circle $x^2 + y^2 - 25 = 0$ and the line $4x + 3y + k = 0$ for (a) $k = -20$; (b) $k = -25$; (c) $k = -65$.

*3. (a) Prove that every circle [i.e., curve with equation $A(x_1^2 + x_2^2) + Bx_1x_0 + Cx_2x_0 + Dx_0^2 = 0$] passes through I and J.

(b) Prove that every real conic through I and J is a circle; i.e., that, if the coordinates of I and J satisfy $ax_0^2 + bx_1^2 + cx_2^2 + dx_0x_1 + ex_0x_2 + fx_1x_2 = 0$, with all the coefficients being real numbers, then $b = c$ and $f = 0$.

(c) Prove the following stronger version of (b): Every real conic through either I or J is a circle. [*Hint:* Remember that two complex numbers $u_1 + iv_1$, $u_2 + iv_2$ are equal if and only if $u_1 = u_2$ and $v_1 = v_2$.]

4. In three-dimensional space of the complex domain, find the points of intersection of the sphere with equation $x^2 + y^2 + z^2 = 4$ and the line with equations

$$\frac{x - 3}{1} = \frac{y - 2}{1} = \frac{z - 4}{-1}.$$

*5. *Definition.* If the complex number x can be written as $x = u + iv$, u, v real, then the complex number $\bar{x} = u - iv$ is called the *conjugate* of x. (Note that if $\bar{x}$ is the conjugate of x, then x is the conjugate of $\bar{x}$; i.e., $\overline{(\bar{x})} = x$. We may call x and $\bar{x}$ a pair of "conjugate complex numbers.")

(a) With the hint of Problem 3(c) above, show that a complex number equals its conjugate if and only if the number is real.

(b) If p and q are complex numbers, show that $\overline{p \pm q} = \bar{p} \pm \bar{q}$, and that $\overline{p \cdot q} = \bar{p} \cdot \bar{q}$.

*6. *Definitions.* (i) The conjugate of a point P is the point $\bar{P}$ each of whose coordinates (homogeneous or nonhomogeneous) can be written as the conjugate of the corresponding coordinate of P. For example, I and J are conjugate points; so are the points A and B with homogeneous coordinates $(1, 1 + i, 2 - i)$ and $(i, 1 + i, -1 + 2i)$. (ii) The conjugate of the line l whose equation is

$a_0x_0 + a_1x_1 + a_2x_2 = 0$ is the line l whose equation is $\bar{a}_0x_0 + \bar{a}_1x_1 + \bar{a}_2x_2 = 0$.

(a) Verify that A and B of the above example are conjugate points.

(b) Show that a point is the same as its conjugate if and only if the point is real. Likewise for a line.

(c) Show that if point P lies on line l, then $\bar{P}$ lies on $\bar{l}$. [*Hint:* Use the result of Problem 5(b).]

(d) Show that if the imaginary point P lies on line l, then $\bar{P}$ also lies on l if and only if l is real.

(e) Find the equation of the line passing through $P(1, 2 + i, 1 - 2i)$ and $\bar{P}$.

(f) Show that if the imaginary line l passes through point P, then $\bar{l}$ also passes through P if and only if P is real.

(g) Find the coordinates of the point of intersection of line l with equation $x_0 + (2 + i)x_1 + (1 - 2i)x_2 = 0$ and $\bar{l}$.

(h) Use the results of (d) and (f) to show that there is just one real line through each imaginary point and just one real point on each imaginary line.

7. In extended space of the complex domain find any common points of the following.

(a) The 3 planes whose equations are

$$\left.\begin{aligned}
2x_0 + 3x_1 - x_2 - 2x_3 &= 0,\\
3x_0 - x_1 + 5x_2 + 3x_3 &= 0,\\
3x_0 + x_1 + x_2 &= 0.
\end{aligned}\right\} 3 \text{ dimensions}$$

(b) The 3 planes whose equations are

$$\left.\begin{aligned}
2x_0 + 3x_1 - x_2 - 2x_3 &= 0,\\
x_0 \qquad + 4x_2 - x_3 &= 0,\\
5x_0 + 6x_1 + 2x_2 - 5x_3 &= 0.
\end{aligned}\right\} 3 \text{ dimensions}$$

(c) The 3 lines whose equations are

$$\left.\begin{aligned}
3x_0 + 2x_1 + 6x_2 &= 0,\\
2x_0 - 4x_1 + 7x_2 &= 0,\\
x_0 + 6x_1 + x_2 &= 0.
\end{aligned}\right\} 2 \text{ dimensions}$$

(d) The circle $x^2 + y^2 = 25$ and the line $x + y + 9 = 0.$ $\Big\}$ 2 dimensions

(e) The circle $x^2 + y^2 = 25$ and the parabola $y^2 = x - 5.$ $\Big\}$ 2 dimensions

(f) The circles $x^2 + y^2 = 25$ and $x^2 - 8x + y^2 = 9.$ $\Big\}$ 2 dimensions

(g) The parabolas $y^2 = 6x$ and $y^2 = 10 - 4x.$ $\Big\}$ 2 dimensions

8. Let the curve $\mathcal{C}$ have equation $f(x_0, x_1, x_2) = 0$, where f is a polynomial function. Let $\mathcal{C}$ be called *real* if there is an equation equivalent to $f = 0$ with all coefficients real; let $\bar{\mathcal{C}}$ be the curve whose equation is obtained from that of $\mathcal{C}$ by replacing each coefficient by its conjugate. Which of the analogues of Problem 6(c) and (d) are true if l, $\bar{l}$ are replaced by $\mathcal{C}$, $\bar{\mathcal{C}}$?

2–4 HIGHER SPACE

Geometry of two and three dimensions may be studied for either of two reasons: because the subject matter is of inherent interest, or because the methods of geometry or the images conjured up by the use of geometrical language are helpful in the solution of nongeometrical problems.

In relativity theory, for example, one deals with number quadruples, which it is convenient to think of as nonhomogeneous coordinates of "points of four-dimensional space." This does not mean that we can visualize a space of four dimensions. Rather we *define* a point in four dimensions as a quadruple of four complex numbers (x, y, z, w), or alternatively, in terms of homogeneous coordinates, as a set of five complex numbers $(x_0, x_1, x_2, x_3, x_4)$ not all 0. Likewise, a "hyperplane" in four dimensions may be *defined* as the set of points satisfying the linear equation

$$a_1 x + a_2 y + a_3 z + a_4 w + a_0 = 0,$$

in nonhomogeneous coordinates, or

$$a_0 x_0 + a_1 x_1 + a_2 x_2 + a_3 x_3 + a_4 x_4 = 0,$$

in homogeneous coordinates; and a "hypersphere centered at the origin with radius r" may be *defined* as the set of points satisfying the equation

$$x^2 + y^2 + z^2 + w^2 = r^2,$$

or, in homogeneous coordinates,

$$x_1^2 + x_2^2 + x_3^2 + x_4^2 \quad r^2 x_0^2 = 0.$$

With these and other similar definitions, we can describe some of the phenomena associated with relativity theory in geometrical language which is vivid and economical; moreover, the geometrical terminology is often suggestive of the existence of other phenomena and relationships, which we may then explore by algebraic means. (It should be remarked that the definition of distance in the space of relativity theory is not the most obvious extension of the corresponding definition in ordinary two- and three-dimensional spaces.)

Relativity theory is not the only branch of the natural sciences making use of higher dimensional spaces. Theoretical physics and chemistry employ "phase spaces" of many dimensions, and in some applications of mathematics to physical science, it is convenient to speak of "function spaces" of infinitely many dimensions.

Fields other than the physical sciences also find the language of higher dimensional geometry useful for the purposes of discovery and exposition. In multiple factor analysis, for example, psychologists speak of each of a number of factors as determining an axis in a multidimensional coordinate frame, and of each linear equation in these factors as determining a "hyperplane" in the "factor space." Similar phraseology occurs in some work in theoretical economics.

In listing these applications of geometry, we must not overlook another source of concern for higher space; i.e., the traditional interest of the mathematician in generalization and extension. After the mathematician has analyzed features of space of one, two, and three dimensions, he wishes to obtain some results for n dimensions, obtaining general theorems of which the earlier results for $n = 1, 2, 3$ are special cases. This, too, will be part of our purpose.

2–5 SUMMARY

In the intuitive presentation of these introductory chapters, we have indicated how the three-dimensional, ordinary, real space of Euclid may be expanded into the n-dimensional, extended, complex space of modern geometry.* Likewise we have widened the technique of analytic geometry to include the use of homogeneous coordinates. Later, a helpful abridged notation, and coordinates for elements other than points will be introduced when needed.

In our subsequent study of this extended system, we will be able to obtain general results in which we will often find familiar theorems as special cases, and we will be able to see a structure in the whole which is not apparent in the separate parts. To achieve this gain in generality, we must give up the visualization of geometric results—something upon which we have relied heavily, at times, in our intuitive approach. In fact, we have frequently simply given geometric names to algebraic expressions analogous to those for which the names are appropriate in the space we can visualize. It might then be said that we are only expressing algebraic results in geometric language. Indeed the boundary line between the disciplines of algebra and geometry becomes hard to find.

We turn now to a systematic approach to modern geometry and algebra, starting with the development of the complex numbers in the next chapter.

---

* It may be asked why we stop with extended, complex space. Are not further generalizations possible? Indeed they are, but they are not needed for much of geometry. In extended complex space of two dimensions, for example, an algebraic curve of degree m will meet an algebraic curve of degree n in mn points of intersection. This elegant result, a particular case of Bézout's theorem, is based on the Fundamental Theorem of Algebra: In the complex domain, a polynomial equation of degree p has p roots.

CHAPTER 3

Axioms of
Some Algebraic Systems

3-1 AXIOMATIC SYSTEMS

A formal mathematical system consists of unproved statements (axioms) and deductions, by the rules of logic, from these statements (theorems). The axioms are statements about undefined terms (primitive elements), relations among the elements, and operations upon them. We will give some examples of each of these components of a mathematical system, and then comment upon them.

A set of undefined terms or elements. In plane geometry these may be "points"; in ordinary algebra they may be "real numbers." A given mathematical system may deal with more than one set of elements; in plane geometry, for example, "straight lines," as well as "points," are usually primitive elements.

Relations among the elements. Examples of relations in geometry are given by "point P *lies on* line l" or "for the collinear points A, B, C, B *lies between* A and C" or "for the coplanar lines l_1 and l_2, l_1 *is parallel to* l_2." In algebra we have such relations as "$x = y$," and "$x < y$." A relation between two elements is called *binary*; a relation among three elements is called *ternary*, etc.

Operations upon the elements. In geometry we have, for example, the operation of laying off, along a line, one line segment followed by a second, thus obtaining a third line segment. In algebra, we may square a real number to obtain another real number, or we may add two real numbers to obtain a third. An operation on a single element is called *unary*; an operation on two elements is called *binary*, etc.

Axioms. In Euclidean plane geometry, one of the usual axioms is that there is one and only one straight line through two points. In the algebra of real numbers we may assume that if $a < a'$, then $a + b < a' + b$.

REMARKS. (i) It should be emphasized that the axioms are assumptions which it is agreed to use, rather than "self-evident truths" which must be accepted. Synonyms for "axiom" are "postulate" and "assumed proposition."

The choice of axioms is, to some extent, arbitrary. In a given mathematical system it is often possible to assume "Proposition α" (along with certain other assumptions) in which case "Proposition β" follows as a theorem (i.e., deduction from the assumptions); or to assume "Proposition β" (along with certain other assumptions) and to prove "Proposition α" as a theorem. A mathematician may assume some "strong" axioms in order to prove his desired results expeditiously, or he may try to see how "weak" he can make his assumptions and still prove certain theorems (perhaps with considerable difficulty).

Whatever his choice of axioms, the mathematician tries to state all his assumptions explicitly, never appealing to a proposition which hasn't been either assumed or already proved, no matter how "reasonable" that proposition may appear to be. Some propositions are so "obvious" that it is easy to make the mistake of assuming them unconsciously, without ever stating them as assumptions. For example, Euclid attempted to set down all his assumptions explicitly, but he overlooked stating one which seems trivial: if three distinct points are collinear, just one of the points lies on the segment determined by the other two. However, without some axiom of "betweenness" it is impossible to prove certain theorems which Euclid thought that he had proved. (See Problem 1 below.)

(ii) Just as there is some freedom of choice for the mathematician in selecting his axioms for a given system, so also is there some arbitrariness in deciding on the primitive elements. In plane geometry, for example, *circle* is not usually a primitive element, being defined in terms of point, line, and some other notions. It would be possible, however, to take *circle* as one of the primitive elements, in which case *line* might not be primitive, being definable in terms of point, circle, and some other notions.

(iii) It is to be understood that the elements themselves, the operations upon elements, and the relations among elements possess only those properties which are assumed about them or which may be deduced from the axioms, nothing more. Just because we are in the habit of picturing a point as a "dot," for example, does not mean that the point in our geometry will somehow be "infinitely small," unless the axioms state such a property or imply it.

Likewise, in the formal algebra of real numbers, we must be careful to ascribe to the operation "$+$" only those properties which are postulated about it or which can be deduced from the axioms. We must not assume that the "+" operation necessarily obeys all the laws which we have learned about it in some other connection.

(iv) It will be noted that *definition* was not listed as one of the components of a mathematical system. From the logical point of view, a definition is merely an abbreviation (e.g., the single word "ellipse" can be used to replace the lengthy phrase, "in a plane, the locus of points the sum of whose distances from two fixed points is constant"). Hence, definitions are not logically necessary, although they are extremely convenient in practice.

Note that if *ellipse* is defined as above, then any ellipse is the locus of points, in a plane, the sum of whose distances from two fixed points is constant, and conversely, any such locus is an ellipse. In other words, if we use "*A* is *B*" as a definition of *A*, we mean that all *A*'s are *B*'s and also that all *B*'s are *A*'s.

(v) There are certain primitive terms which are used in outlining any system, and which cannot be elucidated within that system. Typical of such terms is "set," introduced without explanation at the beginning of this chapter. The meaning of "set" could be stated only in terms of some other word or words, whose meaning likewise would call for further explanation. Since we must start somewhere, we shall consider "set" to be an "extramathematical," or "metamathematical," term, and leave it at that. (In a course in symbolic logic, a more searching analysis may be made.)

We will, however, deal only with "well-defined" sets. A set S is said to be well-defined when, for any given element x, there is a criterion to determine whether or not x is a member of S (synonomously, whether or not x belongs to S).

(vi) Frequent mention has been made of deducing conclusions from the hypotheses, i.e., of proving theorems based on the axioms. But nothing has been said about the rules of procedure by which we draw the conclusions. For the sake of completeness, these rules should be set down, but to do so is a lengthy business. We will assume that the reader is familiar with the principles of deductive reasoning and will omit explicit mention of them. The interested reader is referred to the following books on logic:

D. HILBERT and W. ACKERMAN, *Mathematical Logic*. New York: Chelsea (1950).

P. C. ROSENBLOOM, *Mathematical Logic*. New York: Dover (1950).

J. B. ROSSER, *Logic for Mathematicians*. New York: McGraw-Hill (1953).

(vii) An essential feature of a mathematical system is that the axioms form a *consistent* set. We do not wish to deal with a system in which it is possible to deduce both a theorem and its negation. In particular, if we have a consistent system and add axioms to form a new system (as often is done, c.f. the ideal points in Section 1–5), we must be sure that the added axioms are consistent with the earlier ones.

PROBLEM SET 3–1

1. Analyze what is wrong with the following well-known "proof" that every triangle is isosceles. Let the perpendicular bisector of side AB and the bisector of $\angle C$ meet at O (Fig. 3–1). Draw OA and OB, and also draw OM perpendicular to CA, and ON perpendicular to CB. Then right triangles OMC and ONC are congruent (hypotenuse and leg of one . . .). Hence $CM = CN$. Also right triangles OMA and ONB are congruent (again, hypotenuse and leg of one . . .). Therefore $MA = NB$. Hence, by subtracting equals, we have $CA = CB$. Q.E.D.

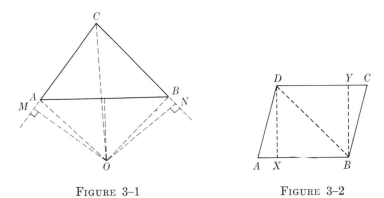

FIGURE 3–1   FIGURE 3–2

2. Analyze what is wrong with the following argument. In quadrilateral $ABCD$ (Fig. 3–2), if $\angle A \cong \angle C$, and if $AD = BC$, we have a parallelogram.

Proof. Draw DX perpendicular to AB, and BY perpendicular to CD. Then $\triangle ADX \cong \triangle CBY$ (hypotenuse and acute angle). Hence $DX = BY$ and $AX = CY$. Draw BD. Then $\triangle BDX \cong \triangle DBY$ (hypotenuse and leg). Hence $XB = YD$. Therefore, $AX + XB = CY + YD$, i.e., $AB = CD$, and so the figure is a parallelogram.

3–2 NOTATIONS, CONVENTIONS, AND ABBREVIATIONS; EQUIVALENCE RELATIONS

There are certain definitions, conventions, and abbreviations which are standard in mathematical literature. Some of them will be explained now in order to simplify the subsequent presentation.

(1) The elements of a set are usually symbolized by letters. We would read $S\{a, b, c, d\}$ as "the set S with elements a, b, c, d," and $T\{x, y, z, \ldots\}$ as "the set T with elements x, y, z, and so on." The fact that the element

u is a member of (belongs to) the set A is symbolized by $u \in A$; if u does not belong to A, we write $u \notin A$.

(2) If each of the elements of a set A is also an element of a set B, we say that A is a *subset* of B, or that A is contained in B, and write $A \subseteq B$. According to this definition, any set is a subset of itself, i.e., $B \subseteq B$. If each of the elements of A is an element of B, but not every element of B is an element of A, we call A a *proper subset* of B and write $A \subset B$. Two sets, P and Q, are *equal* if they have the same elements as members or, equivalently, if every member of P is a member of Q and vice versa; i.e., $P = Q$ is equivalent to $P \subseteq Q$ and $Q \subseteq P$.

(3) If S_1 and S_2 are sets, the *intersection* of S_1 and S_2, symbolized as $S_1 \cap S_2$, is the set whose elements are those common to S_1 and S_2. It is convenient, for reasons which won't be discussed now, to call the set which has no members, the *null set*, symbolized by $\emptyset$. Two sets are called *disjoint* if they have no common elements; in other words S_1 and S_2 are disjoint if $S_1 \cap S_2 = \emptyset$.

The set of elements which lie in S_1 or in S_2 or in both is called the *union* of S_1 and S_2, designated by $S_1 \cup S_2$.

$S_1 \cap S_2$ is usually read as "S_1 cap S_2," and $S_1 \cup S_2$ as "S_1 cup S_2."

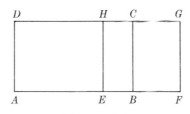

FIGURE 3–3

For example (Fig. 3–3), if S_1 is the set of points inside the rectangle $ABCD$ and if S_2 is the set of points inside and on the rectangle $EFGH$, then $S_1 \cap S_2$ is the set of points inside the rectangle $EBCH$ and on the segment EH, excluding E and H; and $S_1 \cup S_2$ is the set of points inside the rectangle $AFGD$ and on the segments EF, FG, and GH.

Note that $\cap$ and $\cup$ are binary operations on sets, according to the terminology of Example (3), Section 3–1.

(4) Parentheses and brackets are used to indicate grouping and precedence in the order of performing operations. In ordinary arithmetic, for example, since $+$ is a binary operation, we should write $(3 + 2) + 4$ or $3 + (2 + 4)$. However, since $(3 + 2) + 4 = 3 + (2 + 4)$, we can write $3 + 2 + 4$ without ambiguity. Likewise, for the binary operation $\cap$ on sets, we would understand that

$$S = (A \cap B) \cap C$$

is the set obtained by taking the intersection of A and B and finding its intersection with C, and

$$T = A \cap (B \cap C)$$

is the set obtained by finding the intersection of A and the set which is the intersection of B and C. Since $S = T$, as is easy to check, we may omit the grouping symbols and write $A \cap B \cap C$; similarly, with $A \cup B \cup C$.

In ordinary algebra, $a(b + c)$ means that we multiply a and the sum of b and c. If it were intended that we first multiply a and b, and then add c to the product, we might indicate this by $(a \cdot b) + c$. Ordinarily the parentheses are omitted from this expression because of the convention that multiplication takes precedence over addition if there is no indication of a contrary order.

There is no comparable convention in the case of sets and the operations $\cap$ and $\cup$ which permits us to dispense with parentheses. It is clear that $A \cap (B \cup C)$ and $(A \cap B) \cup C$ are generally not the same sets. (See Problem 2 below.)

(5) If p and q are propositions, we shall use $p \Rightarrow q$ for "p implies q," and $p \Leftrightarrow q$ for "p implies q and q implies p"; or "p if and only if q"; or "p is necessary and sufficient for q"; or "p is logically equivalent to q."

In all mathematical systems we have the binary relation "equality." Two symbols a and b are equal if they represent the same entity in the system. Either of two equal symbols may be substituted for the other at any occurrence in a mathematical statement.

The preceding sentence is loosely stated, and could be misinterpreted. For example, if $a = b$, can we substitute b for a in the statement, "The first letter of our alphabet is a"? We shall not take the trouble to make a precise statement about "substitutability" which will rule out misinterpretation. In practice, we will not encounter difficulty.

Many mathematical systems also have a binary relation "equivalence," akin to equality, but somewhat weaker. In a set $\mathcal{S}\{a, b, c, \ldots\}$ a binary relation, $\sim$, existing between some elements, is an *equivalence* provided the following three axioms are satisfied.

For every element p of $\mathcal{S}$, $p \sim p$: (Reflexivity).

If $p \sim q$, then $q \sim p$: (Symmetry).

If $p \sim q$, and if $q \sim r$, then $p \sim r$: (Transitivity).

These axioms will occasionally be referred to as (R), (S), and (T). It is not intended that the use of distinct symbols (p, q, r) in these axioms implies that all the elements which are referred to are distinct. It is clear that equality is an equivalence relation. But there are many other relations which also satisfy these axioms.

EXAMPLE 1. Suppose that S is the set of natural numbers (positive integers), and $x \sim y$ is interpreted to mean that x and y leave the same remainder when divided by 5. Then

$$1 \sim 6 \sim 11 \sim 16 \sim \cdots,$$
$$2 \sim 7 \sim 12 \sim 17 \sim \cdots,$$
$$3 \sim 8 \sim 13 \sim 18 \sim \cdots,$$
$$4 \sim 9 \sim 14 \sim 19 \sim \cdots,$$
$$5 \sim 10 \sim 15 \sim 20 \sim \cdots.$$

Indeed, we have here five subsets of S:

$$A_1\{1, \ \ 6, 11, 16, \ldots\},$$
$$A_2\{2, \ \ 7, 12, 17, \ldots\},$$
$$A_3\{3, \ \ 8, 13, 18, \ldots\},$$
$$A_4\{4, \ \ 9, 14, 19, \ldots\},$$
$$A_5\{5, 10, 15, 20, \ldots\},$$

in which we observe that: (1) any two elements from the same subset are equivalent, according to the given relation; (2) the subsets are "pairwise disjoint," i.e., no two subsets have a common element; and (3) every element of S appears in some subset.

We can write

$$S = A_1 \cup A_2 \cup A_3 \cup A_4 \cup A_5 = \bigcup_{i=1}^{5} A_i,$$

where $A_i \cap A_j = \emptyset$ for $i \neq j$, and can picture the situation as in Fig. 3–4.

What we have in this example is characteristic of equivalence relations. Every equivalence relation over a set divides the set into subsets which are pairwise disjoint and whose union is the entire set (technically, such a division is called a *decomposition* of the set). The subsets consist of equivalent elements, with respect to the given relation, and are known as *equivalence classes*.

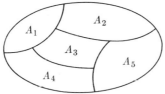

FIGURE 3–4

EXAMPLE 2.   Let S consist of the set of nonnegative integers, and let $x \sim y$ mean that $x - y$ is divisible by 3, i.e., that $x - y = 3k$, where k is an integer (positive, negative, or zero).   This relation is an equivalence (Problem 3a below).   The relation decomposes S into $A_0\{0, 3, 6, 9, \ldots\}$, $A_1\{1, 4, 7, 10, \ldots\}$, $A_2\{2, 5, 8, 11, \ldots\}$, with

$$S = A_0 \cup A_1 \cup A_2, \qquad A_i \cap A_j = \emptyset \quad \text{for} \quad i \neq j.$$

The equivalence classes may be described, respectively, as consisting of integers divisible by 3, of integers leaving a remainder of 1 on division by 3, and of integers leaving a remainder of 2 on division by 3.

Another notation for the relation in this case follows: $x \equiv y$ (mod 3). This is read, "x is congruent to y, modulo 3." The equivalence relation of Example 1 is rendered as $x \equiv y$ (mod 5).

EXAMPLE 3.   Let S consist of all ordered triples of complex numbers (x_0, x_1, x_2) except $(0, 0, 0)$.   Let $(p_0, p_1, p_2) \sim (q_0, q_1, q_2)$ if there is a complex number k such that $p_i = kq_i$, $i = 0, 1, 2$.   This relation is an equivalence (Problem 3(b), below).   If we think of the triads as homogeneous coordinates of points in the extended plane of the complex domain, then all the members of an equivalence class are associated with the same point.   Any triad is a "representative" of the equivalence class to which it belongs.   When we deal with the points of the extended plane in the complex domain, we are in effect working with the equivalence classes as entities, not distinguishing between two different triads of the same equivalence class.

PROBLEM SET 3–2

1. Give an example of three sets A, B, C such that $A \cap B \cap C = \emptyset$, but no pair of the sets is disjoint.

2. (a) With the help of pictures similar to that of Fig. 3–3, verify that if A, B, C are sets, $(A \cup B) \cap C = (A \cap C) \cup (B \cap C)$. Is $(A \cap B) \cup C$ equal to $(A \cup C) \cap (B \cup C)$?

(b) Going back to the definition of equality of sets, establish rigorously the results of (a).

3. (a) Verify that the relation of Example 2 is an equivalence.

(b) Similarly for the relation of Example 3.

4. In each of the following, state which of the axioms (R), (S), (T) of this section are satisfied; and, if the given relation is an equivalence, describe the following equivalence classes.

(a) S = all positive integers, $x \sim y$ means $x + y$ is an even number.

(b) S = all positive integers, $x \sim y$ means $x > y$.

(c) S = all positive integers, $x \sim y$ means $x \geq y$.

(d) S = all real numbers; $x \sim y$ means $|x - y| \leq \frac{1}{2}$.

(e) S = all ordinary lines of the plane; $x \sim y$ means x and y have the same direction.

(f) S = set of all triangles; $x \sim y$ means x is similar to y.

(g) S = $\{1, 2, 4, 6, 10\}$; $x \sim y$ means $x + y$ is divisible by 4.

5. What is wrong with the following "proof" that axioms (S) and (T) imply (R)?

For any p, let $p \sim q$. Then, by (S), $q \sim p$. Hence by (T), since $p \sim q$ and $q \sim p$, we have $p \sim p$. (Cf. Problem 4(g) above.)

6. Let U be a proper subset of a set V, and let R be a relation in V defined as follows: $xRy \Leftrightarrow x, y$ both belong to U. Show that this relation is symmetric and transitive, but not reflexive.

7. Let Axiom (T′) be the following: if $p \sim q$ and $q \sim r$, then $r \sim p$. Show that (R) and (T′) imply (S), and hence (T).

8. To establish $p \leftrightarrow q$, it is necessary to demonstrate two implications: $p \Rightarrow q$ and $q \Rightarrow p$. What is the smallest number of implications which must be demonstrated in order to establish $p_1 \leftrightarrow p_2 \leftrightarrow p_3 \leftrightarrow \cdots \leftrightarrow p_n$?

3–3 AXIOMS AND ELEMENTARY PROPERTIES OF A FIELD

Up to this point we have assumed general agreement as to the properties of the number system of algebra. The time has come to examine our basic number systems carefully and to develop their properties with some precision. We choose to consider first the mathematical system called a field, of which we shall find many examples among the familiar sets of numbers with which we have worked. It will be helpful to you if you keep in mind the properties of the complex numbers while considering the axioms presented below. Some remarks have been interpolated among the axioms for clarity; these remarks are not part of the definition of a field.

Definition 1.   A *field* is a set of elements $\mathcal{F}\{a, b, c, \ldots\}$ with two binary operations designated as "$+$" and "$\cdot$" satisfying the following eleven axioms A1 through A5; M1 through M5; and D.   The operations are read "plus" and "times."

Axiom A1.   *Possibility of Addition.* The sum of any two elements of $\mathcal{F}$ is an element of $\mathcal{F}$.   (For each p, $q \in \mathcal{F}$ there is one $r \in \mathcal{F}$ such that $p + q = r$.)

The situation is sometimes described by saying that $\mathcal{F}$ is "closed under addition."

Axiom A2.   *Commutativity of Addition.* For any elements p, q of $\mathcal{F}$, the sum of p and q is the same as the sum of q and p. $(p + q = q + p.)$

Axiom A3. *Associativity of Addition.* For any elements p, q, r of $\mathfrak{F}$, the result of adding p to the sum of q and r is the same as that of adding the sum of p and q to r. $[p + (q + r) = (p + q) + r.]$

Axiom A4. *An Additive Identity.* There is an element z in $\mathfrak{F}$ which, when added to any element of $\mathfrak{F}$, gives that element for the sum. (There is a z in $\mathfrak{F}$, such that $x + z = x$ for all x in $\mathfrak{F}$.)

Note that we assume the existence of *an* additive identity z; we don't assume that there is only one such. Later we shall prove the uniqueness of the additive identity (Theorem 3–1).

Axiom A5. *An Additive Inverse.* For each p in $\mathfrak{F}$, and each additive identity element z, there is a p' in $\mathfrak{F}$ such that $p + p' = z$.

We shall see (Theorem 3–2) that each element of a field has only one additive inverse.

Axiom M1. *Possibility of Multiplication.* The product of any two elements of $\mathfrak{F}$ is an element of $\mathfrak{F}$. (For each h, $k \in \mathfrak{F}$, there is one $l \in \mathfrak{F}$ such that $h \cdot k = l$.) We say that $\mathfrak{F}$ is "closed under multiplication."

Axiom M2. *Commutativity of Multiplication.* For any elements p, q of $\mathfrak{F}$, $p \cdot q = q \cdot p$.

Axiom M3. *Associativity of Multiplication.* For any elements p, q, r of $\mathfrak{F}$, $p \cdot (q \cdot r) = (p \cdot q) \cdot r$.

Axiom M4. *A Multiplicative Identity.* There is an element u in $\mathfrak{F}$, with $u \neq z$, such that $x \cdot u = x$ for all x in $\mathfrak{F}$.

In Theorem 3–4 we shall prove that there is just one multiplicative identity element in a field.

Axiom M5. *A Multiplicative Inverse.* In $\mathfrak{F}$, for each p other than an additive identity element, and for each multiplicative identity element u, there is a p^* such that $p \cdot p^* = u$.

In Theorem 3–5 we shall prove that an element does not have more than one multiplicative inverse.

Axiom D. *Distributivity of Multiplication over Addition.* For any elements p, q, r in $\mathfrak{F}$, $p \cdot (q + r) = p \cdot q + p \cdot r$.

In everyday language, the (unique) additive identity is called the zero, 0; the additive inverse of an element p is called its negative, $-p$; the multiplicative identity element is called the unit, 1; and the multiplicative inverse of an element p is called its reciprocal, p^{-1}. For short, we may occasionally write $p - q$ for $p + (-q)$ and p/q for $p \cdot q^{-1}$. *Throughout this chapter, the symbols z and u will be reserved for the additive and multiplicative identities.*

Since a field is a mathematical system involving a set of elements and two operations, the following expression is a suggested notation:

$$\mathfrak{F} = \{S; +; \cdot\}.$$

When there is no possibility of misinterpretation, we may omit explicit mention of the operations and refer simply to the field $\mathfrak{F}$.

Definition 2. If a subset of the elements of a field $\mathfrak{F}$ form a field $\mathfrak{G}$ under the same two operations as those of $\mathfrak{F}$, then $\mathfrak{G}$ is called a subfield of $\mathfrak{F}$.

The significance of the concept of a field begins to appear if we consider some familiar sets with complex numbers as elements and with " + " and "·" having their *ordinary* arithmetic meanings. (If such a system is a field, it is called a *number field*.) As you can verify (Problem 1 below), the set of positive integers fails to satisfy several of the field axioms. Likewise the set of all integers is not a field, nor is the set of positive rational numbers. The set $\mathfrak{R}$ of all rational numbers (i.e., all numbers of the form p/q, where p and q are integers, and $q \neq 0$) *is* a field; so also are the set R of real numbers, and the set C of complex numbers. [Roughly speaking, a number field is a system with at least two elements *within* which all four of the arithmetic operations, addition, subtraction, multiplication, and division (except division by 0) can be performed.] Since in our set terminology, $\mathfrak{R} \subset R \subset C$, $\mathfrak{R}$ is a subfield of R, which is in turn a subfield of C.

There are many number fields in addition to the three just mentioned; some others are noted in Problem 4 below. There are many fields other than number fields, too. One important type is illustrated as follows. Let the elements of $\mathfrak{F}$ be the integers 0, 1, 2, 3, 4, and let the operations + and · have their ordinary meanings with the following supplement. After a sum or product has been obtained, we subtract from the result the largest possible multiple of 5 which leaves the difference nonnegative. For example,

$$1 + 2 = 3; \quad 2 + 3 = 0; \quad 4 + 4 = 3;$$

$$3 \cdot 0 = 0; \quad 1 \cdot 4 = 4; \quad 4 \cdot 3 = 2,$$

and so forth.

The entire addition and multiplication tables look like the following tables.

+	0	1	2	3	4
0	0	1	2	3	4
1	1	2	3	4	0
2	2	3	4	0	1
3	3	4	0	1	2
4	4	0	1	2	3

·	0	1	2	3	4
0	0	0	0	0	0
1	0	1	2	3	4
2	0	2	4	1	3
3	0	3	1	4	2
4	0	4	3	2	1

To read the sum of 3 and 1, for instance, we find the number at the intersection of the "3" row and the "1" column of the "+" table. Since our operation "+" is clearly commutative, we expect to find the same number at the intersection of the "1" row and the "3" column. The table is symmetrical about a line joining the upper left-hand corner to the lower right-hand corner.

That this system is a field can be established by checking that all the axioms are satisfied, as follows:

(A1) and (M1). Since all the numbers in the bodies of the two tables are members of $\mathfrak{F}$, the set is closed under + and ·.

(A2) and (M2). Since both tables are symmetrical about a diagonal running from upper left to lower right, the operations are commutative.

(A3) and (M3). By laborious checking, we can determine that both operations are associative.

(A4) and (M4). The additive identity is 0; the multiplicative identity is 1.

(A5) and (M5). Since 0 appears in every row of the addition table, there is an additive inverse or negative of each element. The negative of 0 is 0; of 1, 4; of 2, 3; of 3, 2; and of 4, 1. Since 1 appears in every row, except the "0" row of the multiplication table, there is a multiplicative inverse or reciprocal of each element except 0. The reciprocal of 1 is 1; of 2, 3; of 3, 2; and of 4, 4.

(D) The distributivity of multiplication over addition can be checked (laboriously) by straightforward computation.

Since it is clear that the reduction by multiples of 5 could be postponed to the end of a series of ordinary additions and multiplications, thereby giving the same result as though the reduction by multiples of 5 were performed after each sum or product, we could appeal to the known commutativity, associativity, and distributivity of ordinary arithmetic to establish Axioms A2, A3, A5, M2, M3, M5 and D, if we wished to do so.

The field $\mathfrak{F}\{0, 1, 2, 3, 4\}$ is called "the field of residues, modulo 5," i.e., the field of remainders of integers with respect to division by 5. Since $\mathfrak{F}$ has a finite number of elements (five of them), it is called a *finite field of order* 5. Such "modular fields" are of importance in both algebra and geometry. Note that $\mathfrak{F}$ is *not* a number field, for, although its elements are numbers, the operations are not ordinary addition and multiplication.

We now present a few basic theorems about fields. Other theorems will be considered later.

Theorem 3–1. A field has only one additive identity element.

Proof. Suppose that a field $\mathfrak{F}$ has an additive identity $\tilde{z}$, as well as the postulated additive identity z. Then, $x + \tilde{z} = x$ for all $x \in \mathfrak{F}$. For $x = z$, this gives $z + \tilde{z} = z$. But, by the property of z, $\tilde{z} + z = \tilde{z}$. By the commutativity of addition $\tilde{z} + z = z + \tilde{z}$. Hence, $\tilde{z} = z$.

Theorem 3–2. Each element of a field has only one additive inverse.

Proof. Suppose that a certain element a of $\mathfrak{F}$ has an additive inverse a'' as well as the postulated additive inverse a'. Then $a + a' = z$ and $a + a'' = z$. Hence $a + a' = a + a''$. Keep in mind that this equality means that the element represented by $(a + a')$ is the same element as that symbolized by $(a + a'')$. Hence

$$a' + (a + a') = a' + (a + a'').$$

Now, by associativity and commutativity,

$$a' + (a + a') = (a' + a) + a' = (a + a') + a' = z + a' = a' + z = a',$$

and

$$a' + (a + a'') = (a' + a) + a'' = (a + a') + a'' = z + a'' = a'' + z = a''.$$

Hence $a'' = a'$. (See Problem 9 below.)

Theorem 3–3. *Cancellation law of addition.* If p, q, r are elements of a field, and if $p + r = q + r$, then $p = q$.

Proof. Since $(p + r)$ and $(q + r)$ are the same element, $(p + r) + r' = (q + r) + r'$, where r' is the negative of r. Now, $(p + r) + r' = p + (r + r') = p + z = p$, and, similarly, $(q + r) + r' = q$. Hence $p = q$. There are three analogous theorems about the operation "·":

Theorem 3–4. A field has only one multiplicative identity element.

Theorem 3–5.   Each element of a field, other than the zero, has only one multiplicative inverse.

Theorem 3–6.   *Cancellation law of multiplication.* In a field, if $a \cdot b = a \cdot c$, and if a is not the zero, then $b = c$.

The proofs of these theorems are analogous to those of Theorems 3–1, 3–2, and 3–3 (Problem 10 below).

We observe again that the axioms of a field fall into three sets: Axioms A1 through A5, dealing with "$+$"; Axioms M1 through M5, dealing with "$\cdot$" in analogous fashion, except for the distinguished role of zero in M5; and the lone Axiom D, relating the operations "$+$" and "$\cdot$". In these axioms then, "$+$" and "$\cdot$" fail in two respects to enter symmetrically: every element is assumed to have a negative, but zero is not assumed to have a reciprocal, and $\cdot$ is assumed to be distributive over $+$, but not vice versa (see Problem 13 below).

PROBLEM SET 3–3

*1. Which of the axioms of a field are not satisfied by each of the following sets of numbers, with the operations ordinary addition and multiplication? [Note that if Axiom A1 fails, so also does A2, for the symbol $p + q$ is not defined for some p, q within the universe we are considering.]

  (a) the odd positive integers, $\{1, 3, 5, \ldots\}$;
  (b) the positive integers, $\{1, 2, 3, \ldots\}$;
  (c) the nonnegative integers, $\{0, 1, 2, 3, \ldots\}$;
  (d) all fractions of the form $n/2$, n integral;
  (e) the even integers, positive and negative, including zero;
  (f) all the integers;
  (g) all the positive rational numbers, i.e., fractions p/q, where p and q are positive integers.

2. Which of the axioms of a field are not satisfied by the set $\{0, 1\}$ with the following addition and multiplication tables?

$+$	0	1		$\cdot$	0	1
0	0	1		0	0	1
1	1	0		1	0	1

*3. In Problem 1, since the operations $+$ and $\cdot$ have their ordinary arithmetical meanings, the axioms of commutativity and associativity are necessarily satisfied.

  (a) Verify that for the following sets, the given operations are neither commutative nor associative:

    (i)   the set of integers, ordinary subtraction;
    (ii) $\mathfrak{R}$, the set of rationals, ordinary division;
    (iii) the set of integers, ordinary raising to a power.

(b) We shall later study some significant operations which are associative but not commutative. Verify that for the set of positive integers, the operation "∘" defined as follows is commutative but not associative.

For $x \neq y$, $x \circ y = \max [x, y]$, i.e., the larger of the integers x, y.

For all x, $x \circ x = 1$.

(c) Observe that the operation ∘ defined by $x \circ y = x + 2y$ is neither commutative nor associative. Find all possible values of the ambiguous expression $a \circ a \circ a \circ a$.

(d) Show that, if an operation ∘ is commutative, then the expression $a \circ a \circ a$ is unambiguous. Give an example to show that the expression $a \circ a \circ a \circ a$ may be ambiguous even if the operation is commutative.

(e) Let an operation ∘ be defined for all real numbers as follows:

$$x \circ y = Axy + B(x + y) + C,$$

for fixed real numbers A, B, C. Show that a necessary and sufficient condition for this operation to be associative is that $B^2 - B - AC = 0$.

4. Show that in a field, $(a + b)(c + d) = ac + bc + ad + bd$.

5. Make up the addition and multiplication tables for a field with 2 elements; with 3 elements.

6. *Notation.* $S = \{x + y\sqrt{3}\}$, with x and y rational, designates the set of *all* numbers of the form $x + y\sqrt{3}$, where x and y are rational.

Which of the following sets are number fields?

(a) $\{2x + y\sqrt{5}\}$, with x and y rational;

(b) $\{x + y\sqrt[3]{2}\}$, with x and y rational;

(c) $\{x + i\sqrt{2}\}$, with x rational, $i = \sqrt{-1}$;

(d) $\{x + iy\sqrt{2}\}$, with x and y rational, $i = \sqrt{-1}$.

7. Show that the field of rational numbers is a subfield of every number field. [*Hint:* Every number field contains 1, hence also $1 + 1$, hence, ...]

8. Write out the addition and multiplication tables for each of the following systems and state whether or not it is a field.

(a) $S_7\{0, 1, 2, 3, 4, 5, 6\}$—residues, modulo 7;

(b) $S_2\{0, 1\}$ —residues, modulo 2;

(c) $S_6\{0, 1, 2, 3, 4, 5\}$ —residues, modulo 6.

9. Note that the proof given in the text for Theorem 3–2 makes use of the result of Theorem 3–1. Obtain a shorter proof, not depending on the result of Theorem 3–1, by considering alternative simplifications of the expression $a' + (a + a'')$.

10. (a), (b), (c). Write out proofs of Theorems 3–4 through 3–6.

*11. (a) Show that if $p, q \in \mathfrak{F}$, then there is a unique x in $\mathfrak{F}$ such that $p + x = q$.

(b) Show that if $p, q \in \mathfrak{F}$ and if $p \neq z$, then there is a unique y in $\mathfrak{F}$ such that $p \cdot y = q$.

12. Consider the set of all real numbers greater than 0 with "$a + b$" interpreted as the ordinary product ab and "$a \cdot b$" interpreted as $a^{\log b}$, where the base of logarithms is some positive number different from 1. Is the system a field? (Donald Miller)

13. Are the first ten axioms of a field together with the following alternative to Axiom D consistent?

Axiom $\overline{\text{D}}$. *Distributivity of addition over multiplication.* For all p, q, r of $\mathfrak{F}$, $p + (q \cdot r) = (p + q) \cdot (p + r)$. [*Hint:* Consider the element $u + (u \cdot z)$].

14. Is the set of all real numbers, with a "plus" b defined as $a + b + 1$, and a "times" b defined as $a + b + ab$, a field?

15. Show that in a field, the additive inverse of the sum of two elements equals the sum of the respective additive inverses; likewise for the multiplicative inverse.

16. Which axioms of a field are not satisfied by the set of integers $-k$, $-(k-1), \ldots, 0, 1, \ldots, k$, with operations defined as follows in terms of ordinary addition and multiplication:

$$x \oplus y = \begin{cases} x + y, & \text{if } |x + y| \leq k, \\ 0, & \text{otherwise}, \end{cases}$$

$$x \odot y = \begin{cases} xy, & \text{if } |xy| \leq k, \\ 0, & \text{otherwise}? \end{cases}$$

3–4 FURTHER DISCUSSION OF FIELDS AND RELATED SYSTEMS; ORDERING

Near the beginning of Section 3–3, we set forth a set of axioms for a field, the motivation presumably coming from familiarity with properties of various number systems, including the complex number system. But if you had been asked what you considered to be the fundamental properties of arithmetical operations, it is unlikely that you would have chosen precisely the eleven postulates enumerated in Section 3–3.

You might have thought of the zero, for example, as being the element "which, when added to itself, gives itself."

Axiom A4′. There is an element z in $\mathfrak{F}$ such that $z + z = z$.

If, in the set of eleven axioms, Axiom A4 is replaced by A4′, the resulting set will not define a field; A4′ is weaker than A4. But if, in addition, the cancellation law of addition is assumed:

Axiom A4″. If p, q, r belong to $\mathfrak{F}$, and if $p + r = q + r$, then $p = q$, and we *do* have a field.

Axiom A4″, of course, was proved as Theorem 3–3, deduced from Axioms A1 through A5, M1 through M5, and D. That Axioms A4′ and A4″ can replace A4 in the set of axioms of a field follows from the fact that A4 can be deduced as a theorem from Axioms A1, A3, A4′, and A4″ (Problem 1, below).

Another property of zero which you might be inclined to consider fundamental in arithmetic is that "zero multiplied by any number is zero." This is true in any field, and can be deduced from the basic eleven axioms.

Theorem 3-7. In any field, $z \cdot x = z$.
The proof is left to you (Problem 2 below).

A somewhat more complicated relation involving zero is brought out by the following theorem, which will be recognized as basic to the solution of equations by factoring.

Theorem 3-8. In any field, if $x \cdot y = z$, then $x = z$ or $y = z$.
The proof again is left to you (Problem 3 below).

Remarks on Theorem 3-8. (i) The statement of the conclusion of the theorem does not preclude the possibility that *both* $x = z$ and $y = z$.

(ii) The theorem furnishes a short proof that the set of residues mod 6 is not a field, since $3 \cdot 2 = 0$, although $3 \neq 0$ and $2 \neq 0$. (Cf. Problem 8c of Section 3-3; also Problem 5 below.)

It will be remembered that the intersection and union of a pair of sets S_1 and S_2 were discussed in §(3) of Section 3-2. Suppose now that two operations " $+$ " and "$\cdot$" are defined so that S_1, with these operations, forms a field $\mathfrak{F}_1$, say, and S_2, with the same operations, forms a field $\mathfrak{F}_2$. Then we have the following theorem.

Theorem 3-9. The intersection, $S_1 \cap S_2$, with the same operations as $\mathfrak{F}_1$ and $\mathfrak{F}_2$, forms a field. (It is natural to designate this field as $\mathfrak{F}_1 \cap \mathfrak{F}_2$).

Proof. The proof of the theorem is easy. If $a, b \in (S_1 \cap S_2)$, then $a, b \in S_1$ and $a, b \in S_2$. Hence, $(a + b) \in S_1$ and $(a + b) \in S_2$, by Axiom A1. That is, $(a + b) \in (S_1 \cap S_2)$, which means that Axiom A1 is satisfied for $S_1 \cap S_2$; similarly for the zero, the negative of an element, etc. Commutativity, associativity, and distributivity are known immediately to hold in $S_1 \cap S_2$ because of their holding in S_1 and S_2.

Obviously, $\mathfrak{F}_1 \cap \mathfrak{F}_2$ is the largest field which is a subfield of both $\mathfrak{F}_1$ and $\mathfrak{F}_2$.

If the operations $+$ and $\cdot$ are such as to be meaningful for two elements, one from S_1 and the other from S_2, as well as when both elements come from the same set, we can ask whether $S_1 \cup S_2$ is a field with respect to these operations. But this is not always the case, for if $x \in S_1$ and $y \in S_2$, $x + y$ is not necessarily a member of $S_1 \cup S_2$. Thus, if there is a smallest field which contains both S_1 and S_2, it may include $S_1 \cup S_2$ as a *proper* subset.

EXAMPLE. Let $\mathfrak{F}_1$ be the number field whose elements are $p + q\sqrt{2}$, for p, q rational, and let $\mathfrak{F}_2$ be the number field whose elements are $r + s\sqrt{3}$, for r, s rational. Then clearly, the field $\mathfrak{R}$ of rational numbers is contained in both $\mathfrak{F}_1$ and $\mathfrak{F}_2$, and hence $\mathfrak{R} \subseteq \mathfrak{F}_1 \cap \mathfrak{F}_2$. Moreover, any element in both $\mathfrak{F}_1$ and $\mathfrak{F}_2$ is a rational number (Problem 6 below). Therefore, $\mathfrak{R} = \mathfrak{F}_1 \cap \mathfrak{F}_2$.

The union of $\mathfrak{F}_1$ and $\mathfrak{F}_2$ does not contain numbers of the sort

$$p + q\sqrt{2} + r + s\sqrt{3}$$

for $q \neq 0$, $s \neq 0$. Hence $\mathfrak{F}_1 \cup \mathfrak{F}_2$ is not a field.

In the field of rational numbers, in the field of real numbers, and in some other fields, there is an "ordering relation," symbolized by $<$. A field $\mathfrak{O}$ is "ordered" if the following conditions are satisfied.

Axiom O1. If $a, b \in \mathfrak{O}$, then exactly one of the following holds: (i) $a = b$, (ii) $a < b$, (iii) $b < a$.

Axiom O2. If $a, b, c \in \mathfrak{O}$, if $a < b$, and if $b < c$, then $a < c$ (Transitivity).

Axiom O3. If $a, b, x \in \mathfrak{O}$, and if $a < b$, then $a + x < b + x$.

Axiom O4. If $a, b \in \mathfrak{O}$, if $z < a$, and if $z < b$, then $z < a \cdot b$; (z is the zero).

A *set* is customarily called simply ordered or linearly ordered if Axioms O1 and O2 are satisfied. But for a *field* to be called "ordered" all of Axioms O1 through O4 must be satisfied.

Many fields do not have an order; that is, there is no binary relation between elements of some fields satisfying Axioms O1 through O4. For example, in the field of residues, mod 5, we might try to order the elements in the normal fashion: $0 < 1 < 2 < 3 < 4$. Most of the desired properties of an order relation are preserved in this interpretation, but Axiom O3 fails. Although $1 < 3$, it is *not* true that $1 + 2 < 3 + 2$.

The failure of the attempted ordering does not imply that some different attempt would not suceed. However, it should be easy for you to prove that if $\mathfrak{F}$ is the field of residues, modulo any prime number p, then no assumed ordering of the elements of $\mathfrak{F}$

$$f_1 < f_2 < \cdots < f_p,$$

will satisfy all the Axioms O1 through O4 (Problem 8 below).

Likewise, the field of complex numbers cannot be ordered so as to satisfy Axioms O1 through O4. To see this, assume that i (defined by $i^2 = -1$) is ordered relative to 0 (i.e., z) as follows: $0 < i$. Then writing the relation, $0 < i$, again and applying Axiom O4 gives $0 < -1$. The application of O4 to $0 < -1$, $0 < -1$ yields $0 < 1$; while the application of O3 to $0 < -1$ gives $0 + 1 < -1 + 1$, or $1 < 0$. These contradictory results show that the hypothesis $0 < i$ is incompatible with the ordering axioms. A similar chain of argument would show that $i < 0$ is also inconsistent with Axioms O1 through O4. Since $i \neq 0$, we see that none of the possibilities of Axiom O1 holds for 0 and i. Hence, the impossibility of ordering the field of complex numbers.

PROBLEM SET 3–4

1. Show that Axioms A1, A3, A4′, A4″ imply Axiom A4. [*Hint:* Start with $z + z = z$, and add a to each side.]

2. Prove Theorem 3–7. [*Hint:* Start with $a + z = a$, and multiply each side by x.]

3. Prove Theorem 3–8. [Assume that $x \neq z$ and multiply each side by x^{-1}.]

*4. Is the following system a field?

The set of all polynomials with complex numbers as coefficients, in which the operations are the familiar addition and multiplication of polynomials.

5. *Definition.* An integer is *composite* if it is not a prime number.

(a) Show that the set of residues modulo a composite integer, with addition and multiplication defined as in Section 3–3 for the field of residues mod 5, is not a field.

(b) Show that the set of residues modulo a prime number, with the operations defined as in part (a), *is* a field.

6. Prove that if p, q, r, $s \in \mathfrak{R}$, and if

$$p + q\sqrt{2} = r + s\sqrt{3},$$

then $p = r$ and $q = 0 = s$. In making the proof, you may appeal to any properties of integers and rational numbers that you know.

7. Let $\mathfrak{F}$ be the field of all numbers of the form $a + b\sqrt{2}$, a, b rational, the operations being ordinary addition and multiplication. Show that the only subfields of $\mathfrak{F}$ are $\mathfrak{R}$ (the field of rationals) and $\mathfrak{F}$ itself.

8. (a) Prove the statement in the text that the field of residues, modulo a prime p cannot be ordered so as to satisfy Axioms O1 through O4.

(b) Show that *no* finite field can be ordered so as to satisfy Axioms O1 through O4.

*9. (a) $(a, b \in \mathfrak{F}) \Rightarrow [a' \cdot b = (a \cdot b)']$, where the prime indicates "additive inverse." [*Hint:* Start with $a + a' = z$];

(b) $(a, b \in \mathfrak{F}) \Rightarrow (a' \cdot b' = a \cdot b)$. (This is the familiar "minus times minus is plus" of arithmetic);

(c) $(z = \text{zero}, u = \text{unit, of an ordered field}) \Rightarrow (z < u)$. [*Hint:* Assume $u < z$ and apply Axioms O3 and O4];

(d) $(a, b, c \in$ ordered field; $a < b; z < c) \Rightarrow (a \cdot c < b \cdot c)$. [*Hint:* Start with $a < b$ and add a' to each side];

(e) $(a \in$ ordered field; $z < a) \Rightarrow (z < a^*)$, where a^* is the reciprocal of a. [*Hint:* Assume $a^* < z$ and apply parts (d) and (c) above];

(f) $(a, b \in \Re; a < b) \Rightarrow (a < (a+b)/2 < b)$. [*Hint:* Start with $a < b$; add a to each side; assume as known that $a + a = 2 \cdot a$, where $2 = 1 + 1$, 1 being the unit; also assume that

$$\frac{a+b}{2} = \frac{1}{2} \cdot (a+b),$$

where $\frac{1}{2}$ is the reciprocal of 2.]

10. In a field, it is clear that $z + x = x + z$, and that $p' + p = p + p'$, because of the assumed commutativity of addition (Axiom A2).

Consider a system in which Axioms A1, A3, A4, and A5 hold, but in which commutativity is not assumed. Show that each additive identity element commutes with every element, i.e., that $z + x = x + z = x$; and that each element commutes with each of its additive inverses, i.e., that $p + p' = p' + p = z$. [*Hint:* First prove Theorem 3–3 in this system.]

11. Consider a system consisting of a set S and one operation $(+)$ satisfying the following axioms: Axioms A1, A3, and A4$'$.

Axiom A5$'$.   For each $x \in$ S, there is at least one $\bar{x} \in$ S such that $\bar{x} + x = z$.

Axiom A5$''$.   For each $x \in$ S, there is at most one $\tilde{x} \in$ S such that $x + \tilde{x} = z$.

Show that in this system, Axioms A4 and A5 are satisfied (Olga Taussky).

*12. *Definition.* In a system S, if $a \cdot a = a$, the element a is said to be *idempotent*.

Clearly, the additive and multiplicative identity elements are both idempotent. Moreover, if Axiom M5 is satisfied in S, z and u are the only idempotent elements. (Prove this statement.) If there are interesting examples of idempotency, then they may be expected to be found in systems where not every nonzero element has a multiplicative inverse (cf. Chapter 6).

Let Axiom D$'$ be the following "two-sided" distributive axiom:

Axiom D$'$.   For all $a, b, c, a(b+c) = ab + ac$, and $(b+c)a = ba + ca$.

Show that, if Axioms A1 through A5, M1, and D$'$ are satisfied in S, and if, moreover, *every* element is idempotent, then Axiom M2 is satisfied in S. [*Hint:* Consider $(a+b) \cdot (a+b)$.]

3–5 THE REAL AND COMPLEX NUMBER SYSTEMS; ISOMORPHISM; SUMMARY

The result of Problem 9(f) of the preceding section shows that the rational numbers are *dense*, i.e., that between any two rational numbers there is a rational number (and, hence, that there are infinitely many rationals between any two rationals). This "density" is not enough to make the rational number system adequate for all problems in algebra (and in analytic geometry).

Our next step is to obtain the real number system, namely an ordered field in which every nonempty subset which has an upper bound has a *least* upper bound *in the field.* We explain this concept (formulated by the 19th-century mathematician, Richard Dedekind) by presenting some examples, argued informally, before making a formal statement.

(i) Consider $S = \mathfrak{R}$, and $M = \{x \in \mathfrak{R}; \ |x| \leq \frac{3}{2}\}$, i.e., let M be the subset of the rationals consisting of all rational numbers from $-\frac{3}{2}$ to $\frac{3}{2}$, both ends included. Then M has an upper bound; there is a (rational) number r such that all members of M are $\leq r$. Indeed, there are many upper bounds: 10, 4, $\frac{3}{2}$, are all upper bounds of M. (M is also bounded below in this example.) The least upper bound of M is $\frac{3}{2}$, which, in this case, belongs to M as well as to S.

(ii) Now consider $S = \mathfrak{R}$ again, and let $N = \{x \in \mathfrak{R}; \ x < \frac{3}{2}\}$. The set N is bounded above (but is not bounded below) and has the same least upper bound as M, viz., $\frac{3}{2}$. This least upper bound *is not* a member of N but *is* a member of S.

(iii) Consider, finally, the same set $S = \mathfrak{R}$ and the subset $L = \{x \in \mathfrak{R}; \ x^2 \leq \frac{3}{2}\}$. This set L is bounded and has many upper bounds: 4, 2, $\frac{3}{2}$, $\frac{4}{3}$ are some of them. But, within S, there is no least upper bound; it can be shown that, given any rational upper bound, we can find a smaller one.

In order that the bounded set L may have a least upper bound in S, S must contain the irrational number $\sqrt{\frac{3}{2}}$. If $S = R$, the set of real numbers, then L has a least upper bound in S.

The preceding discussion lacks rigor. There has been no definition of least upper bound, no proof that $\frac{3}{2}$ is a least upper bound of M, no proof that there is no rational least upper bound of L, no proof that $\sqrt{\frac{3}{2}}$ is irrational. But the discussion is intended merely as an introduction to the following formal statements.

Definition 3.   (a) An *upper bound* of an ordered set S is an element b such that $x \leq b$ for all $x \in S$.

(b) A *least upper bound* of an ordered set S (lub of S) is an element b_0 such that (i) b_0 is an upper bound of S, and (ii) if b is any upper bound of S, then $b_0 \leq b$.

It is easy to prove that a set can have only one least upper bound (Problem 1 below).

Axiom LUB (*Dedekind*).   If M is a nonempty subset of R, and if M has an upper bound, then M has a least upper bound in R.

It is suggested that you go over the statement of the least upper bound axiom several times, picturing various sets of numbers as points on a line, in order to become familiar with its statement and content.

Now, if we have a set R, two operations $+$ and $\cdot$, and a relation $<$, satisfying Axioms A1 through A5; M1 through M5; D; O1 through O4; LUB (with $\mathfrak{F}$ replaced by R in Axioms A1 through A5; M1 through M5; D, and with $\mathfrak{O}$ replaced by R in Axioms O1 through O4) we may call R the *real number system*. Or, more briefly, the real number system is the ordered field satisfying the Dedekind axiom. This is meaningful (a) only if the system has the properties which we are accustomed to associate with the arithmetic of real numbers, *and* (b) if there is only one system of the sort. Although we have not made a complete check in the foregoing development, it is clear that the system R does have properties that we expect of real numbers. The system is unique in the sense that two systems satisfying Axioms A1 through A5; M1 through M5; D; O1 through O4; LUB are abstractly identical, differing only in names or symbols.

The technical term for abstract identity is *isomorphism*. The concept of isomorphism is so important in mathematics that a rather complete discussion of the subject will be given now. The word is derived from the Greek "iso" meaning same and "morph" meaning form or structure; thus two systems are *isomorphic* if they have the same structure.

Definition 4.   Suppose that a certain mathematical system consists of a set $S(a, b, c, \ldots)$, with operations "$+$," "$\cdot$," etc., and with relations "$<$," "$\sim$," etc. Suppose that another system consists of a set $S(\bar{a}, \bar{b}, \bar{c}, \ldots)$, with operations $\oplus$, $\odot$, etc., and with relations $\oslash$, $\oslash$, etc. Then, the systems are *isomorphic* if there exists a one-to-one correspondence between their elements, between their operations, and between their relations such that the correspondence preserves operation and relation.

Thus, if an isomorphism is to exist, it is first necessary that it be possible to set up a one-to-one correspondence, such as the following:

$$a \leftrightarrow \bar{a}, \qquad \text{``}+\text{''} \leftrightarrow \oplus, \qquad \text{``}<\text{''} \leftrightarrow \oslash,$$
$$b \leftrightarrow \bar{b}, \qquad \text{``}\cdot\text{''} \leftrightarrow \odot, \qquad \text{``}\sim\text{''} \leftrightarrow \oslash,$$
$$\vdots$$

Moreover, the correspondence must be such that, if a "$+$" $b = c$ and $\bar{a} \oplus \bar{b} = \bar{c}$, then $c \leftrightarrow \bar{c}$. More concisely: a "$+$" $b \leftrightarrow \bar{a} \oplus \bar{b}$. Still another way of putting this requirement is as follows. If $\bar{x}$ symbolizes the element corresponding to x, then it must be true that for all a, b, $(\overline{a \text{ ``}+\text{''} b}) = \bar{a} \oplus \bar{b}$. Likewise, $(\overline{a \text{ ``}\cdot\text{''} b}) = \bar{a} \odot \bar{b}$, etc. When no confusion is possible, we may drop the circles around the symbols for the operations on the right-hand sides of these equations. Finally, the relations must also be preserved under the correspondence: if, for example, a "$<$" b, then it must be the case that $\bar{a} \leqslant \bar{b}$, etc.

EXAMPLE 1. In Problem 5 at the end of Section 3-3, the addition and multiplication tables for a field $\mathfrak{F}$ with 3 elements, would look like the following tables.

$\oplus$	z	u	a
z	z	u	a
u	u	a	z
a	a	z	u

$\odot$	z	u	a
z	z	z	z
u	z	u	a
a	z	a	u

The elements don't have to be symbolized by z, u, a—any 3 symbols would do. But since the field must contain the additive identity and the multiplicative identity, it is convenient to call them z and u; the symbol for the third element is quite arbitrary. Now suppose that we consider R_3, the field of residues mod 3. The elements of this field are 0, 1, 2, and the operations are ordinary addition and multiplication, with the results reduced by multiples of 3. Suppose that we represent these operations by $\oplus$ and $\odot$. Then we have the following one-to-one correspondence: $z \leftrightarrow 0$, $u \leftrightarrow 1$, $a \leftrightarrow 2$, $\vdash \leftrightarrow \oplus$, $\cdot \leftrightarrow \odot$. There is no relation in either field other than that of equality (identity). It is easy to verify that under the correspondence here set up, $\mathfrak{F}_3$ and R_3 are isomorphic (symbolized by $\mathfrak{F}_3 \cong R_3$): if p, q are any elements of $\mathfrak{F}_3$ and if $\bar{p}$, $\bar{q}$ are the corresponding elements of R_3, then $p + q \leftrightarrow \bar{p} \oplus \bar{q}$ and $p \cdot q \leftrightarrow \bar{p} \odot \bar{q}$.

Indeed, *any* two fields with 3 elements are isomorphic, as can be seen from the fact that there is only one way to fill in the addition and multiplication tables for the field with elements z, u, a.

It will be found, in our later work, that it is sometimes possible to set up a correspondence establishing the isomorphism of two systems in more than one way. But it will be found that necessarily the identity elements must correspond to each other. Likewise, if two elements correspond to each other, so also must their inverses correspond. In formal terms we have the following theorem.

Theorem 3-10. (a) Let $\mathcal{S}$, $\bar{\mathcal{S}}$ be two systems satisfying Axioms A1, A3, A4, and A5. Then if $\mathcal{S} \cong \bar{\mathcal{S}}$, the zero of $\mathcal{S}$ must correspond to the zero of $\bar{\mathcal{S}}$. Also, if $a \leftrightarrow \bar{a}$, then the additive inverse of a must correspond to the additive inverse of $\bar{a}$.

(b) Let $\mathfrak{I}$, $\overline{\mathfrak{I}}$ be two systems satisfying Axioms M1, M3, M4, and M5. Then, if $\mathfrak{I} \cong \overline{\mathfrak{I}}$, the unit of $\overline{\mathfrak{I}}$ must correspond to the unit of $\mathfrak{I}$. Also, if $a \leftrightarrow \overline{a}$, $a \neq z$, then the reciprocal of a must correspond to the reciprocal of $\overline{a}$.

The proof of this theorem is left to you (Problem 2 below).

EXAMPLE 2.   The field of rationals $\mathfrak{R}$ is not isomorphic to the field of reals R.

Actually, it can be shown (with some difficulty) that the set of rationals cannot be put into one-to-one correspondence with the set of reals in any way, but we can show the impossibility of the isomorphism more easily. Suppose that a one-to-one correspondence of the desired type were possible. Then, as a consequence of Theorem 3–10, the rational number 1 would have to correspond to the real number 1. Hence the rational number n (an integer) must correspond to the real number n; and, finally, the rational number p/q must correspond to the real number p/q. Thus the system of rationals corresponds to a proper subset of the reals (i.e., the rationals), and there is nothing left among the rationals for correspondence to $\sqrt{2}$, say, and to other irrationals. Hence the assumed isomorphism leads to the conclusion that no isomorphism is, in fact, possible between $\mathfrak{R}$ and R.

Finally (with only two more axioms) we get to the field C of complex numbers. C is a field satisfying the following conditions:

Axiom I 1. There is an i in C such that $i \cdot i = u'$. [Here u is the unit of the field, and u' is its negative.]

Axiom I 2. Every $a \in C$ can be written as $a = x + y \cdot i$, where $x, y \in R$.

SUMMARY

1. A system $\mathfrak{F}$ with two binary operations satisfying Axioms A1 through A5, M1 through M5, and D is a *field*. There are many sorts of fields: finite and infinite, ordered and nonordered. Although we began the discussion of fields to describe the complex numbers (for our complex geometry), we will find that many of the results of our geometry remain true when the "elements" of the geometry are defined in terms of members of an arbitrary field, and need not be restricted to the complex numbers.

2. A field $\mathfrak{O}$ with a binary relation satisfying Axioms O1 through O4 is an *ordered field*. The rationals and the reals are ordered fields.

3. An ordered field R satisfying Axiom LUB is the real number system. (Two ordered fields each satisfying Axiom LUB can be shown to be isomorphic.)

4. A field C having R as subfield and satisfying Axioms I1 and I2 is the complex number system. (Two fields each having R as a subfield and each satisfying Axioms I1 and I2 can be shown to be isomorphic.)

PROBLEM SET 3–5

1. Show that a set has at most one least upper bound. [*Hint:* Use an indirect proof.]

2. Prove Theorem 3–10.

3. (a) Show that if i satisfies $x \cdot x = u'$, then so does i'.

(b) Show that in any field, the equation $x \cdot x = a$ has at most two solutions. Is it possible that there are *no* solutions of this equation? What conclusion can be drawn about solutions, in a field, of the "general" quadratic equation

$$a \cdot x \cdot x + b \cdot x + c - z?$$

4. Let R be the set of real numbers, and let two operations, † and *, be defined in terms of ordinary addition and multiplication as follows: $a \,†\, b = a + b - ab$; $a * b = ab$. Which of Axioms A1 through A5, M1 through M5, and D are satisfied in this system? (Note that † may be interpreted as $+$ and $*$ as $\cdot$, or vice versa.)

*5. Consider a system S satisfying the following axioms of this chapter: Axioms A1 through A5, M1, M3, and D' (see Problem 12, Section 3–4, for Axiom D').

Let $[x, y]$ be an abbreviation for $xy - yx$, called the *commutator* of x and y. The following properties of the commutator are immediate. For all x in S, $[x, x] = 0$; for all x, y in S, $[x, y] = -[y, x]$. Verify the following properties for all u, v, w in S.

(a) $[u + v, w] = [u, w] + [v, w]$

(b) $[u + v, w] + [v + w, u] + [w + u, v] = 0$

(c) $[u, v \cdot w] = [u, v] \cdot w + v \cdot [u, w]$

(d) $[u, [v, w]] + [v, [w, u]] + [w, [u, v]] = 0$ (the Jacobi relation)

6. Let S be a system satisfying the axioms in the preceding problem, and assume, moreover, that $(p + p = 0) \Rightarrow (p = 0)$.) Show that if for all u, v, $uv + vu = 0$, then for all x, $x^2 = 0$, and conversely. [*Hint:* For the converse, express $uv + vu$ in terms of squares.]

7. (a) As we saw in Problem 5(a), Section 3–4, the set $\{0, 1, 2, 3\}$, with the operations of addition and multiplication mod 4, does *not* form a field. By trial, fill in $+$ and $\cdot$ tables for a set $\{z, u, a, b\}$ so as to obtain a field with four elements.

(b) Fill in the operation tables for the system consisting of the four polynomials: $0 + 0x$, $1 + 0x$, $0 + 1x$, $1 + 1x$, where addition is defined in the ordinary way, except that the coefficients are reduced mod 2; and multiplication is defined in the usual way, except that products are reduced mod $(1 + x + x^2)$, and coefficients are reduced mod 2.

(c) Show that the system in (b) is a field isomorphic to the field in (a).

8. Consider a system S consisting of the ordered field of rational numbers, augmented by two symbols α, α' subject to the following rules (suggested by the behavior of ∞ and $-\infty$).

(i) $x + \alpha = \alpha = \alpha + x$, for all $x \neq \alpha'$
(ii) $x + \alpha' = \alpha' = \alpha' + x$, for all $x \neq \alpha$
(iii) $\alpha + \alpha' = 0 = \alpha' + \alpha$
(iv) $x < \alpha$, for all $x \neq \alpha$
(v) $\alpha' < x$, for all $x \neq \alpha'$
(vi) $x\alpha = \alpha = \alpha x$, for all $x > 0$
(vii) $x\alpha = \alpha' = \alpha x$, for all $x < 0$
(viii) $x\alpha' = \alpha' = \alpha' x$, for all $x > 0$
(ix) $x\alpha' = \alpha = \alpha' x$, for all $x < 0$
(x) $0 \cdot \alpha = 1 = \alpha \cdot 0$
(xi) $0 \cdot \alpha' = 1 = \alpha' \cdot 0$

Which of the axioms of an ordered field are not satisfied by S?

3–6 GROUPS

We were led to consider fields because of our experience with number systems, involving, as they do, two binary operations. But there are significant mathematical systems which involve only *one* binary operation. One of the most important of such systems is called a *group*. Before we present the axioms defining a group, let us consider an example which will help to indicate why the particular axioms are chosen.

EXAMPLE. We work with the six expressions:

$$A = x, \qquad B = \frac{1}{x}, \qquad C = 1 - x,$$

$$D = \frac{1}{1 - x}, \qquad E = \frac{x - 1}{x}, \qquad F = \frac{x}{x - 1}.$$

We define a binary operation ∘ on two of these as the expression resulting from the substitution of the second expression for x in the first. Thus

$$D \circ E = \frac{1}{1 - (x - 1)/x} = x.$$

Hence, we write

$$D \circ E = A.$$

It is suggested that you write out the operation table for this set, and check your work against the following table.

∘	A	B	C	D	E	F
A	A	B	C	D	E	F
B	B	A	D	C	F	E
C	C	E	A	F	B	D
D	D	F	B	E	A	C
E	E	C	F	A	D	B
F	F	D	E	B	C	A

We shall encounter these six expressions later when we study "cross ratio" in projective geometry. Now we simply observe some algebraic properties of the system consisting of the set $S\{A, B, C, D, E, F\}$ and the operation ∘.

(1) The result of performing the operation ∘ on any two elements of S is an element of S; i.e., S is closed under the operation.

(2) The operation is not commutative; e.g., $B \circ C = D$ and $C \circ B = E$.

(3) There is an identity element, namely, A. For all P in S, $P \circ A = P$. Moreover, $A \circ P = P$.

(4) Each element has an inverse: $A \circ A = A$; $B \circ B = A$; $C \circ C = A$; $D \circ E = A$; $E \circ D = A$; $F \circ F = A$.

(5) Although it is not obvious, the operation is associative—for all P, Q, R in S, $P \circ (Q \circ R) = (P \circ Q) \circ R$.

We can check the associativity by laborious computation, or we can argue the associativity, in this case, as a property of the composition of functions, but we shall not take the time to do so.

Examples of this sort motivate the definition of a group.

Definition 5. A system consisting of a set S of elements a, b, c, . . . , and a binary operation ∘ is called a *group* if the following four axioms are satisfied.

G1. Possibility of the operation. For any a, $b \in S$ there exists one $c \in S$ such that $a \circ b = c$.

G2. Associativity of the operation.

G3. Existence of a right-identity element. There is an element $e \in S$ such that $x \circ e = x$ for all x in S.

G4. Existence of a right-inverse for each element. For each x in S and for each right-identity element e there is an x^* in S such that $x \circ x^* = e$.

Definition 6. If the operation of a group is commutative ($x \circ y = y \circ x$), then the group is called *Abelian*. (Named for the Norwegian mathematician N. H. Abel.)

As was the case with a field, we do not assume that there is only one identity element, nor do we assume that each element has only one inverse. But we can *prove* these results, by the argument suggested in Problem 10 of Section 3–4, and, in the process, we show that the identity and the inverse are *two sided*.

First we prove right-cancellation.

Theorem 3–11. In a group, if $p \circ r = q \circ r$, then $p = q$.

Proof. Let r^* be a right inverse of r. Then $(p \circ r) \circ r^* = (q \circ r) \circ r^*$. Hence $p \circ (r \circ r^*) = q \circ (r \circ r^*)$; i.e., $p \circ e = q \circ e$. Therefore, $p = q$.

Next we show that a right-identity element is also a left-identity element.

Theorem 3–12. If e is a right-identity element of a group, then $e \circ x = x$, for all x in S.

Proof. $e \circ e = e$. For any x in S, there is an x^* in S such that $x \circ x^* = e$, by G4. Hence $e \circ (x \circ x^*) = x \circ x^*$. Therefore, $(e \circ x) \circ x^* = x \circ x^*$. Thus, $e \circ x = x$, by Theorem 3–11.

It is now simple to show that a group has only one identity.

Theorem 3–13. A group has a unique identity element.

Proof. Suppose that a group has two identities, e_1 and e_2. Then $e_1 \circ e_2 = e_1$ by definition of e_2, and $e_1 \circ e_2 = e_2$, by Theorem 3–12. Hence $e_1 = e_2$.

Next we prove that a right inverse is also a left inverse:

Theorem 3–14. If x is any element of a group, and e is the identity element, and if $x \circ x^* = e$, then $x^* \circ x = e$.

Proof. $(x^* \circ x) \circ x^* = x^* \circ (x \circ x^*) = x^* \circ e = e \circ x^*$. Hence, by right-cancellation, $x^* \circ x = e$. It follows then, that

$$(r \circ p = r \circ q) \Rightarrow (p = q.)$$

Finally, we can prove that each element has only one inverse.

Theorem 3–15. The inverse of each element in a group is unique.

Proof. Suppose that an element x has two inverses, x^* and $\tilde{x}$. Then $x \circ x^* = e = x \circ \tilde{x}$. Hence, by left-cancellation, $x^* = \tilde{x}$.

Using the terminology introduced above, we can describe a field as a set S, with two binary operations, $+$ and $\cdot$, such that (i) under the operation $+$, S is an Abelian group; (ii) under the operation $\cdot$, S, without the $+$ identity, is an Abelian group; (iii) the operation $\cdot$ is distributive over the operation $+$. [This is not a complete description of a field, for it does not specify how the $+$ identity behaves with respect to the operation $\cdot$.]

Sometimes we shall be concerned with groups whose elements are specified as numbers or transformations or the like. If no specific interpretation is in mind, we may refer to the system as an *abstract group*.

Note that Theorem 3–11, the cancellation law for abstract groups, implies both Theorems 3–3 and 3–6 (the two cancellation laws for fields). Likewise Theorem 3–13, on the uniqueness of the identity element in a group, implies Theorems 3–1 and 3–4; and Theorem 3 15, on the uniqueness of the inverse of an element of a group, implies Theorems 3–2 and 3–5.

Definition 7. If a subset $\mathcal{3C}$ of a group $\mathcal{G}$ is itself a group relative to the operation of $\mathcal{G}$, then $\mathcal{3C}$ is called a subgroup of $\mathcal{G}$.

Definition 8. If there is only a finite number n of distinct elements in a group, the group is said to be of *order n*.

A group of order n is completely determined by the specification of its operation table. For example, if a group has the three elements u, a, b, its operation table must be (Problem 1 below) as follows.

$\cdot$	u	a	b
u	u	a	b
a	a	b	u
b	b	u	a

It should be clear that if a square array is to be the operation table of a group, each element of the group must appear once in each row and column. An array of this type, in which each element appears once in each row and column, is called a *Latin square*. Not every Latin square, however, is the operation table of a group (Problem 2 below).

PROBLEM SET 3–6

1. Show that there is just one abstract group of order 1, of order 2, of order 3.

2. (a) Find the abstract groups of order 4.

(b) Show that the fourth roots of unity form a group under ordinary multiplication. This group is isomorphic to which abstract group of order 4?

(c) Let

$$P = \begin{pmatrix} 1 & 2 & 3 & 4 \\ 2 & 3 & 1 & 4 \end{pmatrix}$$

represent the "permutation" in which 1, 2, 3, 4 are transformed respectively into 2, 3, 1, 4. If

$$Q = \begin{pmatrix} 1 & 2 & 3 & 4 \\ 2 & 4 & 1 & 3 \end{pmatrix},$$

then the "product," PQ is the permutation obtained by applying first P and then Q, i.e.,

$$PQ = \begin{pmatrix} 1 & 2 & 3 & 4 \\ 4 & 1 & 2 & 3 \end{pmatrix}.$$

With this terminology, show that the permutations

$$P_1 = \begin{pmatrix} 1 & 2 & 3 & 4 \\ 1 & 2 & 3 & 4 \end{pmatrix},$$

$$P_2 = \begin{pmatrix} 1 & 2 & 3 & 4 \\ 2 & 1 & 4 & 3 \end{pmatrix},$$

$$P_3 = \begin{pmatrix} 1 & 2 & 3 & 4 \\ 3 & 4 & 1 & 2 \end{pmatrix},$$

$$P_4 = \begin{pmatrix} 1 & 2 & 3 & 4 \\ 4 & 3 & 2 & 1 \end{pmatrix}$$

form a group. This group is isomorphic to which abstract group of order 4?

*3. Show that the following systems are groups:

(a) the set of all integers, the operation being ordinary addition;

(b) the set of residues modulo an integer n, the operation being addition mod n;

(c) the set of nonzero residues modulo a prime p, the operation being multiplication mod p;

(d) the set of all rotations in Euclidean three-space about a fixed point in that space, the operation being one rotation *followed by* another.

4. Prove the following statement. If the set of nonzero residues modulo n is a group with respect to multiplication mod n, then n is a prime.

*5. Let a rigid motion which makes a square coincide with itself be called a *symmetry* of the square. If the edges of the square are numbered as shown in Fig. 3–5, the symmetries can be listed by starting with edge 1 on top, facing the reader,

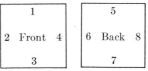

FIGURE 3–5

and indicating which edge assumes this position:

$1 \rightarrow 2$ is called R_1 (rotation through 90° clockwise),

$1 \rightarrow 3$ is called R_2 (rotation through 180° clockwise),

$1 \rightarrow 4$ is called R_3 (rotation through 270° clockwise),

$1 \rightarrow 1$ is called I (rotation through 360°, or 0°, clockwise),

$1 \rightarrow 5$ is called V (reflection in the vertical axis of symmetry),

$1 \rightarrow 6$ is called D_1 (reflection in the diagonal running from upper left to lower right),

$1 \rightarrow 7$ is called H (reflection in the horizontal axis of symmetry),

$1 \rightarrow 8$ is called D_2 (reflection in the diagonal running from upper right to lower left).

Let the "product" of two symmetries be interpreted as the first followed by the second; e.g., $R_1 \cdot V = D_1$.

(a) Verify that this system is a group of order 8. Write out the multiplication table.

(b) Find all the subgroups of this group.

6. (a) Write out the multiplication table for the group of symmetries of an equilateral triangle.

(b) Is this group isomorphic to the group of the example of this Section?

7. Let G be a group and S a subset of G. Show that the set of all elements of G which commute with all elements of S form a subgroup of G.

8. Show that if in a group, $p \circ p$ is not the identity, then there is an element q, different from p and different from the identity, such that $p \circ q = q \circ p$.

9. Let G be a group and S a nonempty subset of G. Prove that a necessary and sufficient condition that S be a subgroup of G is as follows. If a, b are elements of S, then $a \circ b^*$ is in S.

10. For the set of all real numbers, r, $0 \leq r \leq 1$, check whether each of the following operations defines a group.

(a) $x \circ y = \dfrac{x + y}{2}$ (b) $x \circ y = \max [\tfrac{1}{2}, xy]$ (c) $x \circ y = \max [x, y]$

11. Let S be the set of all pairs of real numbers (x, y), with $x \neq 0$. An operation $\cdot$ is defined in terms of ordinary addition and multiplication as follows:

$$(x_1, y_1) \circ (x_2, y_2) = (x_1 x_2, x_1 y_2 + y_1).$$

Is this system a group?

12. Exhibit an isomorphism between the additive group of all real numbers and the multiplicative group of all positive real numbers. Show that the isomorphism can be established in only one way.

13. Let $\{S; +; \cdot\}$ be a system with the following properties:

(a) S is a finite set.

(b) $\{S; +\}$ is an Abelian group.

(c) For each a, b, $c \in S$, $a \neq b$, there is exactly one x such that $xa = xb + c$. Prove that for each p, q, $r \in S$, $p \neq q$, there is exactly one y such that $py = qy + r$. (*American Mathematical Monthly*)

CHAPTER 4

Vector Spaces

For the formal development of the ideas sketched in Chapters 1 and 2, we need the *projective spaces* and *homogeneous projective coordinates* of Chapter 5. A necessary background is found in the study of *finite-dimensional vector spaces*, which are of basic importance in many aspects of mathematics itself and of its applications. We shall now consider this subject in some detail.

4–1 VECTORS; VECTOR SPACES

The concept of a vector quantity as an entity involving both magnitude and direction, and its representation by an arrow, are familiar from physics. For many purposes "location" is of no significance, and we think of the two arrows in Fig. 4–1, which have the same magnitude and direction, as representing the same vector, α. It is therefore possible, once a rectangular coordinate frame is chosen, to represent any vector by an arrow emanating from the origin, or by the point P at the head of the arrow when it is so placed, or by the ordered set of numbers which are the coordinates of P. We will call these numbers the *rectangular coordinates of the vector relative to the given coordinate frame*. The usual rule for adding vectors is the "parallelogram law" (Fig. 4–2). If α is the

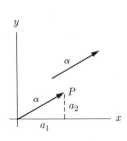

FIGURE 4–1

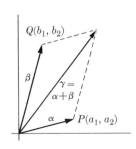

FIGURE 4–2

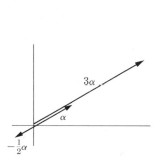

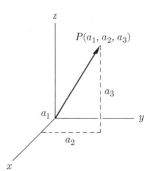

FIGURE 4-3   FIGURE 4-4

vector (a_1, a_2) and β the vector (b_1, b_2) in a certain coordinate frame, then $\alpha + \beta = \gamma$ is the vector $(a_1 + b_1, a_2 + b_2)$ in that frame. If we should have a different rectangular coordinate frame in which α has coordinates (a_1', a_2') and β has coordinates (b_1', b_2'), then $\alpha + \beta$ would still be the same vector γ, which would have coordinates $(a_1' + b_1', a_2' + b_2')$ relative to the new coordinate frame.

Another notion familiar from elementary physics is that of a *scalar quantity*, which has magnitude but not direction. We have the following rule defining the multiplication of a vector by a scalar (see Fig. 4-3). If α is the vector (a_1, a_2) in a certain coordinate frame, and if c is a real number, then $c \cdot \alpha$ is the vector (ca_1, ca_2) in that coordinate frame.

In three-space, each vector has three coordinates relative to a rectangular coordinate frame (Fig. 4-4), and obvious analogues of all the preceding statements about vectors in two dimensions hold.

The above definitions of vectors and of operations on vectors are chosen because of their usefulness in handling problems involving such quantities as force, velocity, and acceleration. We shall now generalize these ideas on vectors to give them a broader scope, including the geometry which is one of our principal concerns. To do this, we shall think of a vector ξ as an ordered n-tuple $(x_1, x_2, \ldots, x_n)$ of elements of a field $\mathfrak{F}$. The elements of $\mathfrak{F}$ will be called *scalars*, and the scalars $x_1, x_2, \ldots, x_n$ will be called *components* of ξ. It must be understood that no coordinate frame is yet involved, and the components of a vector are not to be confused with coordinates of a vector, to be introduced later. (It will be found that the coordinates of a vector depend upon the choice of coordinate frame, as would be expected, but the components of a vector do not. There is one choice of coordinate frame for which the components and coordinates are the same.)

Note also that our use of the term "component" is different from that often found in elementary physics, where the component of a vector in a given direction is defined as a *vector*.

We cannot adequately define vectors without defining the relation of equality among them and operations involving them; hence our formal definition is of a *vector space*, rather than of a vector.

Definition 1.   *A vector space over a field* $\mathfrak{F}$ *is a set* S, of ordered n-tuples of elements of $\mathfrak{F}$, $\xi = (x_1, x_2, \ldots, x_n)$, such that (i) two n-tuples, $\alpha = (a_1, a_2, \ldots, a_n)$ and $\beta = (b_1, b_2, \ldots, b_n)$, are *equal* if and only if $a_i = b_i$, $i = 1, 2, \ldots, n$; (ii) if $\alpha = (a_1, a_2, \ldots, a_n)$ and $\beta = (b_1, b_2, \ldots, b_n)$, then the *sum* of α and β, $\alpha + \beta$, is the n-tuple $(a_1 + b_1, a_2 + b_2, \ldots, a_n + b_n)$; (iii) if $k \in \mathfrak{F}$ and $\xi = (x_1, x_2, \ldots, x_n)$, then the *product* of k and ξ, $k \cdot \xi$, is the n-tuple $(kx_1, kx_2, \ldots, kx_n)$; (iv) the set S is *closed* under the operations of addition and multiplication by scalars, i.e., (1) if ξ, $\eta \in S$, then $(\xi + \eta) \in S$, and (2) if $k \in \mathfrak{F}$ and $\xi \in S$, then $k \cdot \xi \in S$.

The set of *all* n-tuples $(x_1, x_2, \ldots, x_n)$, $x_i \in \mathfrak{F}$, constitutes a vector space, designated as $V_n(\mathfrak{F})$. Each n-tuple of $V_n(\mathfrak{F})$ is called a *vector*. If 0 is the zero element of $\mathfrak{F}$, the vector $(0, 0, \ldots, 0)$ is called the *zero vector* or *null vector*, symbolized by o. The set consisting of o alone is a vector space, too simple to be interesting.

Definition 2.   If all the vectors of a vector space S are also members of a vector space T, then S is called a *subspace* of T.

It should be clear that if each of the vectors of a vector space S has n components which are elements of $\mathfrak{F}$, then S is a subspace of $V_n(\mathfrak{F})$. The trivial space $\{o\}$ and $V_n(\mathfrak{F})$ itself are called *improper* subspaces of $V_n(\mathfrak{F})$; all others are *proper*.

EXAMPLE.   Suppose that $\mathfrak{F} = R$, the field of real numbers, and $n = 3$. Then the set of all triples of the form $(x_1, 0, 0)$, $x_1 \in R$, *is* a vector space S, say. Likewise the set of all triples of the form $(x_1, x_2, 0)$, $x_1, x_2 \in R$, is a vector space, which we may call T. Finally, the set of all triples (x_1, x_2, x_3), $x_i \in R$, is the space we call $V_3(R)$. Clearly, S is a subspace of T, and T, in turn, is a subspace of $V_3(R)$.

If we choose a rectangular coordinate frame in three-space, and picture the components of the vectors in this example as coordinates of points relative to the chosen coordinate frame, then S may be visualized as the x-axis, T as the xy-plane, and $V_3(R)$ as the entire three-space.

Our definition of a vector space is a "natural" extension of our earlier description of vectors in two- and three-dimensional real space. But if $n > 3$ or if the vector components are not all real numbers, we can no longer visualize the vectors, although such spaces have physical application.

It is of the utmost importance to appreciate that, even if $n \leq 3$ and if all the vector components are real numbers, there is nothing in the above definition which necessitates an interpretation along the lines of Figs. 4–1 through 4–4, or of the latter part of the example; i.e., the components of a vector are *not* necessarily the coordinates of the head of an arrow in a rectangular coordinate frame or in *any* coordinate frame.

We will consistently use Greek letters as symbols for vectors (except in the case of the null vector) and Latin letters to represent scalars. The following results are immediate consequences of the definition of $V_n(\mathfrak{F})$ and the properties of fields:

(1) if $\alpha, \beta, \gamma \in V_n(\mathfrak{F})$, then $\alpha + (\beta + \gamma) = (\alpha + \beta) + \gamma$ (the associative property);

(2) if $\alpha, \beta \in V_n(\mathfrak{F})$, then $\alpha + \beta = \beta + \alpha$ (the commutative property);

(3) for all $\alpha \in V_n(\mathfrak{F})$, $\alpha + o = \alpha$ (the null vector is an additive identity element);

(4) for each $\alpha \in V_n(\mathfrak{F})$ there is a vector $(-\alpha) \in V_n(\mathfrak{F})$ such that $\alpha + (-\alpha) = o$;

(5) for all $\alpha \in V_n(\mathfrak{F})$, $1 \cdot \alpha = \alpha$, where 1 is the multiplicative identity element in $\mathfrak{F}$;

(6) for all $\alpha, \beta \in V_n(\mathfrak{F})$ and $k \in \mathfrak{F}$, $k \cdot (\alpha + \beta) = (k \cdot \alpha) + (k \cdot \beta)$;

(7) for all $k_1, k_2 \in \mathfrak{F}$ and $\alpha \in V_n(\mathfrak{F})$, $(k_1 + k_2) \cdot \alpha = (k_1 \cdot \alpha) + (k_2 \cdot \alpha)$;

(8) for all $k_1, k_2 \in \mathfrak{F}$ and $\alpha \in V_n(\mathfrak{F})$, $(k_1 k_2) \cdot \alpha = k_1 \cdot (k_2 \cdot \alpha)$.

We have stated our definitions and basic results about vector spaces over any field $\mathfrak{F}$; but, for the purposes of our geometry, we will be chiefly concerned with $V(C)$, where C is the field of complex numbers.

PROBLEM SET 4–1

1. Illustrate each of the results (1), (2), (6), (7), and (8) listed at the end of this section by a vector diagram in two dimensions.

*2. Let $\xi = (x_1, x_2, \ldots, x_n)$ be an arbitrary vector of $V_n(C)$. Which of the following subsets of $V_n(C)$ constitute subspaces?

(a) All ξ with $x_n = 0$

(b) All ξ with $x_n = 1$

(c) All ξ with either x_1 or x_2 equal to 0

(d) All ξ with all $x_1, x_2, \ldots, x_n$ real

(e) All ξ with $2x_1 + 3x_2 = 0$

(f) All ξ with $2x_1 + 3x_2 = 5$

(g) All ξ with $k_1 x_1 + k_2 x_2 + \cdots + k_n x_n = 0$ and $l_1 x_1 + l_2 x_2 + \cdots + l_n x_n = 0$, where $k_1, \ldots, k_n, l_1, \ldots, l_n$ are fixed complex numbers.

*3. Let α, β be fixed vectors of $V_n(\mathfrak{F})$, and k, l arbitrary elements of $\mathfrak{F}$. Is the set of vectors $\{k \cdot \alpha + l \cdot \beta\}$ a subspace of $V_n(\mathfrak{F})$?

4–2 BASIC RESULTS ON SUBSPACES OF $V_n(C)$

Problems (2) and (3) of the preceding set exemplify certain important ideas about subspaces of $V_n(C)$.

(i) The subset described in Problem 2(a) above *is* a subspace of $V_n(C)$; in analogy with the situation in real Euclidean space of three dimensions, this subspace may be called the *"projection* of $V_n(C)$ onto the $x_1 x_2 \ldots x_{n-1}$-hyperplane."

(ii) Problems 2(e) and (g) above indicate an important relation between vector spaces and the solution of homogeneous linear equations.

If a system of linear equations in the variables x_1, $x_2, \ldots, x_n$ has a solution $x_1 = r_1$, $x_2 = r_2, \ldots, x_n = r_n$, we may think of the numbers $r_1, r_2, \ldots, r_n$ as the components of a vector ρ, say, and we may call ρ a *solution vector* of the system of equations. Using this language we can state the following result.

Theorem 4–1. The set of all solution vectors of a system of linear homogeneous equations in n variables with coefficients in C constitutes a subspace of $V_n(C)$.

The proof is straightforward (Problem 1 below).

Note that in Theorem 4–1, the equations must be homogeneous; the set described in Problem 2(f) above is *not* a subspace.

(iii) It is convenient to make the following definition.

Definition 3. If α_1, $\alpha_2, \ldots, \alpha_p$ are vectors and k_1, $k_2, \ldots, k_p$ are scalars, then the vector $k_1 \cdot \alpha_1 + k_2 \cdot \alpha_2 + \cdots + k_p \cdot \alpha_p$, which is abbreviated

$$\sum_{i=1}^{p} k_i \cdot \alpha_i,$$

is called a *linear combination* of the vectors $\alpha_1, \alpha_2, \ldots, \alpha_p$.

Problem 3 above generalizes easily to the following result.

Theorem 4–2. The set of all linear combinations of a fixed set of vectors of $V_n(C)$ constitutes a subspace of $V_n(C)$.

The proof is left to you (Problem 2 below).

In analogy with Theorem 3–9, we can state a result about the intersection of subspaces.

Theorem 4–3. If S, T are subspaces of $V_n(C)$, then $S \cap T$ is a subspace of $V_n(C)$.

The proof is easy (Problem 4 below).   Clearly, $S \cap T$ is the largest subspace of $V_n(C)$ contained in both S and T.   We have the following chains of inclusion:

$$(S \cap T) \subseteq S \subseteq V_n(C); \qquad (S \cap T) \subseteq T \subseteq V_n(C).$$

The union of S and T is not particularly interesting, but another concept, that of linear sum, proves to be fruitful.

Definition 4.   If S, T are subsets of $V_n(C)$, the *linear sum* of S and T, symbolized by $S + T$, is the set of all vectors of the form $\xi + \eta$ where $\xi \in S$ and $\eta \in T$.

For example, if S consists of the set of all vectors of the form $(0, x_2, x_3)$, for $x_2, x_3 \in \mathfrak{F}$, and if T consists of the set of all vectors of the form $(x_1, 0, 0)$ for $x_1 \in \mathfrak{F}$, then $S + T$ consists of the set of all vectors of the form (x_1, x_2, x_3), which is $V_3(\mathfrak{F})$.   Similarly, if S is as before, and U consists of the single vector $(1, 2, 0)$, then $S + U$ consists of all vectors of the form $(1, 2 + x_2, x_3)$, which is the same set as $(1, x_2, x_3)$ for arbitrary x_2, x_3 Note that this linear sum is not a vector space.

We can state the following theorem about linear sums of vector spaces.

Theorem 4–4.   If S, T are subspaces of $V_n(C)$, then $S + T$ is a subspace of $V_n(C)$.   Moreover, $S + T \supseteq S$ and $S + T \supseteq T$; and, if Q is a subspace of $V_n(C)$ containing both S and T, then $Q \supseteq S + T$ (i.e., $S + T$ is the "smallest" subspace containing both S and T).

The proof is straightforward (Problem 5 below).

PROBLEM SET 4–2

1. Prove Theorem 4–1.

2. Prove Theorem 4–2.

3. Using as a model of $V_3(R)$ ordinary Euclidean three-space, in which the components of vectors are interpreted as the coordinates of points relative to a fixed rectangular coordinate frame, describe $S \cap T$ and $S + T$ in each of the following cases.
  (a) S = the x-axis; T = the z-axis
  (b) S = the xy-plane; T = the yz-plane
  (c) S = the xy-plane; T = the z-axis
  (d) S = the xy-plane; T = the y-axis
  (e) S = the plane with equation $3x + 4y - 2z = 0$; T = the line with equations $x/1 = y/2 = z/5$
  (f) S = same plane as in (e); T = the line with equations $x/2 = y/{-3} = z/{-3}$.

4. Prove Theorem 4–3.

5. Prove Theorem 4–4.

6. (a) Let A and B be arbitrary subspaces of $V_n(\mathfrak{F})$, and let $T = A \cup B$, $U = A + B$. Which, if any, of the following is correct: $T = U$, $T \subseteq U$, $U \subseteq T$?

(b) What is the answer to (a) if A and B are arbitrary *subsets* of $V_n(\mathfrak{F})$?

7. (a) Let A, B, C be arbitrary subspaces of $V_n(\mathfrak{F})$, and let $P = A + (B \cap C)$, $Q = (A + B) \cap (A + C)$. Which of the following is correct: $P = Q$, $P \subseteq Q$, $Q \subseteq P$?

(b) How may the hypotheses of (a) be weakened without altering the conclusion?

8. (a) Let A, B, C be arbitrary subspaces of $V_n(\mathfrak{F})$, and let $R = A \cap (B + C)$, $S = (A \cap B) + (A \cap C)$. Which of the following is correct: $R = S$, $R \subseteq S$, $S \subseteq R$?

(b) How may the hypotheses of (a) be weakened without altering the conclusion?

9. Let $\mathcal{I}_p$, p a prime, be the field $\{0, 1, 2, \ldots, p - 1\}$, with addition and multiplication (mod p). List all subspaces of $V_3(\mathcal{I}_2)$ and of $V_2(\mathcal{I}_3)$.

4–3 LINEAR DEPENDENCE AND INDEPENDENCE

The important ideas of linear independence, of vectors spanning a space, and of basis vectors for a space will be introduced in the first part of this section in intuitive fashion. The latter part of the section will deal with a more rigorous and more general approach to these topics.

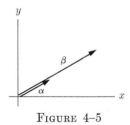

FIGURE 4–5

Suppose that, in the ordinary Euclidean plane, we have two vectors, α and β, with the same direction and different magnitudes (Fig. 4–5). Then, if neither α nor β is the null-vector, there is a real constant k, different from zero, such that $\beta = k \cdot \alpha$, or $\alpha = (1/k) \cdot \beta$. We can express this relationship more symmetrically by writing it as

$$c_1 \cdot \alpha + c_2 \cdot \beta = o, \qquad c_1 \neq 0, \quad c_2 \neq 0. \tag{1}$$

Because of the definition of equality of vectors, this vector equation is equivalent to a pair of ordinary algebraic equations. If a_1, a_2 are the components of α, and b_1, b_2 the components of β, then Eq. (1) is equivalent to

$$c_1 a_1 + c_2 b_1 = 0, \qquad c_1 a_2 + c_2 b_2 = 0, \qquad c_1 \neq 0, \quad c_2 \neq 0. \qquad (2)$$

Unless $a_2 = 0 = b_2$, Eqs. (2) have a solution for c_1, c_2 if and only if $a_1 : a_2 = b_1 : b_2$. We say that α and β are *linearly dependent*, a concept which is essentially the same as that of proportionality of components in this case. Actually, we have a slight generalization of the notion of proportionality; for even if α, say, is the null vector, there exist c_1, c_2 satisfying Eq. (1), if we permit one of the c's to be zero, namely c_1 arbitrary and $c_2 = 0$. To take this situation into account, we make the following definition of linear dependence. Two vectors, α and β, are *linearly dependent* if there exist constants c_1, c_2, *not both zero*, such that

$$c_1 \cdot \alpha + c_2 \cdot \beta = o.$$

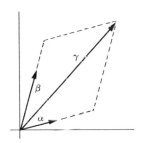

FIGURE 4–6

If α and β do not have the same direction (Fig. 4–6), then Eq. (1) cannot be satisfied, i.e., there are no constants c_1, c_2, such that $c_1 \cdot \alpha + c_2 \cdot \beta = o$, unless $c_1 = 0 = c_2$. Now however, if γ is a third vector in the plane, there are constants k, l such that $\gamma = k \cdot \alpha + l \cdot \beta$. (In Fig. 4–6, $k = 2$ and $l = \frac{3}{2}$. The figure suggests a geometric proof of the existence of k and l.) In terms of the phraseology already introduced, we see that γ is expressible as a linear combination of α and β. We can make the expression more symmetrical by writing it in the following way. There are constants c_1, c_2, c_3, not all zero, such that

$$c_1 \cdot \alpha + c_2 \cdot \beta + c_3 \cdot \gamma = o. \qquad (3)$$

The three vectors α, β, γ are said to be linearly dependent.

It is instructive to visualize under what circumstances one or more of the c's can be zero (Problem 1(a) below).

In the situation illustrated in Fig. 4–6, where every vector in the plane is expressible as a linear combination of α and β, these two vectors are said to *span* the plane, or to form a set of *generators* for the plane. Actually α, β, and γ also span the plane, but any one of the three vectors is superfluous for the purpose: the three vectors are not what we shall presently define as "linearly independent." A set of linearly independent vectors which span the plane is called a *basis* for the plane (defined formally below). The simplest basis consists of the two "unit vectors": $\epsilon_1 = (1, 0)$ and $\epsilon_2 = (0, 1)$. Any vector $\xi = (x_1, x_2)$ is expressible as

$$\xi = x_1 \cdot \epsilon_1 + x_2 \cdot \epsilon_2.$$

Neither the set of vectors α, β nor the set α, β, γ of Fig. 4–6 suffices to span three-space. For this purpose we need, in addition to vectors α, β of the xy-plane, a third vector not in that plane. In fact, any three vectors not all in a plane constitute a basis for three-space (Problem 2(b) below). The material thus far presented in intuitive fashion will now be formalized for $V_n(\mathcal{F})$.

Definition 5. (i) Vectors $\alpha_1, \alpha_2, \ldots, \alpha_p$ are *linearly dependent* if there exist $c_1, c_2, \ldots, c_p \in \mathcal{F}$, not all zero, such that

$$\sum_{i=1}^{p} c_i \cdot \alpha_i = o.$$

(ii) Vectors $\alpha_1, \alpha_2, \ldots, \alpha_p$ are *linearly independent* if they are *not* linearly dependent.

An alternative form of (ii) follows.

(ii′) Vectors $\alpha_1, \alpha_2, \ldots, \alpha_p$ are *linearly independent* if

$$\sum_{i=1}^{p} c_i \cdot \alpha_i = o$$

implies that $c_1 = 0 = c_2 = \cdots = c_p$.

Theorem 4–5. If $\alpha_1, \alpha_2, \ldots, \alpha_p$ are linearly dependent, then at least one of the α's can be expressed as a linear combination of the other α's.

The proof is immediate, and incidentally shows why it would be incorrect to state that *any* of the α's can be expressed as a linear combination of the other α's (Problem 3 below).

Definition 6. (i) Vectors $\alpha_1, \alpha_2, \ldots, \alpha_p$ *span* V_n (or, a subspace S of V_n) if every vector of V_n (or of S) is expressible as a linear combination of $\alpha_1, \alpha_2, \ldots, \alpha_p$.

(ii) Vectors $\alpha_1, \alpha_2, \ldots, \alpha_p$ form a *basis* for V_n (or, for a subspace S of V_n) if $\alpha_1, \alpha_2, \ldots, \alpha_p$ *span* V_n (or S) and are linearly independent.

Thus a basis is both a "minimal spanning set" and a "maximal linearly independent set."

Definition 7.   The vectors $\epsilon_1 = (1, 0, 0, \ldots, 0, 0)$, $\epsilon_2 = (0, 1, 0, \ldots, 0)$, $\epsilon_3 = (0, 0, 1, 0, \ldots, 0), \ldots, \epsilon_n = (0, 0, \ldots, 0, 1)$ are called the *unit vectors* of V_n.

Theorem 4–6.   The unit vectors $\epsilon_1, \epsilon_2, \ldots, \epsilon_n$ form a basis for V_n.

The proof, which is straightforward, is left to you (Problem 4 below).

Theorem 4–7.   Suppose that ξ is expressible as a linear combination of $\alpha_1, \alpha_2, \ldots, \alpha_p$. Then $\alpha_1, \alpha_2, \ldots, \alpha_p$ are linearly independent $\Leftrightarrow$ the expression for ξ is unique.

Proof.   (a) "$\Rightarrow$." Suppose, on the contrary, that

$$\xi = c_1 \cdot \alpha_1 + c_2 \cdot \alpha_2 + \cdots + c_p \cdot \alpha_p,$$

and that also

$$\xi = d_1 \cdot \alpha_1 + d_2 \cdot \alpha_2 + \cdots + d_p \cdot \alpha_p,$$

where not every d_i equals the corresponding c_i. Then

$$c_1 \cdot \alpha_1 + c_2 \cdot \alpha_2 + \cdots + c_p \cdot \alpha_p = d_1 \cdot \alpha_1 + d_2 \cdot \alpha_2 + \cdots + d_p \cdot \alpha_p,$$

or

$$(c_1 - d_1) \cdot \alpha_1 + (c_2 - d_2) \cdot \alpha_2 + \cdots + (c_p - d_p) \cdot \alpha_p = o.$$

But, since not every coefficient is zero, this equation contradicts the assumed independence of the α's.

(b) "$\Leftarrow$." Suppose, on the contrary, that the α_i are not linearly independent. Then there exist $k_1, k_2, \ldots, k_p$, not all zero, such that $k_1 \cdot \alpha_1 + k_2 \cdot \alpha_2 + \cdots + k_p \cdot \alpha_p = o$. By hypothesis, ξ is expressible as a linear combination of the α's:

$$\xi = l_1 \cdot \alpha_1 + l_2 \cdot \alpha_2 + \cdots + l_p \cdot \alpha_p,$$

say. Then ξ can also be written as

$$\xi = (l_1 + k_1) \cdot \alpha_1 + (l_2 + k_2) \cdot \alpha_2 + \cdots + (l_p + k_p) \cdot \alpha_p,$$

which contradicts the assumed uniqueness of the expression for ξ. $\square$

This theorem embodies the background necessary for the introduction of a coordinate system in a vector space. To fix the ideas, let us consider $V_2(R)$, interpreted as the ordinary Euclidean plane. Suppose that β_1, β_2 form a basis for $V_2(R)$. Then any vector ξ, with components x_1, x_2, of

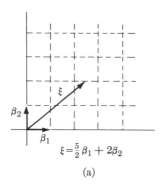

$$\xi = \tfrac{5}{2}\beta_1 + 2\beta_2$$

(a)

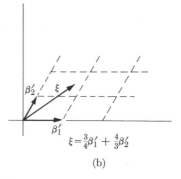

$$\xi = \tfrac{3}{4}\beta_1' + \tfrac{4}{3}\beta_2'$$

(b)

FIGURE 4–7

$V_2(R)$ can be expressed as a linear combination of β_1 and β_2:

$$\xi = y_1 \cdot \beta_1 + y_2 \cdot \beta_2,$$

say. Since, according to Theorem 4–7, y_1, y_2 are uniquely determined in this case, the ordered pair (y_1, y_2) may be thought of as characterizing ξ relative to β_1, β_2; or (y_1, y_2) may be called the *coordinates* of ξ in the frame determined by β_1 and β_2. Since $\beta_1 = 1 \cdot \beta_1 + 0 \cdot \beta_2$, the coordinates of β_1 in this frame are $(1, 0)$; similarly the coordinates of β_2 are $(0, 1)$. If β_1, β_2 are pictured as arrows of equal length perpendicular to each other, we can think of the plane as covered by the familiar square grid of a rectangular cartesian coordinate system (Fig. 4–7a), but if β_1', β_2' are not perpendicular, nor of equal length, we have the oblique coordinate frame and parallelogram grid of Fig. 4–7(b).

In general, if $B = \{\beta_1, \beta_2, \ldots, \beta_r\}$ is a basis for a vector space V, any vector ξ of V can be uniquely expressed as $\xi = c_1 \cdot \beta_1 + c_2 \cdot \beta_2 + \cdots + c_r \cdot \beta_r$. The scalars $c_1, c_2, \ldots, c_r$ are called the *coordinates of ξ relative to B*. In V_n, if B is chosen as the set of unit vectors (Definition 7), then the coordinates of any vector ξ relative to B are the same as the components of ξ.

EXAMPLE.   Let S be the subspace of $V_3(R)$ determined by

$$2x_1 + 3x_2 - x_3 = 0$$

[i.e., S is the set of all solution vectors of this equation (Theorem 4–1)]. It is easy to verify that $\beta_1 = (1, 1, 5)$ and $\beta_2 = (1, 0, 2)$ belong to S. Moreover, β_1 and β_2 constitute a basis for S, as can be seen in the following way.

Any vector ξ of S has components $(x_1, x_2, 2x_1 + 3x_2)$. We try to determine scalars c_1, c_2 such that $\xi = c_1 \cdot \beta_1 + c_2 \cdot \beta_2$. If c_1, c_2 exist, they must satisfy the equations

$$1 \cdot c_1 + 1 \cdot c_2 = x_1,$$
$$1 \cdot c_1 + 0 \cdot c_2 = x_2, \qquad (4)$$
$$5 \cdot c_1 + 2 \cdot c_2 = 2x_1 + 3x_2.$$

By means of elementary algebra we can determine that these three equations have a unique solution:

$$c_1 = x_2, \qquad c_2 = x_1 - x_2.$$

Thus, any vector of S can be expressed uniquely as a linear combination of β_1 and β_2; hence, from Theorem 4–7, we know that β_1 and β_2 form a basis for S.

Now, Eqs. 4 give us the expression for any vector of S in terms of β_1 and β_2. For example, if $\alpha = (1, -1, -1)$, then

$$\alpha = -1 \cdot \beta_1 + 2 \cdot \beta_2.$$

Thus the coordinates of α relative to $\{\beta_1, \beta_2\}$ are $(-1, 2)$.

PROBLEM SET 4–3

1. (a) If $c_1 \cdot \alpha + c_2 \cdot \beta + c_3 \cdot \gamma = o$, describe in geometrical language under what conditions one or more of the scalars will be zero.

(b) Show that if one member of a set of vectors is the null vector, then the vectors of the set are linearly dependent.

(c) Show that if the vectors of a set S are linearly independent, then so are the vectors of any subset of S.

(d) Show that if the vectors of a set T are linearly dependent, then so are the vectors of any set containing T.

2. (a) State the geometric argument leading to the conclusion that, in Fig. 4–6, any vector γ can be expressed as a linear combination of α and β.

(b) Give an analogous argument, applicable to vectors in real three-space, to show that any three vectors not in a plane constitute a basis of the space.

3. (a) Prove Theorem 4–5 and indicate clearly why it would be incorrect to state that *any* one of the vectors in a linearly dependent set can be expressed as a linear combination of the others.

(b) Prove that if $\alpha_1, \alpha_2, \ldots, \alpha_m$ are linearly independent and if $\alpha_1, \alpha_2, \ldots, \alpha_m, \alpha_{m+1}$ are linearly dependent, then α_{m+1} can be expressed as a linear combination of $\alpha_1, \alpha_2, \ldots, \alpha_m$.

4. Prove Theorem 4–6.

5. Show that if a set of linearly dependent vectors S spans a vector space, then there is a proper subset of S which also spans the space.

*6. This problem is intended to help fix in mind the intuitive significance of the concepts presented in Section 4–3. Interpret each of the vectors in this problem as an arrow in ordinary three-space and sketch the vectors so as to see the relationships among them. Let $\alpha = (1, 1, 1), \beta = (3, 2, 0), \gamma = (2, 1, -1)$, $\eta = (7, 4, -2), \delta = (7, 5, 2), \zeta = (5, 3, 0)$.

(a) Show that α, β, γ are linearly dependent.
(b) Express η as a linear combination of α, β, γ in three ways.
(c) Express η as a linear combination of α and β.
(d) Express ζ as a linear combination of $\alpha, \beta, \gamma, \delta$ in two ways.
(e) Express ζ as a linear combination of α, β, δ.
(f) Write the equation of the plane spanned by $\alpha, \beta, \gamma, \eta$.
(g) Write the equation of the plane for which δ and ζ form a basis.

7. In $V_3(C)$ express $(1, 0, 1)$ as a linear combination of $(2i, 1, 0), (2, -i, 1)$, $(0, 1 + i, 1 - i)$.

*8. Show that (a) the coordinates of $\xi + \eta$ relative to B are the sums of the respective coordinates of ξ and η relative to B; and (b) the coordinates of $k \cdot \xi$ relative to B are k times the respective coordinates of ξ relative to B.

9. This problem refers to the space S and the vectors α, β_1, β_2 of the example in Section 4–3.

(a) Find the coordinates of $\gamma = (0, 1, 3)$ relative to $\{\beta_1, \beta_2\}$.
(b) Show that γ and β_1 form a basis for S, and find the coordinates of β_2 relative to $\{\gamma, \beta_1\}$.
(c) What are the coordinates of γ, as a vector of $V_3(R)$, relative to the set of unit vectors $\{\epsilon_1, \epsilon_2, \epsilon_3\}$?
(d) Show that $\{\beta_1, \beta_2, \epsilon_1\}$ constitute a basis for $V_3(R)$, and find the coordinates of $\lambda = (3, 1, 7)$ relative to this basis; likewise for α, for γ, and for $\mu = (2, 1, 5)$.

4–4 DIMENSION

The models of the first part of Section 4–3 suggest that for a plane, a basis consists of two vectors not in the same line, and that for three-space, a basis consists of three vectors not in the same plane. It seems reasonable to define dimension, for a general vector space, in terms of the number of vectors in a basis. But thus far we don't know that two bases for a vector space necessarily have the same number of vectors. Worse than this—although we do know that V_n has a basis consisting of the n unit vectors, we have not yet shown that an arbitrary vector space can be spanned by a finite number of vectors.

To discuss the general problem rigorously, we proceed in the following way, leading up to the important Grassmann-Steinitz replacement theorem.

Suppose that a vector space V is spanned by a finite set of vectors $\alpha_1, \alpha_2, \ldots, \alpha_p$, not necessarily independent. Moreover, suppose that

$\beta_1, \beta_2, \ldots, \beta_r$ is a set of linearly independent vectors in V, not necessarily spanning V. We shall show that $p \geq r$, and that a new spanning set of vectors can be formed by replacing some r of the α's by the r β's.

In the first place, β_1 can be expressed as a linear combination of α_1, $\alpha_2, \ldots, \alpha_p$; hence $\beta_1, \alpha_1, \alpha_2, \ldots, \alpha_p$ is a set of linearly dependent vectors. Hence, there exist scalars $b_1, a_1, a_2, \ldots, a_p$, not all zero, such that

$$b_1 \cdot \beta_1 + a_1 \cdot \alpha_1 + a_2 \cdot \alpha_2 + \cdots + a_p \alpha_p = o.$$

Not all the a_i can be zero (why?). Let j be the greatest index such that $a_j \neq 0$. Then α_j can be expressed as a linear combination of β_1, α_1, $\alpha_2, \ldots, \alpha_{j-1}$. (Conceivably, j might be 1 or p, or any integer between them.) Since any vector of V can be expressed as a linear combination of $\alpha_1, \alpha_2, \ldots, \alpha_p$, it is also true that any vector of V can be expressed as a linear combination of $\beta_1, \alpha_1, \alpha_2, \ldots, \alpha_{j-1}, \alpha_{j+1}, \ldots, \alpha_p$; i.e., this last-named set of p vectors spans V.

Repeating the argument, we observe that β_2 can be expressed as a linear combination of $\beta_1, \alpha_1, \ldots, \alpha_{j-1}, \alpha_{j+1}, \ldots, \alpha_p$; hence, the vectors $\beta_1, \beta_2, \alpha_1, \ldots, \alpha_{j-1}, \alpha_{j+1}, \ldots, \alpha_p$ are linearly dependent. In the equation expressing the linear dependence,

$$b_1' \cdot \beta_1 + b_2' \cdot \beta_2 + a_1' \cdot \alpha_1 + \cdots + a_{j-1}' \cdot \alpha_{j-1}$$
$$+ a_{j+1}' \cdot \alpha_{j+1} + \cdots + a_p' \cdot \alpha_p = o,$$

it is impossible for all the coefficients of the α's to be zero. (Why?)

Let k be the greatest index such that $a_k' \neq 0$. Thus α_k can be expressed as a linear combination of $\beta_1, \beta_2, \alpha_1, \ldots, \alpha_{j-1}, \alpha_{j+1}, \ldots, \alpha_{k-1}$. (The index k might be less than or greater than the index j.) Then we obtain $\rho_1, \beta_2, \alpha_1, \ldots, \alpha_{j-1}, \alpha_{j+1}, \ldots, \alpha_{k-1}, \alpha_{k+1}, \ldots, \alpha_p$ as a set of p vectors spanning V.

Repetition finally gives $\beta_1, \beta_2, \ldots, \beta_r, \alpha_{i_1}, \alpha_{i_2}, \ldots, \alpha_{i_{p-r}}$ as a set of p vectors spanning V. It is possible that there are no α's left in the set and hence that $\beta_1, \ldots, \beta_r$ span V, but it is impossible that fewer than r β's alone span V. (Why? Problem 1 below.) Hence $p \geq r$. We have proved the Grassmann-Steinitz exchange theorem.

Theorem 4–8. The number of vectors in any set spanning a vector space V is at least as great as the number of vectors in any linearly independent set in V. If $\alpha_1, \alpha_2, \ldots, \alpha_p$ span V and if $\beta_1, \ldots, \beta_r$ are linearly independent vectors in V, then there are $(p - r)$ of the α's which, together with the r β's, span V.

This rather involved statement has a beautifully simple, important corollary.

Corollary. If a vector space has two finite bases, then the bases consist of the same number of vectors.

Proof. If $\gamma_1, \ldots, \gamma_r$ and $\delta_1, \ldots, \delta_s$ are two sets of linearly independent vectors each spanning V, then, by Theorem 4–8, $r \leq s$ and $s \leq r$. Hence, $r = s$.

Since $\epsilon_1, \epsilon_2, \ldots, \epsilon_n$ constitute a basis for V_n, it follows that any basis for V_n will consist of n vectors. By Theorem 4–8 we know that V_n cannot contain a set of more than n linearly independent vectors. Hence, any subspace $V \subseteq V_n$ likewise cannot contain more than n linearly independent vectors. If V is not the subspace consisting of the null vector alone, V contains a nonzero vector, which is linearly independent. Thus, there must be a maximum integer r $(1 \leq r \leq n)$ such that V contains a set of r linearly independent vectors, $\beta_1, \beta_2, \ldots, \beta_r$, say. If ξ is an arbitrary vector of V, the set $\beta_1, \beta_2, \ldots, \beta_r, \xi$, consisting of more than r vectors, must be linearly dependent; i.e., there exist $b_1, \ldots, b_r, k$ such that $b_1 \cdot \beta_1 + b_2 \cdot \beta_2 + \cdots + b_r \cdot \beta_r + k \cdot \xi = o$. Moreover, $k \neq 0$. (Why?) Hence, ξ can be expressed as a linear combination of $\beta_1, \ldots, \beta_r$; or $\beta_1, \ldots, \beta_r$ constitute a basis for V. We have thus proved the following theorem.

Theorem 4–9. Every vector space $V \subseteq V_n$ has a finite basis.

In view of the corollary of Theorem 4–8, it makes sense to define dimension as follows.

Definition 8. The number of vectors in a basis for V is called the *dimension* of the space, denoted by $d(V)$. We assign the dimension 0 to the space consisting of the null vector alone.

Corollary. Any n linearly independent vectors form a basis for V_n *and* any n vectors spanning V_n form a basis for V_n. Indeed, any k linearly independent vectors of a k-dimensional subspace S of V_n form a basis for S, and any k vectors spanning S form a basis for S. The proof is left to you (Problem 2 below).

Theorem 4–10. If S, T are subspaces of V, then

$$d(S) + d(T) = d(S \cap T) + d(S + T).$$

Proof. Suppose that $\alpha_1, \alpha_2, \ldots, \alpha_p$ form a basis for $S \cap T$. Then, by Theorem 4–8, there is a basis for S of the form $\alpha_1, \ldots, \alpha_p, \beta_1, \ldots, \beta_q$ and a basis for T of the form $\alpha_1, \ldots, \alpha_p, \gamma_1, \ldots, \gamma_r$. We can show that $\alpha_1, \ldots, \alpha_p, \beta_1, \ldots, \beta_q, \gamma_1, \ldots, \gamma_r$ form a basis for $S + T$ (Problem 3 below). Then we obtain the desired conclusion from the fact that

$$(p + q) + (p + r) = p + (p + q + r).$$

PROBLEM SET 4-4

1. If $\beta_1, \beta_2, \ldots, \beta_r$ are linearly independent vectors of a vector space, why is it impossible that fewer than r of the β's span the space?

2. Prove the corollary of Theorem 4-9.

3. Show that, in the proof of Theorem 4-10, the vectors $\alpha_1, \ldots, \alpha_p, \beta_1, \ldots, \beta_q, \gamma_1, \ldots, \gamma_r$ form a basis for $S + T$. [*Hint:* First show that these vectors span $S + T$; then show that the assumption of their linear dependence leads to a contradiction.]

4. As a help in visualizing the result of Theorem 4-10, verify its truth for each part of Problem 3, Section 4-2.

5. For each of the following cases, find the dimensions of S, of T, of $S \cap T$, and of $S + T$. Also find bases for $S \cap T$ and for $S + T$.

	S spanned by	T spanned by
(a)	$(2, 4, 6), (3, 6, 9), (1, 0, 1)$	$(0, 0, 1)$
(b)	$(2, 4, 6), (1, 0, 1)$	$(1, 6, 7)$
(c)	$(2, 4, 6), (1, 0, 1)$	$(0, 0, 1), (3, 1, -1)$
(d)	$(2, 4, 6, 1), (1, 0, 1, 1)$	$(0, 0, 1, 1), (3, 1, -1, 1)$
(e)	$(2, 4, 6, 2), (1, 0, 1, 1)$	$(0, 0, 1, 1), (3, 1, -1, -2)$
(f)	$(2, 1, 0, 3), (0, 2, -1, 1), (2, 3, -1, 0)$	$(1, 1, 2, 1), (-1, 1, 1, 0), (1, 0, 0, 1).$

*6. *Definition.* If S, T are vector spaces with $S \cap T = \{o\}$, then $V = S + T$ is called the *direct sum* of S and T. In this case S and T are called *complementary* subspaces in V; S is called a *complement* of T in V, and, likewise, T a complement of S.

(i) If V is the direct sum of its subspaces S and T,
     (a) what relation exists among the dimensions of V, S, and T?
     (b) how can a basis for V be expressed in terms of given bases for S and T?
     (c) show that any vector of V has a *unique* expression as the sum of a vector of S and a vector of T.

(ii) Let V be a subspace of $V_n(\mathfrak{F})$, and let S, T be subspaces of V. Show that if every vector of V has a unique expression as the sum of a vector from S and a vector from T, V is the direct sum of S and T.

(iii) Note that there is no unique complement of a subspace in a given vector space. If S is the set of vectors $(x_1, x_2, 0)$, exhibit several complements of S in V_3.

(iv) If S is a subspace of V, show that there exists a subspace T of V such that V is the direct sum of S and T; i.e., show that any subspace of V has a complement in V. [*Hint:* Use Theorem 4-8.]

7. In $V_4(R)$, let A be the subspace generated by $(1, 0, 1, 1)$ and $(0, 1, 0, 1)$; B, the subspace generated by $(1, 2, 1, 2)$; C, the subspace generated by $(3, 0, 3, 2)$; and D, the subspace generated by $(1, 2, 2, 1)$. Find bases for each of the following subspaces:

$$A \cap (B + C); \qquad (A + B) \cap (A + C); \qquad (A + B) \cap (A + D).$$

8. As an interpretation of $V_3(R)$ consider the familiar Euclidean three-space in which points are given by their coordinates relative to a certain rectangular frame.

(a) If S = the xy-plane, T = the z-axis, write the unique expression for α, (a_1, a_2, a_3), as $\alpha = \xi + \eta$, $\xi \in S$, $\eta \in T$.

(b) If U = the xy-plane, W = the xz-plane, write several expressions for α, (a_1, a_2, a_3), as $\alpha = \zeta + \theta$, $\zeta \in U$, $\theta \in W$.

9. For the integers m, n let (m, n) represent their greatest common divisor and $[m, n]$ their least common multiple. Use the idea of the proof of Theorem 4–10 to prove that

$$m \cdot n = (m, n) \cdot [m, n].$$

4–5 CHANGE OF BASIS

The material of Sections 4–3 and 4–4 indicates that it may be appropriate to think of a basis of a vector space as a sort of generalized "coordinate frame" in that space. Just as a shift from one coordinate frame to another is an important consideration in analytic geometry (rotation of axes), so a change from one basis to another is significant in a study of vector spaces.

Suppose that $A = \{\alpha_1, \alpha_2, \ldots, \alpha_r\}$ and $B = \{\beta_1, \beta_2, \ldots, \beta_r\}$ are two bases of a vector space $V \subseteq V_n$. Suppose further that a vector, $\lambda \in V$, has coordinate vector $\gamma = (c_1, c_2, \ldots, c_r)$ relative to A, and coordinate vector $\delta = (d_1, d_2, \ldots, d_r)$ relative to B. (Note that each of λ, the α_i, and the β_i has n components.) Then we have two expressions for λ:

$$\lambda = c_1 \cdot \alpha_1 + c_2 \cdot \alpha_2 + \cdots + c_r \cdot \alpha_r = \sum_{i=1}^{r} c_i \cdot \alpha_i \tag{1}$$

and

$$\lambda = d_1 \cdot \beta_1 + d_2 \cdot \beta_2 + \cdots + d_r \cdot \beta_r = \sum_{i=1}^{r} d_i \cdot \beta_i. \tag{2}$$

What is the relation between γ and δ? If we know the coordinates of a vector relative to one basis, how can we find its coordinates relative to another basis?

The answers to these questions hinge upon the relation between the α_i and the β_i. Since *every* vector of V can be expressed as a linear combination of the β_i, there must exist scalars t_{ij} such that

$$\begin{aligned}
\alpha_1 &= t_{11} \cdot \beta_1 + t_{12} \cdot \beta_2 + \cdots + t_{1r} \cdot \beta_r, \\
\alpha_2 &= t_{21} \cdot \beta_1 + t_{22} \cdot \beta_2 + \cdots + t_{2r} \cdot \beta_r, \\
&\vdots \\
\alpha_r &= t_{r1} \cdot \beta_1 + t_{r2} \cdot \beta_2 + \cdots + t_{rr} \cdot \beta_r.
\end{aligned} \tag{3}$$

If we substitute the expression for each α_i from Eqs. (3) into Eq. (1) and collect the coefficients of each β_i, we obtain

$$\lambda = (c_1 t_{11} + c_2 t_{21} + \cdots + c_r t_{r1}) \cdot \beta_1 + (c_1 t_{12} + c_2 t_{22} + \cdots$$

$$+ c_r t_{r2}) \cdot \beta_2 + \cdots + (c_1 t_{1r} + c_2 t_{2r} + \cdots + c_r t_{rr}) \cdot \beta_r. \qquad (4)$$

Since the expression of any vector in terms of a basis is unique, a comparison of Eqs. (2) and (4) yields

$$t_{11} c_1 + t_{21} c_2 + \cdots + t_{r1} c_r = d_1,$$

$$t_{12} c_1 + t_{22} c_2 + \cdots + t_{r2} c_r = d_2, \qquad (5)$$

$$\vdots$$

$$t_{1r} c_1 + t_{2r} c_2 + \cdots + t_{rr} c_r = d_r.$$

For two given bases, A and B, the t_{ij} are fixed. Thus *each coordinate of a vector λ relative to one basis is a certain linear combination of the coordinates of λ relative to another basis.* We describe the situation by saying that a change of basis effects a *linear transformation* of the coordinates of vectors. A thorough study of linear transformations, including a convenient abbreviated symbolism, will be made in Chapter 6.

We can make one more general observation now. Equations (5) give us the components of δ (coordinates of λ relative to B) in terms of those of γ (coordinates of λ relative to A). If we wish to reverse the process, we may attempt to solve Eqs. (5) for the c_i in terms of the d_i. Since we might have reversed the roles of A and B throughout the entire argument, the attempted solution will surely succeed and will lead to a unique result. Thus we know that one particular type of system of linear equations has a unique solution. This question will be studied carefully in Chapter 7.

PROBLEM SET 4–5

1. In $V_4(R)$ let $A = \{(2, 1, 4, 2), (2, 1, 3, 1), (1, 1, 3, 2)\}$; $B = \{(1, 0, 1, 0), (0, 0, 1, 1), (1, 1, 2, 1)\}$; $\lambda = (1, 1, 4, 3)$.

(a) Verify that A forms a basis for a three-dimensional space S.

(b) Verify that B forms a basis for a three-dimensional space T.

(c) Show that $S = T$ and that $\lambda \in S$.

(d) Find the coordinates of λ in S relative to A.

(e) Find the coordinates of λ in S relative to B.

(f) Express the coordinates of any vector in S relative to B in terms of the coordinates of that vector relative to A.

(g) Use the result of (f) to obtain the answer to (e) from the answer to (d).

(h) Express the coordinates of any vector in S relative to A in terms of the coordinates of that vector relative to B.

(i) Use the result of (h) to obtain the answer to (d) from the answer to (e).

4–6 LENGTH AND ANGLE; ORTHOGONALITY

In some of the preceding sections reference to familiar Euclidean models of vector spaces carried (implicit) connotations of lengths of vectors and of angles between vectors. It should be noted, however, that none of the formal work up to this point has made use of the concepts of *length* or *angle;* the idea of *measurement* has not yet entered.

Indeed, if we wish to introduce *length* and *angle* into a vector space, we must define these quantities. We choose definitions which are motivated by our experience with Euclidean models (Fig. 4–8).

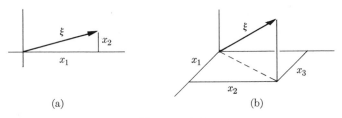

(a)   (b)

FIGURE 4–8

In two dimensions the Pythagorean theorem gives for the length (or "norm") of the vector ξ

$$\|\xi\| = \sqrt{x_1^2 + x_2^2};$$

and, similarly, in three dimensions,

$$\|\xi\| = \sqrt{x_1^2 + x_2^2 + x_3^2}.$$

In $V_n(R)$, then, we make the following definition: if

$$\xi = (x_1, x_2, \ldots, x_n), \qquad \|\xi\| = \sqrt{x_1^2 + x_2^2 + \cdots + x_n^2}.$$

[The definition is restricted to the case where the real numbers form the base field because of the complications which may arise in considering square roots in arbitrary fields. In $V_n(C)$, it is common to define $\|\xi\|$ as $\sqrt{x_1\bar{x}_1 + x_2\bar{x}_2 + \cdots + x_n\bar{x}_n}$, where $\bar{x}_i$ is the conjugate of x_i.]

It is convenient to introduce the notion of *inner product* of two vectors, particularly for the definition of angle to be made shortly.

Definition 9. If

$$\xi = (x_1, x_2, \ldots, x_n), \qquad \eta = (y_1, y_2, \ldots, y_n)$$

are two vectors of $V_n(R)$, the *inner product of ξ and η* is given by

$$\xi \cdot \eta = x_1y_1 + x_2y_2 + \cdots + x_ny_n.$$

Note that the inner product of two vectors is a scalar quantity. It is sometimes called the *scalar product* of the vectors, in contrast with another sort of product of vectors which is itself a vector. We shall not have occasion to consider the "vector product" of two vectors.

It is easy to verify (Problem 1 below) that the inner product has the following properties, for α, β, γ, any vectors of $V_n(R)$:

(i) $(\alpha + \beta) \cdot \gamma = \alpha \cdot \gamma + \beta \cdot \gamma$,

(ii) $(k \cdot \alpha) \cdot \beta = k \cdot (\alpha \cdot \beta)$, all $k \in R$,

(iii) $\alpha \cdot \beta = \beta \cdot \alpha$,

(iv) $\alpha \cdot \alpha > 0$, unless $\alpha = o$.

In terms of the inner product, we can put our definition of the length of a vector as follows.

Definition 10. $\|\xi\| = \sqrt{\xi \cdot \xi}$.

From (i) and (iii) above we can verify (Problem 1 below) that

(v) $\|\alpha \pm \beta\| = \sqrt{(\alpha \cdot \alpha) \pm 2 \cdot (\alpha \cdot \beta) + (\beta \cdot \beta)}$.

We are now ready for a definition of the angle between two vectors. In Euclidean two- or three-dimensional space, the law of cosines gives (Fig. 4-9)

$$\|\beta - \alpha\|^2 = \|\alpha\|^2 + \|\beta\|^2 - 2\|\alpha\| \cdot \|\beta\| \cos \phi.$$

Making use of (v) and cancelling some terms leads to

$$\cos \phi = \frac{\alpha \cdot \beta}{\|\alpha\| \cdot \|\beta\|}.$$

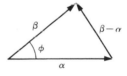

FIGURE 4-9

Now we follow the same procedure which we used in the definition of length. Having obtained a formula for angle valid in two- and three-dimensional Euclidean spaces, we choose it to *define* angle in general.

Definition 11. If ξ, η are two vectors of $V_n(R)$, the *angle ϕ between them* is given by

$$\cos \phi = \frac{\xi \cdot \eta}{\|\xi\| \cdot \|\eta\|}.$$

It remains to be shown that our definitions of length and angle, motivated as they were by our experience with two- and three-dimensional Euclidean spaces, are "good" generalizations in the sense of preserving some fundamental properties of length and angle.

If a vector is multiplied by a scalar, its length should also be multiplied by the scalar, or rather by the absolute value of the scalar (Fig. 4–10). It is not hard to show that this is so (Problem 4 below).

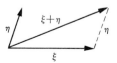

$$\alpha \qquad 3\alpha$$

FIGURE 4–10

(1) For any $k \in R$ and any $\xi \in V_n(R)$, $\|k \cdot \xi\| = |k| \cdot \|\xi\|$.

The length of a vector should always be positive, unless the vector is o. That is,

(2) for all $\xi \in R$, $\|\xi\| > 0$, unless $\xi = o$. This is immediate from our definition of length.

In order that the definition of angle give rise to a real angle, it is necessary that $|\cos \phi|$ be ≤ 1. In other words we would like to have the property that

(3) for all ξ, $\eta \in V_n(R)$, $|\xi \cdot \eta| \leq \|\xi\| \cdot \|\eta\|$. This important relation is known as the *Schwarz-Buniakowsky inequality*. The following is one of several standard proofs of it.

If $\xi = o$, (3) is immediate. We can then assume that $\xi \neq o$. For any $x \in R$,

$$\|x \cdot \xi + \eta\|^2 = (x \cdot \xi + \eta) \cdot (x\xi + \eta) = x^2 \cdot \|\xi\|^2 + 2x \cdot \xi \cdot \eta + \|\eta\|^2.$$

Now $\|x\xi + \eta\|^2 \geq 0$; hence

$$\|\xi\|^2 \cdot x^2 + 2 \cdot (\xi \cdot \eta)x + \|\eta\|^2 \geq 0.$$

This inequality holds for all real x; therefore, the discriminant of the quadratic must be ≤ 0. (Why?) Hence,

$$[2 \cdot (\xi \cdot \eta)]^2 - 4\|\xi\|^2\|\eta\|^2 \leq 0.$$

Therefore,

$$(\xi \cdot \eta)^2 \leq \|\xi\|^2 \cdot \|\eta\|^2, \qquad \text{or} \qquad |\xi \cdot \eta| \leq \|\xi\| \cdot \|\eta\|.$$

Finally, wanting a straight line to be "the shortest distance between two points," we would like it to be true that

$$\eta \qquad \xi + \eta \qquad \eta$$
$$\xi$$

FIGURE 4–11

(4) for all ξ, $\eta \in V_n(R)$, $\|\xi + \eta\| \leq \|\xi\| + \|\eta\|$ (the triangle inequality). The proof follows from a use of (3) (Problem 5 below).

If the cosine of the angle between two vectors is zero, the vectors are said to be orthogonal (perpendicular). We symbolize the orthogonality of ξ and η by writing $\xi \perp \eta$. Clearly, $\xi \perp \eta$ if and only if $\xi \cdot \eta = 0$. Some basic properties of orthogonality are contained in Problem 6 below.

PROBLEM SET 4-6

1. Verify (i) through (v) of p. 87.

2. Carry through the algebraic details leading to the formula for $\cos \phi$ on p. 87.

3. Obtain the formula for the cosine of the angle between two vectors in two- and three-dimensional Euclidean space by straightforward methods of analytic geometry.

4. Prove (1) of p. 88.

5. Prove the triangle inequality. *Hint:* Start with

$$\|\xi + \eta\|^2 = (\xi + \eta) \cdot (\xi + \eta) - \cdots .$$

*6. Prove the following statements.

(a) If $\xi \perp \eta$, then $k \cdot \xi \perp l \cdot \eta$ for all $k, l \in R$.

(b) $\xi \perp \xi$ if and only if $\xi = o$.

(c) If $\xi \perp \eta_i$, $i = 1, 2, \ldots, m$, then

$$\xi \perp \sum_{i=1}^{m} c_i \cdot \eta_i$$

for all $c_i \in R$.

(d) If a vector is orthogonal to each vector of a set S, then it is orthogonal to every vector of the subspace spanned by the vectors of S.

(e) If each of $\xi_1, \xi_2, \ldots, \xi_p$ is orthogonal to every vector of a set S, then every vector of the space spanned by the ξ_i is orthogonal to every vector of S.

7. In $V_4(R)$, let $\alpha = (1, 1, 2, 0)$, $\beta = (0, 1, 2, 1)$, $\gamma = (1, 2, 3, 1)$.

(a) Find all vectors orthogonal to every vector of the space spanned by α, β, γ.

(b) Find all vectors orthogonal to every vector of the space spanned by α and β.

(c) Find all vectors of the form $k \cdot \alpha + l \cdot \beta + (9, 9, 9, 9)$ orthogonal to every vector of the space spanned by β and γ.

*8. Prove the following statement: If, in a set of vectors $\delta_1, \delta_2, \ldots, \delta_p$, no $\delta_i = o$, and if $\delta_i \perp \delta_j$ for every $i \neq j$, then the vectors form a linearly independent set. [*Hint:* Assume the contrary; write the equation expressing linear dependence, and take the inner product of each side of this equation with each δ_i in turn.]

9. Prove that in $V_n(R)$, $\alpha \perp \beta \Leftrightarrow \|\alpha - r\beta\| \geq \|\alpha\|$ for all real r.

4–7 NORMAL ORTHOGONAL BASES

In $V_n(R)$, the basis consisting of the unit vectors $\epsilon_1 = (1, 0, \ldots, 0)$, $\epsilon_2 = (0, 1, 0, \ldots, 0), \ldots, \epsilon_n = (0, 0, \ldots, 0, 1)$ has two features of simplicity: each of the vectors is of unit length, and each vector is orthogonal to each of the other vectors (the vectors are "mutually orthogonal").

Starting with any basis of a Euclidean vector space E, it is possible to construct a *normal orthogonal basis*, i.e., a basis in which each vector is of unit length and the vectors are mutually orthogonal. The construction is known as the *Gram-Schmidt orthogonalization process*. It will be introduced in terms of the familiar Euclidean model in two dimensions.

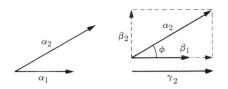

FIGURE 4–12

We first attempt to find an orthogonal basis, leaving until the end the question of obtaining vectors of unit length. Suppose that α_1, α_2 constitute a basis for $V_2(R)$. We set about finding an orthogonal basis β_1, β_2 as follows: Choose

$$\beta_1 = \alpha_1. \tag{1}$$

Express α_2 as $\gamma_2 + \beta_2$, where γ_2 lies in the space spanned by β_1, and $\beta_2 \perp \beta_1$ (Fig. 4–12). Now γ_2 is the "projection" of α_2 in the direction of β_1, so $\gamma_2 = k \cdot \beta_1$, where k represents the number of times that the length of β_1 is contained in the length of the projection of α_2. Thus

$$k = \frac{\|\alpha_2\| \cdot \cos \phi}{\|\beta_1\|} = \frac{\|\alpha_2\|}{\|\beta_1\|} \frac{(\alpha_2 \cdot \beta_1)}{\|\alpha_2\| \cdot \|\beta_1\|} = \frac{(\alpha_2 \cdot \beta_1)}{(\beta_1 \cdot \beta_1)}.$$

Hence

$$\gamma_2 = \frac{(\alpha_2 \cdot \beta_1)}{(\beta_1 \cdot \beta_1)} \cdot \beta_1.$$

Finally, $\beta_2 = \alpha_2 - \gamma_2$, so

$$\beta_2 = \alpha_2 - \frac{(\alpha_2 \cdot \beta_1)}{(\beta_1 \cdot \beta_1)} \cdot \beta_1. \tag{2}$$

We have the desired orthogonal basis for $V_2(R)$.

In three dimensions, suppose that we start with a basis α_1, α_2, α_3. We obtain β_1 and β_2 from α_1 and α_2 as above. We express α_3 as $\gamma_3 + \beta_3$, where γ_3 lies in the two-dimensional space spanned by β_1 and β_2, and β_3

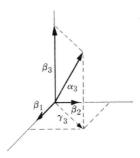

FIGURE 4–13

is $\perp$ to that space (Fig. 4–13). Now γ_3, the "projection" of α_3 onto the $\beta_1\beta_2$-plane, is the sum of the "projections" of α_3 onto the β_1- and β_2-directions. Hence, using the argument of the previous example, we get

$$\gamma_3 = \frac{(\alpha_3 \cdot \beta_2)}{(\beta_2 \cdot \beta_2)} \cdot \beta_2 + \frac{(\alpha_3 \cdot \beta_1)}{(\beta_1 \cdot \beta_1)} \cdot \beta_1.$$

Thus

$$\beta_3 = \alpha_3 - \frac{(\alpha_3 \cdot \beta_2)}{(\beta_2 \cdot \beta_2)} \cdot \beta_2 - \frac{(\alpha_3 \cdot \beta_1)}{(\beta_1 \cdot \beta_1)} \cdot \beta_1. \tag{3}$$

In general, if $\alpha_1, \alpha_2, \ldots, \alpha_r$ form a basis for an r-dimensional subspace S of $V_n(R)$, we can proceed to find an orthogonal basis $\beta_1, \beta_2, \ldots, \beta_r$ in accordance with a set of formulas of which the first three are numbered above, ending with the formula:

$$\beta_r = \alpha_r - \frac{(\alpha_r \cdot \beta_{r-1})}{(\beta_{r-1} \cdot \beta_{r-1})} \cdot \beta_{r-1} - \cdots - \frac{(\alpha_r \cdot \beta_1)}{(\beta_1 \cdot \beta_1)} \cdot \beta_1. \tag{4}$$

It is easy to check that all the β's belong to S (Problem 1 below). We can verify successively that $\beta_2 \perp \beta_1; \beta_3 \perp \beta_2$ and $\beta_3 \perp \beta_1; \ldots; \beta_r \perp \beta_{r-1}, \beta_r \perp \beta_{r-2}, \ldots, \beta_r \perp \beta_1$. Thus the β's are mutually orthogonal. Finally, that the β's form a basis for S follows from Problem 8 of Section 4–6 and the corollary of Theorem 4–9.

Note that if a subset of the α's constitutes a set of mutually orthogonal vectors, we could renumber the α's so that $\alpha_1, \alpha_2, \ldots, \alpha_m$, say, formed this mutually orthogonal set; and the Gram-Schmidt process would give $\beta_i = \alpha_i, i = 1, 2, \ldots, m$. Moreover, if we have any set of mutually orthogonal vectors, none of which is the zero-vector, they can be included in a basis of the space (Problem 8, Section 4–6 and Theorem 4–8), and hence in an orthogonal basis of the space (by the preceding remark).

Now for the *normalization:* If $\xi \neq o$, then the vector ξ' defined by $\xi' = \xi/\|\xi\|$ has length 1. Hence, from any orthogonal basis we can easily obtain a *normal* basis which will still be orthogonal by Problem 6(a) of Section 4–6.

In Problem 6, Section 4–4, the concepts of *direct sum* and *complementary subspaces* were introduced. We now extend these ideas to discuss *orthogonal complements*. As always, in this work it will be helpful to visualize general statements in terms of the familiar Euclidean three-dimensional model.

In Problem 6(e), Section 4–6, we saw that the set of all vectors orthogonal to every vector of a set $S \subset V_n(R)$ constitutes a subspace. If S is itself a subspace, a stronger statement can be made.

Theorem 4–11. In $V_n(R)$, the set of all vectors orthogonal to every vector of a subspace S is a subspace complementary to S.

The proof is omitted (Problem 6 below).

Definition 12. In $V_n(R)$, if S, T are complementary subspaces with $S \perp T$ (i.e., each vector of S is orthogonal to each vector of T), then S and T are called *orthogonal complements* of each other in $V_n(R)$.

Theorem 4–11 ensures the existence of orthogonal complements.

Theorem 4–12. In $V_n(R)$, each subspace has a unique orthogonal complement.

Proof. Problem 7 below.

Let us designate the orthogonal complement of A by A'. In all cases we refer to a fixed universe, $V_n(R)$.

Theorem 4–13. $(A')' = A$.

Theorem 4–14. If P, Q are subspaces with $P \subset Q$, then $P' \supset Q'$.

The proofs are omitted (Problems 8 and 9 below).

Theorem 4–15. $(A + B)' = A' \cap B'$.

Proof. First we show that $A' \cap B' \subseteq (A + B)'$.

$\xi \in A' \cap B' \Rightarrow \xi \in A'$ and $\xi \in B' \Rightarrow \xi \perp \alpha$, all α in A, and $\xi \perp \beta$, all β in $B \Rightarrow \xi \perp (\alpha + \beta)$, all α in A and all β in $B \Rightarrow \xi \in (A + B)'$. Thus $A' \cap B' \subseteq (A + B)'$.

Next we show the inclusion relation in the opposite direction.

Since $A + B \supseteq A$, we know that $(A + B)' \subseteq A'$ by Theorem 4–14; similarly, $(A + B)' \subseteq B'$. Therefore, $(A + B)' \subseteq A' \cap B'$.

Theorem 4–16. $(A \cap B)' = A' + B'$.

Proof. It is possible to prove Theorem 4–16 in a form analogous to that used in proving Theorem 4–15. A neater method is to let P', Q' play the roles of A, B in Theorem 4–15: $(P' + Q')' = (P')' \cap (Q')'$. Hence $(P' + Q')' = P \cap Q$. Therefore $[(P' + Q')']' = (P \cap Q)'$; i.e., $P' + Q' = (P \cap Q)'$. $\square$

PROBLEM SET 4–7

1. Show that $\beta_1, \beta_2, \ldots, \beta_r$ as determined by the Gram-Schmidt process all belong to S, the space spanned by $\alpha_1, \alpha_2, \ldots, \alpha_r$.

2. Show that the β's, as determined by the Gram-Schmidt process, form a mutually orthogonal set.

3. Show that $\xi/\|\xi\|$ has length 1.

4. Find normal orthogonal bases for the subspaces of $V_4(R)$ spanned by the following.

  (a) $(0, 1, 1, 1)$, $(2, 1, 0, -1)$, $(2, 1, 1, 0)$
  (b) $(0, 1, 1, 0)$, $(2, 1, 0, 1)$, $(2, 1, 1, 1)$

[*Hint:* Follow the Gram-Schmidt process of first finding orthogonal bases, and then normalizing.]

5. Find the projection of $\alpha = (0, 1, 0, 1)$ onto the subspace of Problem 4(a); of $\beta = (0, 1, 0, 0)$ onto the same subspace.

6. Prove Theorem 4-11. [*Hint:* Use the result of the Gram-Schmidt orthogonalization process.]

7. Prove Theorem 4-12. [Outline of proof: Assume that a subspace S has two orthogonal complements A and B; express an arbitrary vector $\alpha \in A$ as $\alpha = \sigma + \beta$, $\sigma \in S$, $\beta \in B$; and take the inner product of both sides of this equation with σ.]

8. Prove Theorem 4-13. [*Hint:* Use Theorem 4-12.]

9. Prove Theorem 4-14.

10. In $V_4(R)$ consider the subspace S spanned by $\alpha_1, \alpha_2, \alpha_3$, where $\alpha_1 = (0, 0, 1, 0)$, $\alpha_2 = (0, 1, 1, 0)$, $\alpha_3 = (1, 1, 1, 0)$.

  (a) Prove that $A = \{\alpha_1, \alpha_2, \alpha_3\}$ is a basis of the space S.

  (b) The space S can be regarded as the solution-space consisting of all vectors (x_1, x_2, x_3, x_4) whose components satisfy a single homogeneous equation

$$a_1 x_1 + a_2 x_2 + a_3 x_3 + a_4 x_4 = 0.$$

Use the fact that the components of $\alpha_1, \alpha_2, \alpha_3$ satisfy this equation to find the a_i.

  (c) Perform the Gram-Schmidt construction to obtain from A an orthonormal basis $B = \{\beta_1, \beta_2, \beta_3\}$ for S. (Minimize mistakes by checking your results at each stage.)

(d) Express the elements of basis B in terms of those of basis A; that is, find $t_{ij} \in R$ such that

$$\beta_i = t i_1 \cdot \alpha_1 + t i_2 \alpha_2 + t i_3 \alpha_3, \qquad i = 1, 2, 3.$$

(e) Express the elements of basis A in terms of those of basis B.

(f) Let $\xi \in S$. Express the coordinates (x_1, x_2, x_3) of ξ relative to basis A in terms of the coordinates (x_1', x_2', x_3') of ξ relative to basis B.

(g) Describe the subspace T whose equation is

$$x_1 + x_2 - x_3 = 0;$$

that is, describe this solution-space T by finding a basis of T.

(h) Find a basis of $S \cap T$ and compute $d(S \cap T)$. (One could solve the equations in (b) and (g) simultaneously, or use a "basis" approach.)

(i) Compute $d(S + T)$ and find a basis of $S + T$.

11. Let S, T be subspaces of V_n. Prove that if $S \subseteq T$ and $d(s) = d(T)$, then $S = T$.

4–8 FURTHER RESULTS ON SUBSPACES

A few more results on subspaces have intrinsic interest and will be needed in our development of projective geometry. [These results might have been incorporated into Section 4–4.]

Theorem 4–17. Let U be an r-dimensional subspace of $V_n(\mathfrak{F})$, where $0 \leq r \leq n$. Then U is isomorphic to $V_r(\mathfrak{F})$.

Proof. We must show the existence of a one-to-one correspondence between the vectors of U and those of V_r, a correspondence which preserves the operations of vector addition and of multiplication by scalars.

Suppose that $\phi_1, \phi_2, \ldots, \phi_r$ are basis vectors of U and that $\psi_1, \psi_2, \ldots, \psi_r$ are basis vectors of V_r. Let us set up the correspondence between the vectors of U and V as follows. To the vector

$$\alpha = \sum_{i=1}^{r} c_i \phi_i$$

of U let correspond the vector

$$\tilde{\alpha} = \sum_{1}^{r} c_i \psi_i$$

of V_r. It is easy to verify that this correspondence has all the requisite properties (Problem 1 below).

Theorem 4–17 implies that all vector spaces of dimension k are essentially the same, i.e., isomorphic to V_k.

Lemma. In $V_n(\mathfrak{F})$, if $\beta_1, \beta_2, \ldots, \beta_k$ are independent, then so are

$$\beta_1' = (\beta_1 + c_1 \cdot \beta_k),$$
$$\beta_2' = (\beta_2 + c_2 \cdot \beta_k),$$
$$\vdots$$
$$\beta_{k-1}' = (\beta_{k-1} + c_{k-1} \cdot \beta_k),$$

where $c_i \in \mathfrak{F}$, $i = 1, 2, \ldots, k - 1$.

Proof. Suppose, on the contrary, that there exist

$$l_i \in \mathfrak{F}, \ i = 1, 2, \ldots, k - 1,$$

not all $l_i = 0$, such that

$$l_1 \cdot \beta_1' + l_2 \cdot \beta_2' + \cdots + l_{k-1} \cdot \beta_{k-1}' = o.$$

Then

$$l_1 \cdot \beta_1 + l_2 \cdot \beta_2 + \cdots + l_{k-1} \cdot \beta_{k-1} + (l_1 c_1 + l_2 c_2 + \cdots + l_{k-1} c_{k-1})\beta_k = o.$$

Since not all the $l_i = 0$, we have a contradiction of the assumed independence of $\beta_1, \ldots, \beta_k$.

Theorem 4–18. Let $\beta_1, \beta_2, \ldots, \beta_n$ be basis vectors of $V_n(C)$. Consider the set S of all vectors of the form $\sum_1^n x_i \cdot \beta_i$, subject to the condition that $\sum_1^n p_i \cdot x_i = 0$, for fixed scalars $p_1, p_2, \ldots, p_n$, not all zero. Then S is a vector space of dimension $(n - 1)$.

Proof. There will be no loss in generality if the β_i are renumbered so that $p_n \neq 0$. Then

$$x_n = -\frac{p_1}{p_n} x_1 - \frac{p_2}{p_n} x_2 - \cdots - \frac{p_{n-1}}{p_n} x_{n-1},$$

so that the generic vector, ξ, of S can be written as

$$\xi = x_1 \cdot \left(\beta_1 - \frac{p_1}{p_n} \beta_n\right) + x_2 \cdot \left(\beta_2 - \frac{p_2}{p_n} \beta_n\right) + \cdots$$
$$+ x_{n-1} \cdot \left(\beta_{n-1} - \frac{p_{n-1}}{p_n} \beta_n\right).$$

Designating $[\beta_1 - (p_1/p_n)\beta_n]$ as β_1', $\ldots$, $[\beta_{n-1} - (p_{n-1}/p_n)\beta_n]$ as β_{n-1}', we observe that $\beta_1', \ldots, \beta_{n-1}'$ are independent, according to our lemma. Hence, the set S consists of all linear combinations of $(n - 1)$ independent vectors; i.e., S is an $(n - 1)$-dimensional space, which was to be proved.

PROBLEM SET 4–8

1. Show that the correspondence set up in the proof of Theorem 4–17 establishes the desired isomorphism.

2. Show directly that the set S of Theorem 4–18 is a vector space.

3. Generalize the lemma of this section.

*4. Consider the set T of all vectors $\eta:(y_1, y_2, \ldots, y_n)$ of $V_n(C)$ subject to the condition that $a_1 y_1 + \cdots + a_n y_n = 0$ where the fixed scalars a_i are not all zero. Show that T is an $(n - 1)$-dimensional vector space. [*Hint:* Choose a vector, γ, not lying in T, and show that V_n is the direct sum of T and Γ, where Γ is the (one-dimensional) vector space spanned by γ.]

5. In $V_n(R)$ consider the set U of all vectors $\eta:(y_1, y_2, \ldots, y_n)$ subject to the conditions that

$$a_{11} y_1 + a_{12} y_2 + \cdots + a_{1n} y_n = 0,$$
$$a_{21} y_1 + a_{22} y_2 + \cdots + a_{2n} y_n = 0,$$
$$\vdots$$
$$a_{r1} y_1 + a_{r2} y_2 + \cdots + a_{rn} y_n = 0,$$

where the r vectors

$$\alpha_1: (a_{11}, a_{12}, \ldots, a_{1n}),$$
$$\alpha_2: (a_{21}, a_{22}, \ldots, a_{2n}),$$
$$\vdots$$
$$\alpha_r: (a_{r1}, a_{r2}, \ldots, a_{rn})$$

form a linearly independent set. Show that U is an $(n - r)$-dimensional vector space. [*Hint:* Merely show that U is the orthogonal complement of the space spanned by the α's.]

4–9 OTHER DEFINITIONS OF VECTOR SPACES

We have been using what might be termed the definition of a "concrete" vector space up to this point, since the definition in Section 4–1 sets up vectors as ordered n-tuples of elements from a field. In more abstract fashion, we might define a vector space as a set of undefined elements (called "vectors") which behave in certain prescribed ways with respect to some undefined operations. It turns out that a useful definition may be put, informally, as follows.

An abstract vector space is a system consisting of a set of elements (called *vectors*) and a field (whose elements will be called *scalars*), satisfying the eight properties listed in Section 4–1.

The first four of those eight properties may be combined into a single statement by use of the phrase "Abelian group," and this is what we do in the following formal definition.

Definition 13. An *abstract vector space*, V, is a mathematical system $\{S, \mathfrak{F}, +, \cdot\}$ which satisfies the following axioms.

(1) $\{S, +\}$ is an Abelian group.
(2) For each $\alpha \in S$, and each k in the field $\mathfrak{F}$, $k \cdot \alpha$ is an element of S.
(3) For all $\alpha \in S$, $1 \cdot \alpha = \alpha$, where 1 is the multiplicative identity element in $\mathfrak{F}$.
(4) For all $\alpha, \beta \in S$, and all $k \in \mathfrak{F}$, $k \cdot (\alpha + \beta) = (k \cdot \alpha) + (k \cdot \beta)$.
(5) For all $k_1, k_2 \in \mathfrak{F}$ and all $\alpha \in S$, $(k_1 + k_2) \cdot \alpha = (k_1 \cdot \alpha) + (k_2 \cdot \alpha)$.
(6) For all $k_1, k_2 \in \mathfrak{F}$ and all $\alpha \in S$, $(k_1 k_2) \cdot \alpha = k_1 \cdot (k_2 \cdot \alpha)$.

The elements of S are called *vectors*, and the elements of the field $\mathfrak{F}$ are called *scalars*, of the vector space, V.

REMARK. Note that $+$ is a binary operation within S, and that $\cdot$ is an operation defined for a scalar and a vector. Strictly speaking, we should have separate symbols in V for two more operations, namely, addition and multiplication within the field $\mathfrak{F}$. You will note that we have used "$+$" in two senses in axiom (5): on the left side of the equation, "$+$" refers to an operation within $\mathfrak{F}$ (addition of scalars), while on the right side of the same equation, "$+$" refers to an operation within S (addition of vectors). There is a similar ambiguity with respect to "$\cdot$" in axiom (6). In practice, no harm results from this ambiguity, and it would be a nuisance to have separate symbols for the four operations.

EXAMPLE. Let $S = \{a_1 x^2 + a_2 x \mid a_3\}$, $a_1, a_2, a_3 \in R$; i.e., S is the set of all polynomials of degree two or less in one variable with real numbers as coefficients.

Two polynomials are equal if their respective coefficients are equal; the *sum* of the polynomials $a_1 x^2 + a_2 x + a_3$ and $b_1 x^2 + b_2 x + b_3$ is the polynomial $(a_1 + b_1)x^2 + (a_2 + b_2)x + (a_3 + b_3)$; the *product* of the real number k and the polynomial $a_1 x^2 + a_2 x + a_3$ is the polynomial $(ka_1)x^2 + (ka_2)x + (ka_3)$. It is easy to verify that the system $\{S, R, +, \cdot\}$, with $+$ and $\cdot$ defined as in the preceding sentence, is an abstract vector space. Moreover, this vector space is isomorphic to $V_3(R)$ (Problem 1 below).

We see here another illustration of the power of the abstract approach. Just as the axioms of a group enable us to deduce certain theorems about all groups, not merely about *special* groups or about particular *interpretations* of groups, so likewise the axioms of an abstract vector space lead us to theorems of greater generality than are obtained when vectors are defined in terms of "ordered n-tuples." For example, from the axioms listed above for an abstract vector space we can obtain results valid for infinite dimensional, as well as for finite dimensional, vector spaces.

Precisely because of the greater generality, we must add some assumptions to the axioms of an abstract vector space in order to obtain certain results which appear automatically in the case of vectors defined as n-tuples. For example, every vector space whose elements are ordered n-tuples is finite dimensional and has a finite number of vectors in a basis, but we must postulate some statement about the existence of a finite basis if we wish to deal with finite-dimensional abstract vector spaces.

For a treatment of the subject which carries through the abstract approach, you are referred to any of the following books.

P. HALMOS, *Finite-Dimensional Vector Spaces*. Princeton: van Nostrand (1958).

G. BIRKHOFF and S. MACLANE, *Survey of Modern Algebra*. New York: Macmillan (1953).

R. STOLL, *Linear Algebra and Matrix Theory*. New York: McGraw-Hill (1952).

For our work, finite dimensional vector spaces will be sufficient. And it can be shown that any n-dimensional vector space over $\mathfrak{F}$, according to the abstract definition, is isomorphic to $V_n(\mathfrak{F})$, Definition 1. In other words, we are really considering "all" finite dimensional vector spaces in our presentation.

It is likewise possible to define a Euclidean vector space (in which "length" and "angle" will be meaningful terms) in the following abstract fashion. A *Euclidean vector space* is an abstract vector space over R in which, for any two vectors, an inner product is defined satisfying properties (i)–(iv) of Section 4–6.

PROBLEM SET 4–9

1. (a) Verify that the system of the example in Section 4–9 is an abstract vector space.

(b) Show that this vector space is isomorphic to $V_3(R)$. [*Hint:* $a_1x^2 + a_2x + a_3$ corresponds to (a_1, a_2, a_3).]

2. (a) Let $\{P_n(x),\ R,\ +,\ \cdot\}$ be the system of all polynomials with real coefficients of degree $\leq n$, "$+$" and "$\cdot$" designating the usual addition of polynomials and multiplication of a polynomial by a real number. Show that this system is isomorphic to $V_n(R)$.

(b) Show that the subsystem involving those polynomials of $P_n(x)$ which vanish at a particular $x = a$ is isomorphic to a subspace T of $V_n(R)$. Find a "basis" for this subspace, i.e., a set of polynomials in one-to-one correspondence with a basis of T.

3. In the abstract vector space $\{S, \mathfrak{F}, +, \cdot\}$ let o represent the identity element of the group $\{S, +\}$, and 0 the additive identity element of the field $\mathfrak{F}$. Prove the following statements.

(a) For all $\xi \in S$, $0 \cdot \xi = o$.

(b) For all $x \in \mathfrak{F}$, $x \cdot o = o$.

4. Let $\{S, \mathfrak{F}, +, \cdot\}$ be an abstract vector space, and let T be a subset of S which is closed under vector addition and multiplication of vectors by scalars; i.e.,

$$\alpha, \beta \in T \Rightarrow \alpha + \beta \in T,$$

and

$$\alpha \in T, k \in \mathfrak{F} \Rightarrow k \cdot \alpha \in T.$$

Show that $\{T, \mathfrak{F}, +, \cdot\}$ is an abstract vector space.

5. Show that the set of complex numbers C, with the usual addition and multiplication by complex numbers, is a vector space isomorphic to $V_1(C)$ and to $V_2(R)$.

CHAPTER 5

Projective Spaces

Starting with the vector spaces of the preceding chapter, we can now develop another type of space in which we can easily introduce homogeneous coordinates. These coordinates, as we know, are needed to deal analytically with the ordinary and ideal elements of projective geometry. This chapter will present some basic results which stem from the introduction of a coordinate system into a projective space, leaving the detailed geometric treatment until later.

5–1 PROJECTIVE SPACES; HOMOGENEOUS COORDINATES

First we need to define a *ray* in a vector space (Fig. 5–1).

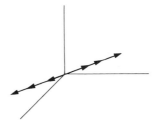

FIGURE 5–1

Definition 1. For a given vector $\alpha \in V_n(C)$, the ray $[\alpha]$ is the set of all vectors of the form $k \cdot \alpha$, $k \in C$.

It is clear that, for $0 \neq p \in C$, $[p \cdot \alpha] = [\alpha]$, i.e., that the ray $[p \cdot \alpha]$ and the ray $[\alpha]$ consist of the same vectors. The ray $[\alpha]$ is the one-dimensional space generated by α. The everyday connotation of "ray" is a sort of "half-line," so the word "ray" is perhaps not an ideal name for this set of vectors, but it is more or less standard.

Definition 2. The rays $[\alpha_1], [\alpha_2], \ldots, [\alpha_r]$ are called linearly dependent or independent according as the vectors $\alpha_1, \alpha_2, \ldots, \alpha_r$ are linearly dependent or independent.

We should check that this is a reasonable definition in the sense that the linear dependence or independence of a set of rays will be unchanged by the use of any nonzero multiples of the original vectors to determine the rays. It is easy to see that this is so.

Definition 3.   *A projective space of dimension* n, *designated by* $S_n(C)$, is *any* set of elements in one-to-one correspondence with the rays of $V_{n+1}(C)$, with elements of S_n linearly dependent if and only if the corresponding rays of V_{n+1} are linearly dependent.

When no other interpretation of the space is in mind, the elements of S_n will be called "points."

Note that the definition describes a projective space as a mathematical system with one relation—that of linear dependence—and no operations. We seem to have imposed very few conditions on our space and might expect, therefore, to be able to draw few conclusions from a system with so much generality. However, we will see that the conditions of one-to-one correspondence with the rays of a vector space, preserving the relation of linear dependence, are sufficient to imply many interesting results. In particular, they enable us to introduce a coordinate system into S_n with no appeal to the notion of distance.

Before we turn to the introduction of a coordinate system in S_n, let us examine some models of S_1 and S_2 described in terms of familiar geometrical configurations in the real domain.

EXAMPLE 1. S_1: the points of a semicircle, including one end point and excluding the other, in natural correspondence with the rays through the center of the circle (Fig. 5–2).

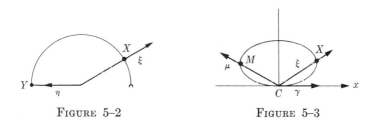

FIGURE 5–2   FIGURE 5–3

EXAMPLE 2. S_1: the points of an ellipse tangent to the x-axis as in Fig. 5–3, in natural correspondence with the rays through the origin. (The point C corresponds to the x-axis.)

EXAMPLE 3. S_2: the points on the surface of a sphere tangent to the xy-plane, not including the point O of tangency, plus the points of a semicircle in the xy-plane with center O, including one end point but not the

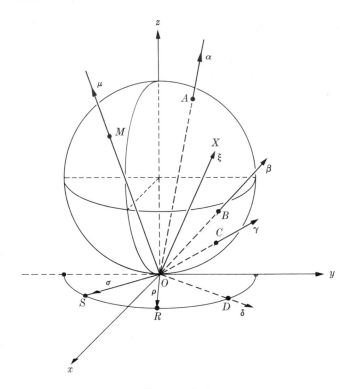

FIGURE 5–4

other, in natural correspondence with rays through O (Fig. 5–4). The vectors α, β, γ, δ are linearly dependent (coplanar); hence the points A, B, C, and D are linearly dependent.

EXAMPLE 4. S_2: the points of the xy-plane plus the points of a semicircle in a plane parallel to the xy-plane, including one end point of the semicircle but not the other, in natural correspondence with the rays through the center of the semicircle (Fig. 5–5).

The rays $[\alpha]$, $[\beta]$, $[\gamma]$, $[\delta]$, being coplanar, are linearly dependent; hence the points A, B, C, and D are linearly dependent. In intuitive language, we may say that D is "the point at infinity" on the line ABC.

Note also that any three or more points on the semicircle are linearly dependent.

It will be instructive if you manufacture some of your own examples of S_1's and S_2's.

We now develop a coordinate system in a projective space. In studying the following exposition of the introduction of a coordinate system into S_n, you should first consider carefully the case $n = 2$, i.e., you should

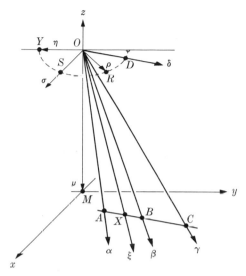

FIGURE 5–5

consider a two-dimensional projective space in relation to a three-dimensional vector space, visualizing the latter as ordinary Euclidean three-space.

Suppose that A_0, A_1, A_2, ..., A_n are $n + 1$ linearly independent points of S_n in one-to-one correspondence with the rays $[\alpha_0]$, $[\alpha_1]$, $[\alpha_2]$, ..., $[\alpha_n]$ of V_{n+1}. Then, by Definitions 3 and 2, the vectors α_0, α_1, ..., α_n are linearly independent, and, hence, by the corollary of Theorem 4–9, these vectors form a basis for V_{n+1}. Suppose further that D is a point of S_n, not one of the A's, and that D corresponds to the ray $[\delta]$ of V_{n+1}. The vector δ can be expressed as a linear combination of the basis vectors α_0, α_1, ..., α_n in only one way:

$$\delta = d_0\alpha_0 + d_1\alpha_1 + \cdots + d_n\alpha_n,$$

say.

We assume that D is so chosen that none of the d_i is zero. (What does this mean in the language of the two-dimensional model?) Let us write

$$d_0 \cdot \alpha_0 = \alpha_0', \quad d_1 \cdot \alpha_1 = \alpha_1', \quad \ldots, \quad d_n \cdot \alpha_n = \alpha_n'.$$

The vectors α_0', α_1', ..., α_n' also constitute a basis for V_{n+1}, of course. Now, let X be an arbitrary point of S_n, corresponding to the ray $[\xi]$, say. The vector ξ is expressible in one and only one way as a linear combination of the basis vectors α_0', α_1', ..., α_n':

$$\xi = x_0 \cdot \alpha_0' + x_1\alpha_1' + \cdots + x_n\alpha_n'.$$

We now make the following definition.

Definition 4.   The ordered set $(x_0, x_1, \ldots, x_n)$ constitutes the *homogeneous coordinates of* X *relative to the* $n + 2$ *fundamental points,* $A_0, A_1, \ldots, A_n, D$.

The set of homogeneous coordinates of a point of S_n relative to a fixed set of $n + 2$ fundamental points is *not* unique. We might have used $k_0 \cdot \alpha_0, k_1 \cdot \alpha_1, \ldots, k_n \cdot \alpha_n$, with none of the k's equal to zero, rather than $\alpha_0, \alpha_1, \ldots, \alpha_n$, to determine the rays $[\alpha_0], [\alpha_1], \ldots, [\alpha_n]$. Likewise, we might have used $l \cdot \delta$, $l \neq 0$, rather than δ, to determine the ray $[\delta]$, and $m \cdot \xi$, $m \neq 0$, rather than ξ, to determine the ray $[\xi]$. Had we used these alternatives, we would have had

$$l \cdot \delta = \frac{ld_0}{k_0} \cdot (k_0 \cdot \alpha_0) + \frac{ld_1}{k_1} \cdot (k_1 \cdot \alpha_1) + \cdots + \frac{ld_n}{k_n} \cdot (k_n \cdot \alpha_n).$$

We would then have set

$$\frac{ld_0}{k_0} \cdot (k_0 \cdot \alpha_0) = \tilde{\alpha}_0, \ldots, \frac{ld_n}{k_n} \cdot (k_n \cdot \alpha_n) = \tilde{\alpha}_n.$$

In other words, we would have had

$$\tilde{\alpha}_0 = l \cdot \alpha_0', \qquad \tilde{\alpha}_1 = l \cdot \alpha_1', \ldots, \tilde{\alpha}_n = l \cdot \alpha_n'.$$

Finally, then, we would have had

$$m \cdot \xi = mx_0 \cdot \alpha_0' + mx_1 \cdot \alpha_1' + \cdots + mx_n \cdot \alpha_n'$$
$$= \frac{m}{l} x_0 \cdot \tilde{\alpha}_0 + \frac{m}{l} x_1 \cdot \tilde{\alpha}_1 + \cdots + \frac{m}{l} x_n \cdot \tilde{\alpha}_n.$$

Thus we would have obtained, as the coordinates of X relative to the $n + 2$ fundamental points $A_0, A_1, \ldots, A_n, D$, the set $[(m/l)x_0, (m/l)x_1, \ldots, (m/l)x_n]$ instead of $(x_0, x_1, \ldots, x_n)$. We see that homogeneous coordinates are determined to within a common nonzero factor.

Coordinates of D in this coordinate frame are $(1, 1, \ldots, 1)$; D is called the unit point.

Coordinates of A_0 are $(1, 0, \ldots, 0)$; of A_1, $(0, 1, 0, \ldots, 0)$; of A_n, $(0, 0, \ldots, 0, 1)$. The points $A_0, A_1, \ldots, A_n$ are called the vertices of *the simplex of reference:* a triangle in two dimensions, and a tetrahedron in three dimensions.

In the homogeneous coordinate system intuitively presented in Section 2–1 by extension of a rectangular coordinate system, A_0 would be called the *origin* and $A_1, A_2, \ldots, A_n$ would be called *ideal points*. But in our present formulation there is absolutely no distinction between "ordinary points" and "ideal points."

Since o does not determine a ray, there is no point of S_n corresponding to "$[o]$," and hence there is no point of S_n with coordinates $(0, 0, \ldots, 0)$.

EXAMPLE 5.   Let us consider a numerical case in S_2, which we choose to describe as in Example 4.   Our S_2 will consist of the points of the xy-plane plus the points of a semicircle in a plane one unit from the xy-plane, including one end point of the semicircle but not the other (Fig. 5–6).   (Note that in terms of the x- and y-axes, we have a simple coordinate representation for some of the points of the S_2—those in the xy-plane—but not for the points of the semicircle.)   Again, as in Example 4, let us consider the natural correspondence between the points of our S_2 with the rays through the center of the semicircle.   For convenience in specifying the rays of V_3 let us set up an $x_1x_2x_3$-coordinate frame as in Fig. 5–6.   Then the point (a, b) of the xy-plane corresponds to the ray $[(1, a, b)]$ of V_3.

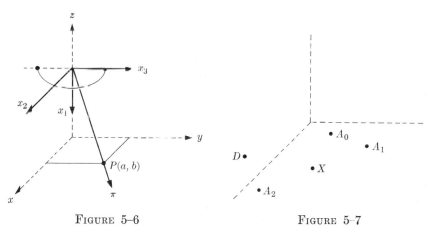

FIGURE 5–6   FIGURE 5–7

We choose three noncollinear points as vertices of the triangle of reference, and a fourth point, not on a side of this triangle, as the unit point. Take, for example, $A_0(1, 2)$, $A_1(2, 5)$, $A_2(6, 1)$, $D(3, -2)$, and $X(4, 3)$ (Fig. 5–7).   We seek homogeneous coordinates for X with reference to the triangle $A_0A_1A_2$ and the unit point D.

Now, the point A_0 of our S_2 corresponds to the ray $[\alpha_0]$ of the V_3, where $\alpha_0 = (1, 1, 2)$; similarly for our other points.   Thus, in the terminology of Example 4,

$$\alpha_0 = (1, 1, 2), \quad \alpha_1 = (1, 2, 5), \quad \alpha_2 = (1, 6, 1),$$
$$\delta = (1, 3, -2), \quad \xi = (1, 4, 3).$$

We can check that

$$\delta = \tfrac{12}{8}\alpha_0 - \tfrac{9}{8}\alpha_1 + \tfrac{5}{8}\alpha_2.$$

Hence we set

$$\alpha_0' = (\tfrac{12}{8}, \tfrac{12}{8}, \tfrac{24}{8}), \qquad \alpha_1' = (-\tfrac{9}{8}, -\tfrac{18}{8}, -\tfrac{45}{8}), \qquad \alpha_2' = (\tfrac{5}{8}, \tfrac{30}{8}, \tfrac{5}{8}).$$

We can check that

$$\xi = 0 \cdot \alpha_0' - \tfrac{4}{9} \cdot \alpha_1' + \tfrac{4}{5} \cdot \alpha_2'.$$

Hence, coordinates of X relative to the fundamental points A_0, A_1, A_2, D, are $(0, -\tfrac{4}{9}, \tfrac{4}{5})$, or $(0, 5, -9)$. Thus in the language of Section 2–1, X is an "ideal" point. But X is *not* "infinitely far out"; it is on the line A_1A_2.

What we have done may be thought of as simply changing triangles of reference and unit points. For "rectangular" (homogeneous) coordinates the vertices of the triangle of reference are the origin and the ideal points on the axes.

Whether or not the first coordinate of a point in S_n is 0 depends solely on the choice of the $n + 2$ fundamental points of the coordinate system, not on any notion of *distance*.

EXAMPLE 6. Another example of the introduction of a coordinate system into S_2 may be useful to emphasize that it is not necessary to assume that some coordinate system has already been established. As our S_2, consider the points on the surface of a hemisphere, including half of the bounding great circle, in natural correspondence with rays through the center.

We introduce a coordinate system into this S_2 as follows. We choose three points, A_0, A_1, A_2, on the hemisphere, not all lying in a plane through the center of the sphere, and choose a fourth point D on the hemisphere, not lying on any of the great circles A_0A_1, A_1A_2, A_2A_0 (Fig. 5–8). Let α_0, α_1, α_2, δ be the vectors drawn from the center of the sphere to the points A_0, A_1, A_2, D.

Suppose that the plane through α_2 and δ intersects the plane through α_0 and α_1 in the line l. Along the line l we choose a vector λ, and by drawing lines through the head of λ parallel to α_0 and to α_1 we can determine λ as a linear combination of α_0 and α_1:

$$\lambda = c_0 \cdot \alpha_0 + c_1 \cdot \alpha_1,$$

say. (In Fig. 5–8, c_0 is $\tfrac{4}{3}$ and c_1 is $\tfrac{5}{4}$.) Through D we draw lines parallel to λ and α_2, thus determining δ as a linear combination of λ and α_2:

$$\delta = h_0 \cdot \lambda + h_1 \cdot \alpha_2,$$

say. (In Fig. 5–8, h_0 is $\tfrac{1}{8}$ and h_1 is 1.) We can now express δ as a linear

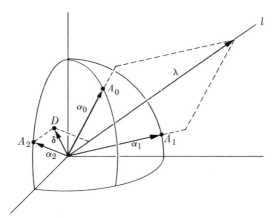

FIGURE 5–8

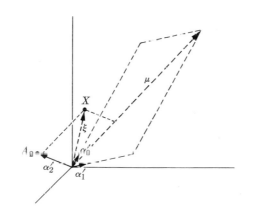

FIGURE 5–9

combination of α_0, α_1, α_2:

$$\delta = h_0 c_0 \cdot \alpha_0 + h_0 c_1 \cdot \alpha_1 + h_1 \cdot \alpha_2.$$

We set

$$h_0 c_0 \cdot \alpha_0 = \alpha_0', \qquad h_0 c_1 \cdot \alpha_1 = \alpha_1', \qquad h_1 \alpha_2 = \alpha_2'.$$

Now, for the vector ξ joining the center of the sphere to an arbitrary point X of the hemisphere, we express ξ as a linear combination of α_0', α_1', α_2' by the same geometrical constructions used to express δ as a linear combination of α_0, α_1, α_2 (Fig. 5–9):

$$\xi = x_0 \cdot \alpha_0' + x_1 \cdot \alpha_1' + x_2 \cdot \alpha_2',$$

say. (In Fig. 5–9, for example, $\mu = 10\alpha_0' + 4\alpha_1'$, and $\xi = \frac{1}{3}\mu + \frac{7}{8}\alpha_2'$, so that $\xi = \frac{10}{3}\alpha_0' + \frac{4}{3}\alpha_1' + \frac{7}{8}\alpha_2'$.)

Then (x_0, x_1, x_2) are homogeneous coordinates of X, in terms of the triangle of reference $A_0A_1A_2$, and the unit point D.

It will be convenient to borrow the notation of vector spaces in referring to homogeneous coordinates of points. If a point X has coordinates $(r_0, r_1, \ldots, r_n)$, we may abbreviate the coordinates as ρ, and call ρ a *coordinate vector* of X (cf. the phrase "solution vector" of a set of equations, introduced in Section 4–2). Clearly, $k \cdot \rho$ is a coordinate vector of the same point X for any $k \neq 0$. If ρ, σ are coordinate vectors of two points, then $\rho + \sigma$ is a coordinate vector of a third point.

The following theorem will prove useful.

Theorem 5–1. Let the points $B_1, B_2, \ldots, B_k$ have coordinate vectors $\rho_1, \rho_2, \ldots, \rho_k$ relative to some coordinate frame in S_n. Then the points $B_1, B_2, \ldots, B_k$ form a dependent set $\Leftrightarrow$ the vectors $\rho_1, \rho_2, \ldots, \rho_k$ of V_{n+1} form a dependent set.

Proof. By definition of S_n, there are rays $[\beta_1], [\beta_2], \ldots, [\beta_k]$ of V_{n+1} in one-to-one correspondence with the points $B_1, B_2, \ldots, B_k$ with the points B_i forming a dependent set if and only if the rays $[\beta_i]$ form a dependent set. Moreover, if the coordinate vector ρ_i has components $r_{i0}, r_{i1}, \ldots, r_{in}$, then, by definition of coordinates,

$$\beta_i = r_{i0}\alpha'_0 + r_{i1}\alpha'_1 + \cdots + r_{in}\alpha'_n,$$

where the $[\alpha'_i]$ are rays corresponding to the vertices of the simplex of reference. Now the set of B's is linearly dependent if and only if there exist $c_1, c_2, \ldots, c_k$, not all zero, such that $c_1\beta_1 + c_2\beta_2 + \cdots + c_k\beta_k = o$. Making use of the expressions for the β's in terms of the α's, we have then

$$(c_1r_{10} + c_2r_{20} + \cdots + c_kr_{k0})\alpha'_0 + (c_1r_{11} + c_2r_{21} + \cdots + c_kr_{k1})\alpha'_1 + \cdots$$
$$+ (c_1r_{1n} + c_2r_{2n} + \cdots + c_kr_{kn})\alpha'_n = o.$$

Since the α's are a linearly independent set, this last equation implies that each of the coefficients of the α's is zero:

$$c_1r_{10} + c_2r_{20} + \cdots + c_kr_{k0} = 0,$$
$$c_1r_{11} + c_2r_{21} + \cdots + c_kr_{k1} = 0,$$
$$\vdots$$
$$c_1r_{1n} + c_2r_{2n} + \cdots + c_kr_{kn} = 0.$$

These n equations can be abbreviated as the single vector equation:

$$c_1\rho_1 + c_2\rho_2 + \cdots + c_k\rho_n = o.$$

Thus we have $\{B_1, B_2, \ldots, B_k\}$ is a dependent set $\Leftrightarrow$ $\{\beta_1, \beta_2, \ldots, \beta_k\}$ is a dependent set $\Leftrightarrow$ $\{\rho_1, \rho_2, \ldots, \rho_k\}$ is a dependent set.

Corollary. Suppose that the points $X_i, i = 1, \ldots, k$, lie in both S_l and S_m, which are subspaces of S_n; and suppose that X_i has coordinate vector λ_i relative to some frame in S_l and coordinate vector μ_i relative to some frame in S_m. Then the vectors $\lambda_1, \lambda_2, \ldots, \lambda_k$ form a dependent set $\Leftrightarrow$ the vectors $\mu_1, \mu_2, \ldots, \mu_k$ form a dependent set.

PROBLEM SET 5–1

1. Check the arithmetical details of Example 5.

2. In the same framework as that of Example 5, find the coordinates of
(a) $V(-1, 1)$ relative to the triangle of reference $A_0 A_1 A_2$ and the unit point D, and
(b) Y relative to the triangle of reference $A_0 A_1 A_2$ and the unit point $E(3, \frac{8}{3})$.
Answer: (a) $(21, 7, -9)$; (b) $(28, -7, -5)$.

3. Show that each of the following sets in ordinary Euclidean space can be considered as a projective space by exhibiting a correspondence between its elements and the rays of a vector space of appropriate dimension.
(a) S_1: points of a line plus one point not on the line,
(b) S_1: points on the x-axis with $x \geq 0$,
(c) S_2: points of the xy-plane with $x \geq 0$, less those points on the y-axis with $y < 0$.

4. Prove the corollary of Theorem 5–1.

5–2 CHANGE OF COORDINATE FRAME; SUBSPACES; HYPERPLANES

A change from one simplex of reference $A_0, A_1, \ldots, A_n$ and unit point D to another simplex of reference $B_0, B_1, \ldots, B_n$ and unit point E effects a change of coordinate frame in a projective space. How are the coordinates of a point in one frame related to its coordinates in a different frame? The answer is furnished by our study of a change of basis in a vector space (Section 4–5), because of the correspondence between points of S_n and rays of V_{n+1}. We found that the coordinates of a *vector*, relative to two bases [Eqs. (5) of Section 4–5], are related by a linear transformation. Hence we conclude that the coordinates of a *point* of S_n, relative to two coordinate frames, are also related by a linear transformation. However, because of the fact that homogeneous coordinates are not unique, the familiar constant of proportionality appears in the equations of the transformation.

Specifically, if a point has coordinates $(x_0, x_1, \ldots, x_n)$ relative to one coordinate frame, and coordinates $(y_0, y_1, \ldots, y_n)$ relative to another coordinate frame, then

$$ry_0 = t_{00}x_0 + t_{01}x_1 + \cdots + t_{0n}x_n,$$
$$ry_1 = t_{10}x_0 + t_{11}x_1 + \cdots + t_{1n}x_n, \qquad r \neq 0 \qquad (1)$$
$$\vdots$$
$$ry_n = t_{n0}x_0 + t_{n1}x_1 + \cdots + t_{nn}x_n.$$

Carry through the details of the argument leading to this result (Problem 2 below).

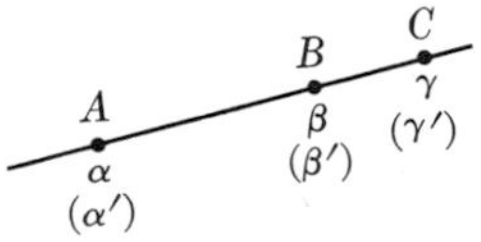

FIGURE 5–10

EXAMPLE 1.   In S_2, suppose that collinear points A, B, C have coordinate vectors α, β, γ, relative to one coordinate frame, and coordinate vectors α', β', γ', relative to another coordinate frame (Fig. 5–10). Suppose further that $\gamma = h \cdot \alpha + k \cdot \beta$. What is the expression for γ' as a linear combination of α' and β'? We proceed as follows:

$$r_1 a'_0 = t_{00}a_0 + t_{01}a_1 + t_{02}a_2,$$
$$r_1 a'_1 = t_{10}a_0 + t_{11}a_1 + t_{12}a_2, \qquad\qquad (2)$$
$$r_1 a'_2 = t_{20}a_0 + t_{21}a_1 + t_{22}a_2,$$

$$r_2 b'_0 = t_{00}b_0 + t_{01}b_1 + t_{02}b_2, \quad \text{etc.,} \qquad (3)$$

$$r_3 c'_0 = t_{00}c_0 + t_{01}c_1 + t_{02}c_2, \quad \text{etc.} \qquad (4)$$

The constant of proportionality which appears in the linear transformation expressing the change of coordinates is not necessarily the same for different points.

Now

$$c_0 = ha_0 + kb_0, \qquad c_1 = ha_1 + kb_1, \qquad c_2 = ha_2 + kb_2. \qquad (5)$$

Substituting from Eqs. (5) into Eqs. (4), and making use of Eqs. (2) and (3), we obtain

$$r_3 c'_0 = r_1 ha_0 + r_2 kb_0, \quad \text{etc.,}$$

or

$$r' = \frac{r_1}{r_3} h \cdot \alpha + \frac{r_2}{r_3} k \cdot \beta.$$

The algebra of this example will be much less tedious when we use matrix methods (Chapter 6).

We have studied subspaces of V_n; we will also concern ourselves with subspaces of S_n, in particular those subspaces called *hyperplanes*.

In the intuitive presentation of Chapter 2, we looked upon

$$a_0 x_0 + a_1 x_1 + a_2 x_2 = 0$$

as the equation of a line in two-dimensional space and upon

$$a_0 x_0 + a_1 x_1 + a_2 x_2 + a_3 x_3 = 0$$

as the equation of a plane in three-dimensional space. In generalization of these ideas, we make the following definition.

Definition 5. The set of all points $(x_0, x_1, \ldots, x_n)$ of $S_n(C)$ satisfying a single linear homogeneous equation

$$p_0 x_0 + p_1 x_1 + \cdots + p_n x_n = 0$$

is called a *hyperplane* (or *prime* or *flat.*)

Thus, from our present, formal, point of view, a *line* is a hyperplane of $S_2(C)$, and a *plane* is a hyperplane of $S_3(C)$.

It is not, perhaps, immediately evident that this definition is meaningful; for, can we be sure that a certain set of points which is a hyperplane with respect to one coordinate frame will also be a hyperplane with respect to a different frame? That the answer is "yes" follows from the linear transformation (Eqs. 1) which characterizes a change of coordinate frame.

Making use of some of the results on vector spaces, we can prove that a hyperplane in S_n is an $(n - 1)$-dimensional linear projective space.

Theorem 5–2. A hyperplane in S_n is an S_{n-1}.

Proof. By the definitions of hyperplane and S_n, we know that each point X, with coordinates $(x_0, x_1, \ldots, x_n)$, of the hyperplane defined by $p_0 x_0 + p_1 x_1 + \cdots + p_n x_n = 0$ corresponds to a ray $[\xi]$ of V_{n+1}, where the vector ξ can be written as

$$\xi = x_0 \cdot \alpha_0' + \cdots + x_n \cdot \alpha_n'.$$

By Theorem 4–18, the set $\{\xi\}$ of all such vectors constitutes an n-dimensional vector space; and hence, by Theorem 4–17, the set $\{\xi\}$ is isomorphic to V_n. Thus we conclude that the points of S_n corresponding to these rays constitute an S_{n-1}. $\square$

EXAMPLE 2. Consider the points of S_2 specified as follows with respect to a certain two-dimensional coordinate frame: $S(1, -2, 1)$, $T(1, 1, 4)$,

$X(-1, 5, 2)$, and $Y(0, 1, 1)$. It is easy to verify that these points all lie on the line $3x_0 + x_1 - x_2 = 0$. Let the given coordinate vectors of these four points be represented by σ, τ, ξ, η, respectively. Because the four points lie in an S_1, the points can be put into one-to-one correspondence with the rays of a V_2. Since only two of the rays can be independent, we expect that two of the coordinate vectors can be expressed as linear combinations of the others. Indeed, we can verify that

$$\xi = -2\sigma + \tau,$$

and

$$\eta = -\tfrac{1}{3}\sigma + \tfrac{1}{3}\tau.$$

It is possible to obtain one-dimensional homogeneous coordinates for S, T, X, Y as follows. Choose S, T, X as the fundamental points of the coordinate system, corresponding respectively to the rays

$$[\sigma] = [\alpha_0 - 2\alpha_1 + \alpha_2], \qquad [\tau] = [\alpha_0 + \alpha_1 + 4\alpha_2],$$
$$[\xi] = [-\alpha_0 + 5\alpha_1 + 2\alpha_2],$$

where $[\alpha_0]$, $[\alpha_1]$, $[\alpha_2]$ are rays of V_3 corresponding to the fundamental points A_0, A_1, A_2 of a coordinate system in S_2. Then, as was found above, $\xi = -2\sigma + \tau$; hence we choose $\sigma' = -2\sigma$ and $\tau' = \tau$. Then we find that $\eta = \tfrac{1}{6}\sigma' + \tfrac{1}{3}\tau'$. We thus have the following one-dimensional coordinates:

$$S: \quad (1, 0),$$
$$T: \quad (0, 1),$$
$$X: \quad (1, 1),$$
$$Y: \quad (\tfrac{1}{6}, \tfrac{1}{3}), \text{ or } (1, 2).$$

A simpler procedure would have been as follows: Consider the point Z with coordinate vector $\zeta = \sigma + \tau = (2, -1, 5)$. [Since ζ is a linear combination of σ and τ, Z also is on the line $3x_0 + x_1 - x_2 = 0$.] Then if S, T, Z are chosen as the fundamental points of a one-dimensional coordinate system, the coordinates are as follows:

$$S: \quad (1, 0),$$
$$T: \quad (0, 1),$$
$$Z: \quad (1, 1),$$
$$X: \quad (-2, 1),$$
$$Y: \quad (-\tfrac{1}{3}, \tfrac{1}{3}), \text{ or } (-1, 1).$$

EXAMPLE 3.   In S_3, what sort of set of points is common to the two hyperplanes

$$P:\ \ 3x_0 - x_1 - x_2 - x_3 = 0,$$

$$Q:\ \ 4x_0 - x_1 - 2x_2 - x_3 = 0?$$

Our experience with analytic geometry tells us that the set of points common to planes P and Q is a line; let us verify that this is the case, according to our present definitions.

The hyperplane P is an S_2; we can obtain a two-dimensional coordinate system in P by choosing the fundamental points

$$A_0(1, 1, 2, 0), \qquad A_1(1, 0, 0, 3), \qquad A_2(0, 1, 1, -2), \qquad D(2, 2, 3, 1).$$

Since the coordinate vector of D equals the sum of the coordinate vectors of A_0, A_1, A_2, we can proceed without modification.   If $X(x_0, x_1, x_2, x_3)$ is an arbitrary point of P, then two-dimensional coordinates of X are (y_0, y_1, y_2) where

$$(x_0, x_1, x_2, x_3) = y_0(1, 1, 2, 0) + y_1(1, 0, 0, 3) + y_2(0, 1, 1, -2).$$

Thus

$$x_0 = y_0 + y_1, \qquad x_1 = y_0 + y_2, \qquad x_2 = 2y_0 + y_2, \qquad x_3 = 3y_1 - 2y_2.$$

If X is also a point of Q, we conclude that

$$4(y_0 + y_1) - (y_0 + y_2) - 2(2y_0 + y_2) - (3y_1 - 2y_2) = 0,$$

or

$$y_0 - y_1 + y_2 = 0.$$

In P (an S_2), the set of points whose coordinates satisfy a linear equation is a hyperplane of that S_2—a line, as we expected.

We can make use of elementary algebra to establish two basic "theorems on incidence" of points and lines.

Theorem 5–3.   In S_2, two distinct points determine a unique line (*or both points lie on just one line*).

Theorem 5–4.   In S_2, two distinct lines determine a unique point (*or both lines pass through just one point*).

Sketch of proofs.   If $A(a_0, a_1, a_2)$, $B(b_0, b_1, b_2)$ are two points, they lie on the line with equation

$$p_0x_0 + p_1x_1 + p_2x_2 = 0$$

if and only if

$$p_0 a_0 + p_1 a_1 + p_2 a_2 = 0 \quad \text{and} \quad p_0 b_0 + p_1 b_1 + p_2 b_2 = 0.$$

If the a_i are not proportional to the b_i, then these two equations determine p_0, p_1, p_2 to within a common, nonzero factor. If

$$p_0 x_0 + p_1 x_1 + p_2 x_2 = 0 \quad \text{and} \quad q_0 x_0 + q_1 x_1 + q_2 x_2 = 0$$

are the equations of two lines in S_2, then the point $R(r_0, r_1, r_2)$ lies on both lines if and only if, . . . , etc.

Note that in Theorem 5–3, the assumption that the points lie in S_2 is superfluous, for two points *always* lie in an S_2. The corresponding assumption is not superfluous in Theorem 5–4, and is included in Theorem 5–3 to suggest a similarity between the theorems. (See Section 5–3 below.)

The general analysis of the sets of points common to subspaces, S_p and S_q, of S_n involves questions on the number of solutions of a system of linear equations, and will therefore be deferred until Chapter 7. However, one generalization of what we have thus far done is simple, and is included in Problem 5 below. Moreover, the discussion on intersection and linear sum of vector spaces (Sections 4–2 and 4–4) carries over intact.

Theorem 5–5. If T and U are subspaces of S_n, then $T \cap U$ is also a subspace of S_n.

Note that T and U may have just one point in common, in which case $d(T \cap U) = 0$; or T and U may have *no* points in common—in this case we say that T and U are *skew to each other*, and we assign $T \cap U$ the dimension -1.

Definition 6. If T and U are subspaces of S_n, the smallest space containing both T and U is called the *join* of T and U, symbolized by $[T, U]$.

The join of T and U is *not* just the union of the two point sets T and U. We risk the slight possibility of confusion here for the sake of expressive geometrical language—the join of the two points (zero-dimensional spaces) A and B is the line AB, etc.

The analogue of Theorem 4–10 is easy to prove.

Theorem 5–6. If T, U are subspaces of S_n, then $d(T) + d(U) = d(T \cap U) + d([T, U])$.

An important corollary is immediate.

Theorem 5–7. If $[T, U] = S_n$ and if T and U are skew to each other, then $d(T) + d(U) = n - 1$.

PROBLEM SET 5–2

1. (a) In S_2, relative to the coordinate frame A_0, A_1, A_2, D, the point X has coordinates $(1, 2, 1)$. Relative to the coordinate frame B_0, B_1, B_2, E, A_0 has coordinates $(1, -1, 0)$; A_1, $(2, -1, -1)$; A_2, $(0, 1, 1)$. What are the coordinates of X relative to B_0, B_1, B_2, E?

(b) In S_2, relative to the coordinate frame B_0, B_1, B_2, E, we have points with the following coordinates: $X(1, 2, 1)$; $A_0(1, -1, 0)$; $A_1(2, -1, -1)$; $A_2(0, 1, 1)$; $D(3, 0, 1)$. What are the coordinates of X relative to the coordinate frame A_0, A_1, A_2, D?

2. Carry through the details of the argument leading to Eqs. (1) as the expression for the relationship between coordinates of a point relative to two coordinate frames. [*Hint:* Assume one simplex of reference A_0, A_1, ..., A_n and unit point D, and another simplex of reference B_0, B_1, ..., B_n and unit point E.]

3. (a) Verify the algebraic details of Example 1.
(b) Same for Example 2.

4. (a) Complete the proof of Theorem 5–3.
(b) In Theorem 5–4.

*5. In view of Example 3 and of Theorem 5–4, formulate and prove a statement about the set of points common to two hyperplanes in S_n.

6. Prove Theorem 5–5.

7. Prove Theorem 5–6.

8. Prove Theorem 5–7.

5–3 DUALITY

There is a reciprocal relationship between Theorems 5–3 and 5–4, which exemplifies the principle of duality in projective geometry. Duality proves useful in several branches of mathematics, and in some of the sciences as well, but its application in projective geometry is particularly elegant and especially fruitful. Most of this section will be devoted to a discussion of duality in two dimensions; at the end of the section brief mention will be made of duality in n dimensions.

Let us represent a particular two-dimensional projective space by S_2. In S_2 consider a line $\mathfrak{a}$ with equation $a_0x_0 + a_1x_1 + a_2x_2 = 0$. We may designate $\mathfrak{a}$ briefly by the ordered triad of coefficients (a_0, a_1, a_2). Since $ka_0x_0 + ka_1x_1 + ka_2x_2 = 0$, for any $k \neq 0$, is also an equation of $\mathfrak{a}$, the triad (ka_0, ka_1, ka_2) represents the same line as does (a_0, a_1, a_2).

It begins to look as though the ordered triad (a_0, a_1, a_2) forms a set of "homogeneous coordinates" for $\mathfrak{a}$. We can show that this is actually the case, as follows.

Make the ray $[\lambda]$ of V_3 correspond to an arbitrary line with equation $l_0x_0 + l_1x_1 + l_2x_2 = 0$ in S_2, where the vector λ has components l_0,

l_1, l_2. Then there is a one-to-one correspondence between the lines of S_2 and the rays of V_3. Let us define linear dependence of the lines by the linear dependence of the corresponding rays. Thus, *the lines of S_2 constitute the elements of a two-dimensional projective space.* Let us designate by Σ_2 this space, whose elements are lines of S_2.

We can set up a coordinate system in Σ_2 by choosing the lines with equations

$$x_0 = 0, \qquad x_1 = 0, \qquad x_2 = 0, \qquad x_0 + x_1 + x_2 = 0$$

as fundamental elements. The rays of V_3 corresponding to these lines are $[\epsilon_1]$, $[\epsilon_2]$, $[\epsilon_3]$, and $[(1, 1, 1)]$, where

$$\epsilon_1 = (1, 0, 0), \qquad \epsilon_2 = (0, 1, 0), \qquad \epsilon_3 = (0, 0, 1).$$

Note that $(1, 1, 1) = 1 \cdot \epsilon_1 + 1 \cdot \epsilon_2 + 1 \cdot \epsilon_3$. The ray $[\alpha]$, where $\alpha = (a_0, a_1, a_2)$, corresponds to the line $\mathcal{C}$ considered above. Since $\alpha = a_0 \cdot \epsilon_1 + a_1 \cdot \epsilon_2 + a_2 \cdot \epsilon_3$, we conclude that (a_0, a_1, a_2) are homogeneous coordinates of $\mathcal{C}$ in Σ_2.

Thus, associated with a two-dimensional projective space S_2, there is a two-dimensional projective space, Σ_2, whose elements are the lines (hyperplanes) of S_2. This is only half the story. What are the hyperplanes of Σ_2? They are the points of S_2, in the following sense.

By the definition of hyperplane, we know that a hyperplane of Σ_2 is the set of lines with coordinates x_0, x_1, x_2 satisfying a fixed linear equation $a_0x_0 + a_1x_1 + a_2x_2 = 0$. Since each of these lines is a set of points of S_2, the hyperplane in Σ_2 is a certain "set of sets" of points of S_2. But how are these lines related? They all pass through a point—indeed, the point of S_2 with coordinates (a_0, a_1, a_2) (Problem 1 below). This point, which is common to all the lines constituting the hyperplane, we choose to call "the hyperplane." This completes the reciprocal relationship:

	S_2	Σ_2
Elements	points	lines
Hyperplanes	lines	points

Essentially the relationship is based on the following fact: The element of S_2 (point) with homogeneous coordinates (p_0, p_1, p_2) lies on the element of Σ_2 (line) with homogeneous coordinates (q_0, q_1, q_2) if and only if

$$q_0p_0 + q_1p_1 + q_2p_2 = 0.$$

This is precisely the condition that the element of Σ_2 (line) with homogeneous coordinates (p_0, p_1, p_2) pass through the element of S_2 (point) with homogeneous coordinates (q_0, q_1, q_2).

EXAMPLE 1. Solving the equations

$$2x_0 - x_1 - 4x_2 = 0 \quad \text{and} \quad 6x_0 + 2x_1 - 7x_2 = 0 \quad (1)$$

simultaneously gives $x_0 : x_1 : x_2 = 3 : -2 : 2$ (Problem 2 below).

We can give the following two geometric interpretations of this algebraic result.

(i) The two hyperplanes of S_2 (lines) given by Eqs. (1) intersect in the element of S_2 (point) with coordinates $(3, -2, 2)$, *or* an alternative wording of (i): The two elements of Σ_2 (lines) with coordinates $(2, -1, -4)$ and $(6, 2, -7)$ intersect in the element of S_2 (point) with coordinates $(3, -2, 2)$.

(ii) The two hyperplanes of Σ_2 (points) given by Eqs. (1) are joined by the element of Σ_2 (line) with coordinates $(3, -2, 2)$, *or* an alternative wording of (ii): The two elements of S_2 (points) with coordinates $(2, -1, -4)$ and $(6, 2, -7)$ are joined by the element of Σ_2 (line) with coordinates $(3, -2, 2)$.

This example, with its relation to Theorems 5–3 and 5–4, illustrates the advantage of the ambiguity inherent in algebraic formulation of statements in projective geometry: every theorem (valid proposition) of S_2 may be interpreted as a theorem of Σ_2 and hence, as *another* theorem of S_2. This is the principle of duality in two dimensions. To obtain the dual of a statement in S_2 one simply interchanges the terms "point" and "line," making such other changes in wording ("point *lies on* line" becomes "line *passes through* point," etc.) as are needed for idiomatic expression.

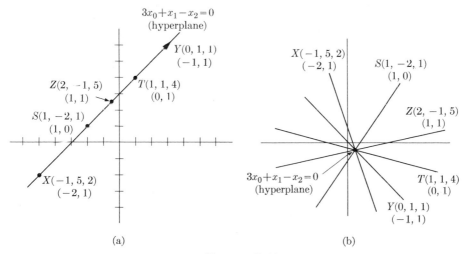

FIGURE 5–11

EXAMPLE 2.   In Example 2 of Section 5–2, we considered, in S_2, a number of points lying in a hyperplane.   The configuration is pictured here in E_2 relative to a rectangular coordinate frame, with both the two-dimensional and the one-dimensional homogeneous coordinates of each point noted (Fig. 5–11a).

Figure 5–11(b) shows the dual configuration.   Note that these lines, all belonging to a hyperplane of Σ_2, lie in a one-dimensional projective space, and, as such, can be given one-dimensional coordinates.   We have chosen a coordinate frame in which the lines S, T, Z are the fundamental elements.

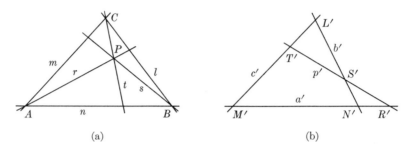

(a)   (b)

FIGURE 5–12

EXAMPLE 3.   Consider Fig. 5–12(a) in which we have four points, A, B, C, P, no three collinear, and the six lines, l, m, n, r, s, t, joining pairs of these points.

The dual figure (Fig. 5–12b) consists of four lines, a', b', c', p', no three concurrent, and the six points, L', M', N', R', S', T', of intersection of pairs of these lines.   In Fig. 5–12(a) points A and B are joined by the line n; in the dual figure, the lines a' and b' intersect in the point N', etc.

Another way to express the relationship is to say that the triangle with vertices A, B, C and sides l, m, n dualizes to the triangle with sides a', b', c' and vertices L', M', N' (a triangle is a "self-dual" figure), and that the three lines r, s, t, one through each vertex and concurrent at P, dualize to three points R', S', T', one on each side and collinear on p'.

A generalization of the foregoing discussion of duality in two dimensions would start out as follows.   The set of all hyperplanes of S_n forms an n-dimensional projective space, Σ_n.   A projective theorem in S_n can be dualized to obtain another theorem by interchanging "point" and "hyperplane" etc.   This time it will be necessary to interchange S_2's with S_{n-2}'s, and, in general, S_r's with S_{n-r}'s.   We will not pursue the generalization here, except to remark that, in three dimensions, *point* and *plane* are dual elements, while *line* is a self-dual element.

PROBLEM SET 5-3

1. Verify that in Σ_2, lines whose coordinates satisfy a fixed linear equation, $a_0x_0 + a_1x_1 + a_2x_2 = 0$, all pass through a point of S_2 with coordinates (a_0, a_1, a_2).

2. Verify the algebra of Example 1.

3. (a) In S_2, find the equation of the line joining the points with homogeneous coordinates $(1, 0, 2)$ and $(0, 1, 1)$.

(b) Hence, what are the coordinates of the point of intersection of the lines with equations $x_0 + 2x_2 = 0$ and $x_1 + x_2 = 0$?

(c) Likewise, in Σ_2, what are the coordinates of the line joining the points with equations $y_0 + 2y_2 = 0$ and $y_1 + y_2 = 0$?

4. Give two geometric interpretations of the following algebraic statement: "If $z_0 + 3z_1 + z_2 = 0$, and $z_0 - 2z_1 - z_2 = 0$, then $z_0:z_1:z_2 = 1:-2:5$."

5. In S_2, find the equation of the line joining the points with the following homogeneous coordinates.
(a) $(1, 1 + i, 2 - i)$ and $(2, 1, 1)$
(b) $(0, 1, i)$ and $(0, 1, -i)$

6. In Σ_2, find the equation of the point of intersection of the lines with the following homogeneous coordinates.
(a) $(1, 1 + i, 2 - i)$ and $(i, 1 + i, -1 + 2i)$
(b) $(1, 0, i)$ and $(0, 1, i)$

7. In Σ_2, find the coordinates of the line joining the points with equations $3y_0 - y_1 + 4y_2 = 0$ and $y_0 + 2y_2 = 0$.

8. (a) In S_3, find the equation of the plane passing through the points with homogeneous coordinates $(1, 0, 2, -1)$, $(0, 3, -2, 0)$, and $(-1, 1, 0, 1)$.

(b) Hence, in Σ_3, what are the coordinates of the plane passing through the points with equations $y_0 + 2y_2 - y_3 = 0$, $3y_1 - 2y_2 = 0$, and $-y_0 + y_1 + y_3 = 0$?

(c) In Σ_3, what is the equation of the point of intersection of the planes with homogeneous coordinates $(1, 0, 2, -1)$, $(0, 3, -2, 0)$, and $(-1, 1, 0, 1)$?

*9. Dualize each of the following configurations.

(a) Three collinear points, and a fourth point not on the line of the other three.

(b) Same as (a), together with the four lines determined by the points.

(c) *Definitions.* The configuration consisting of four coplanar points, no three collinear, and the six lines joining pairs of these points is called a *complete quadrangle*. The points are called the *vertices*, and the lines are called the *sides* of the quadrangle. Two sides which do not pass through a common vertex are called *opposite* sides. The point of intersection of a pair of opposite sides is called a *diagonal point*.

Sketch the configuration described above, and describe the dual figure, called a *complete quadrilateral*, with sides, vertices, opposite vertices, and diagonals.

*10. Let A_1, A_2; B_1, B_2; C_1, C_2 be the pairs of opposite vertices of a complete quadrilateral in the extended Euclidean plane. Show that the midpoints of the segments A_1A_2, B_1B_2, C_1C_2 are collinear.

11. Draw the duals of each of the figures in Fig. 5–13, where the only points considered are those marked heavily, and the only lines considered are those appearing in the figure.

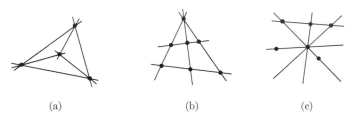

(a)   (b)   (c)

FIGURE 5–13

5–4 SYMBOLIC REPRESENTATIONS

The inner product of two vectors of $V_n(R)$ was introduced in Section 4–6. Actually, the definition may profitably be applied also to other vectors. In particular, if $\alpha = (a_0, a_1, a_2)$ is a coordinate vector of an element A of S_2 ("point") and if $\lambda = (l_0, l_1, l_2)$ is a coordinate vector of an element, l, of Σ_2 ("line"), then A lies on l (or l passes through A) if and only if $\lambda \cdot \alpha = 0$. As was observed on p. 116, this is also the necessary and sufficient condition that the point with coordinate vector λ lie on the line with coordinate vector α, for $\alpha \cdot \lambda = \lambda \cdot \alpha$.

Theorem 5–8. (i) If a coordinate vector of a point X can be written as a linear combination of coordinate vectors of points A and B, then X lies on the line determined by A and B.

(ii) Conversely, a coordinate vector of each point on the line determined by A and B can be written as a linear combination of coordinate vectors of A and B.

We shall present a proof for the case where the space in which the points are imbedded is S_2; then we shall know the truth of the theorem for higher dimensional spaces through an appeal to the corollary of Theorem 5–1.

Proof. (i) Let coordinate vectors of X, A, B be respectively ξ, α, β, with $\xi = h \cdot \alpha + k \cdot \beta$. Let a coordinate vector of the line determined by A and B be λ. Then

$$\lambda \cdot (h\alpha + k\beta) = \lambda \cdot (h\alpha) + \lambda \cdot (k\beta) = h(\lambda \cdot \alpha) + k(\lambda \cdot \beta) = 0 + 0 = 0.$$

(ii) Trivially, coordinate vectors of A and B can be written in the required form, because $\alpha = 1 \cdot \alpha + 0 \cdot \beta$ and $\beta = 0 \cdot \alpha + 1 \cdot \beta$. Consider any other point P on the line AB. It may be identified as the point common to AB and a line m with coordinate vector μ. We already know that $h\alpha + k\beta$ is a coordinate vector of some point on AB. This point will be P provided that it lies on m, i.e., provided that

$$(h\alpha + k\beta) \cdot \mu = 0,$$

or

$$h \cdot (\alpha \cdot \mu) + k \cdot (\beta \cdot \mu) = 0, \qquad \text{or} \qquad h : k = -(\beta \cdot \mu) : (\alpha \cdot \mu).$$

For this value of the ratio $h : k$, $h\alpha + k\beta$ is a coordinate vector of P.

As was stated above, Theorem 5–8 holds no matter what the dimension of the projective space in which the points are imbedded. In particular, if a one-dimensional coordinate system is set up on the line AB, with A and B as fundamental points so as to have respectively the coordinates $\alpha = (1, 0)$ and $\beta = (0, 1)$, then X has coordinate vector $\xi = (x_0, x_1)$, where $\xi = x_0 \cdot \alpha + x_1 \cdot \beta$ (Fig. 5–14).

In S_2, the dual of the set of points on a line (the set of lines through a point) is called a *pencil of lines*. The following theorem is the dual of Theorem 5–8.

Theorem 5–9. (i) If a coordinate vector of a line x can be written as a linear combination of coordinate vectors of lines a and b, then x belongs to the pencil determined by a and b.

(ii) Conversely, a coordinate vector of each line of the pencil determined by a and b can be written as a linear combination of coordinate vectors of a and b.

Note the relationship of this theorem to Problem 10(a) of Section 2–2. It will occasionally be convenient to speak of a linear combination of the *equations* of the lines, in a sense which should be clear from that problem.

Theorem 5–9 requires no separate proof, of course, for from the abstract point of view, it is merely another statement of Theorem 5–8, but it may be instructive for you to dualize the steps of the proof of Theorem 5–8 as an independent proof of Theorem 5–9.

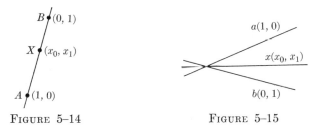

FIGURE 5–14   FIGURE 5–15

Again, the coordinates of the lines of Theorem 5–9 need not be two dimensional, provided that the entire configuration lies in an S_2. In particular, since a pencil of lines is itself a one-dimensional space, we may have a coordinate system as depicted in Fig. 5–15.

We next obtain a result relating linear combinations of points to linear combinations of lines. As a preliminary, we state a lemma on the equation of a line in determinant form. The necessary theorems on determinants will be found in Appendix 2.

Lemma.   In S_2, an equation of the line determined by A, B with respective coordinate vectors (a_0, a_1, a_2), (b_0, b_1, b_2) is

$$\begin{vmatrix} x_0 & x_1 & x_2 \\ a_0 & a_1 & a_2 \\ b_0 & b_1 & b_2 \end{vmatrix} = 0. \tag{1}$$

Proof.   Since (1) is a linear equation it represents some line. If x_0, x_1, x_2 are replaced by a_0, a_1, a_2, respectively, (1) is satisfied, for a determinant with two identical rows is zero. Hence the line passes through A. Likewise the line passes through B. Equation (1), then, is an equation of the line determined by A and B.

Theorem 5–10.   In S_2, let A, B, C be three collinear points, and let P be a point not on the line of the other three points. Let l, m, n be the lines AP, BP, CP. Then an equation of n can be written as the *same* linear combination of the equations of l and m that a coordinate vector of C is of coordinate vectors of A and B.

Proof.   Let coordinate vectors of A, B, C, P be respectively α, β, γ, π; and let $\gamma = h\alpha + k\beta$. Then, by the lemma, equations of l, m, n are:

$$l: \begin{vmatrix} x_0 & x_1 & x_2 \\ a_0 & a_1 & a_2 \\ p_0 & p_1 & p_2 \end{vmatrix} = 0, \qquad m: \begin{vmatrix} x_0 & x_1 & x_2 \\ b_0 & b_1 & b_2 \\ p_0 & p_1 & p_2 \end{vmatrix} = 0,$$

$$n: \begin{vmatrix} x_0 & x_1 & x_2 \\ ha_0 + kb_0 & ha_1 + kb_1 & ha_2 + kb_2 \\ p_0 & p_1 & p_2 \end{vmatrix} = 0.$$

Developing the equation of n by the second row of its determinant leads to

$$h \begin{vmatrix} x_0 & x_1 & x_2 \\ a_0 & a_1 & a_2 \\ p_0 & p_1 & p_2 \end{vmatrix} + k \begin{vmatrix} x_0 & x_1 & x_2 \\ b_0 & b_1 & b_2 \\ p_0 & p_1 & p_2 \end{vmatrix} = 0.$$

PROBLEM SET 5-4

1. Make use of the method of the proof of Theorem 5–8 (ii) to find coordinates of the point of intersection of the line joining the two given points and the line with the given equation.

(a) $(1, 2, 1)$, $(2, 0, 1)$, $2x_0 + 3x_1 - 5x_2 = 0$
(b) $(1, 2, 1)$, $(2, 0, 1)$, $2x_0 + 3x_1 - 4x_2 = 0$

2. Make use of the method dual to that of the proof of Theorem 5–8 (ii) to find an equation of the line which passes through the point of intersection of the two given lines and also through the given point.

(a) $4x_0 + 3x_1 - 2x_2 = 0$, $1 - x_1 - x_2 = 0$, $(1, 1, -2)$
(b) $2x_0 + 5x_1 + 6x_2 = 0$, $x_0 - 3x_1 + 7x_2 = 0$, $(0, 1, -2)$
(c) $x_0 + 2x_1 - x_2 = 0$, $4x_0 - 8x_1 + x_2 = 0$, $(3, -1, 1)$
(d) $5x_0 - x_1 + 4x_2 = 0$, $11x_0 + 2x_1 - 3x_2 = 0$, $(1, -2, 1)$
(e) $x_0 - 2x_1 + x_3 = 0$, $3x_0 - x_1 + 2x_3 = 0$, $(1, 0, 1)$

3. (a) Show that the method of Problem 2 is equally applicable in the ordinary plane when nonhomogeneous coordinates are used.

(b) Find an equation of the line with the given slope passing through the point of intersection of the two given lines.

(i) Slope $= 2$, $5x - y - 4 = 0$, $x + 2y + 6 = 0$
(ii) Slope $= -\frac{1}{2}$, $2x - 3y + 8 = 0$, $x + y - 1 = 0$

4. Use a method similar to that of Problem 2 to find an equation of the plane passing through the line of intersection of the two given planes and also through the given point.

(a) In ordinary space, $x - 3y + 2z + 4 - 0$, $5x - y + z - 6 = 0$, $(1, 2, 2)$
(b) In ordinary space, $2x + 3y - 4z + 5 = 0$, $6x - y + 2z - 7 = 0$, $(1, 1, 1)$
(c) In S_3, $2x_0 - x_1 - 3x_2 = 0$, $x_0 + 3x_2 - 5x_3 = 0$, $(0, 2, 0, 1)$

5. Prove Theorem 5–8 (ii) by considering the correspondence between points of S_2 and rays of V_3.

6. (a) Find coordinates of the point of intersection of the lines with equations $p_0x_0 + p_1x_1 + p_2x_2 = 0$ and $q_0x_0 + q_1x_1 + q_2x_2 = 0$.

(b) Find an equation of the line joining the points (a_0, a_1, a_2) and (b_0, b_1, b_2).

7. Find coordinates of the line which passes through the point of intersection of the lines with coordinates $(1, 2, 1)$ and $(2, -1, 2)$ and also through the point with equation $u_0 + 2u_1 - u_2 = 0$.

8. Use a method similar to that of Problem 2 to find, in the ordinary Euclidean plane, an equation of the circle passing through the points of intersection of the given circles and also through the given point.

(a) $2x^2 + 2y^2 - 19 = 0$, $x^2 - 4x + y^2 + 2y = 0$, $(4, 0)$
(b) $x^2 + y^2 + 3x - 4y + 10 = 0$, $x^2 + y^2 + 2x - 3y + 8 = 0$, $(0, 0)$
(c) $x^2 + y^2 - 2x - 4y + 4 = 0$, $x^2 + y^2 + 2x + 2y - 2 = 0$, $(4, 3)$
(d) $2x^2 + 2y^2 + 5x - 3y - 4 = 0$, $x^2 + y^2 - 2x + 4y - 5 = 0$, $(3, 0)$

9. In ordinary Euclidean three-space, the spheres with equations

$$x^2 + y^2 + z^2 + 2x - 4y + 7z - 10 = 0 \quad \text{and} \quad x^2 + y^2 + z^2 - 6y - 3 = 0$$

intersect in a certain circle. Find an equation of the sphere which passes through this circle and the point $(1, 1, 1)$.

10. Show that the altitudes of a triangle in the ordinary Euclidean plane are concurrent as follows. Let coordinates of the vertices be (a_1, a_2), (b_1, b_2), (c_1, c_2).

(a) Verify that equations of the altitudes are

$$(c_1 - b_1)x + (c_2 - b_2)y - (c_1 - b_1)a_1 - (c_2 - b_2)a_2 = 0,$$
$$(a_1 - c_1)x + (a_2 - c_2)y - (a_1 - c_1)b_1 - (a_2 - c_2)b_2 = 0,$$
$$(b_1 - a_1)x + (b_2 - a_2)y - (b_2 - c_2)c_1 - (b_2 - a_2)c_2 = 0.$$

(b) Use a method similar to that of Theorem 5-9 (i) to show that these three lines are concurrent.

11. In the ordinary plane, with nonhomogeneous coordinates, does a linear combination of the coordinates of A and B always represent a point collinear with A and B? ever represent a point collinear with A and B? (Cf. the "point of division" formula in analytic geometry.)

*12. Let L, M, N be abbreviations respectively for the linear expressions

$$a_0x_0 + a_1x_1 + a_2x_2, \qquad b_0x_0 + b_1x_1 + b_2x_2, \qquad c_0x_0 + c_1x_1 + c_2x_2.$$

Show that the three lines with equations $L - M = 0$, $M - N = 0$, $N - L = 0$ are concurrent.

13. In S_2, suppose that the lines with equations $L = 0$, $M = 0$, and $N = 0$ are not concurrent, but that the lines with equations

$$a_1L + b_1M = 0, \qquad a_2M + b_2N = 0, \qquad a_3N + b_3L = 0$$

are concurrent. What relationship exists among $a_i, b_i, i = 1, 2, 3$?

5-5 DESARGUES' THEOREM AND RELATED RESULTS

Theorems 5-8 and 5-9 of the previous section can be used to prove a basic theorem.

Theorem 5-11 (*Desargues**). If, in two triangles with distinct vertices and sides, the lines joining corresponding vertices are concurrent, then the points of intersection of corresponding sides are collinear, and conversely.

Proof. We have given six distinct points, forming the two triangles ABC and $A'B'C'$ (Fig. 5-16). Suppose that in accordance with the hy-

————————

*Gerard Desargues, an architect from Lyon, was active in mathematics during the first half of the 17th century.

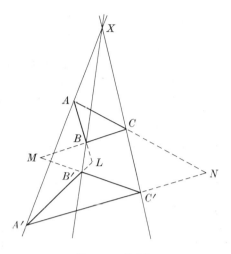

FIGURE 5–16

pothesis of the theorem, AA', BB', CC' meet at X. Let AB and $A'B'$ meet at L; BC and $B'C'$ at M; CA and $C'A'$ at N. We are to show that L, M, N are collinear.

Let coordinate vectors of A, B, C, A', $B,'C'$, L, M, N, X be respectively α, β, γ, α', β', γ', λ, μ, ν, ξ. Since X lies on AA', ξ is a linear combination of α and α', say;

$$\xi = p_1 \cdot \alpha + p_2 \cdot \alpha'.$$

Likewise,

$$\xi - q_1 \cdot \beta + q_2 \cdot \beta' \qquad \text{and} \qquad \xi = r_1 \cdot \gamma + r_2 \cdot \gamma'.$$

Hence

$$p_1 \cdot \alpha - q_1 \cdot \beta = q_2 \cdot \beta' - p_2 \cdot \alpha'.$$

Now $p_1 \cdot \alpha - q_1 \cdot \beta$ is a coordinate vector of a point on AB, while $q_2 \cdot \beta' - p_2 \cdot \alpha'$ is a coordinate vector of a point on $B'A'$. Because the coordinate vectors are equal, they must both represent L, the point common to AB and $A'B'$.

Similarly a coordinate vector of M is

$$q_1 \cdot \beta - r_1 \cdot \gamma \; (= r_2 \cdot \gamma' - q_2 \cdot \beta');$$

and a coordinate vector of N is

$$p_1 \cdot \alpha - r_1 \cdot \gamma \; (= r_2 \cdot \gamma' - p_2 \cdot \alpha').$$

Since

$$(p_1 \cdot \alpha - q_1 \cdot \beta) + (q_1 \cdot \beta - r_1 \cdot \gamma) - (p_1 \cdot \alpha - r_1 \cdot \gamma) = o,$$

we conclude that L, M, N are collinear.

Note that no mention has been made of the dimension of the space S_n in which Fig. 5–16 is embedded. The number of components of the coordinate vectors mentioned in the foregoing argument will depend upon n, but the proof will not be affected. [In extended Euclidean three-space, if ABC, $A'B'C'$ are in different planes, a one-step proof can be given: L, M, N lie on the line of intersection of planes ABC and $A'B'C'$.]

If the entire figure lies in S_2, the converse portion of Desargues' theorem follows by duality. [In S_2, Desargues' theorem is "self-dual."] But, in higher space, duality will not be a help in this proof, and an independent proof of the converse portion is necessary. As a first step, we establish a lemma which will often prove useful.

Lemma 1.   Let L, M, N be distinct points lying respectively on sides AB, BC, CA of triangle ABC (Fig. 5–17). Let coordinate vectors of A, B, C be respectively α, β, γ. Then L, M, N collinear $\Leftrightarrow$ coordinate vectors λ, μ, ν of L, M, N can be chosen so that

$$\lambda = p \cdot \alpha - q \cdot \beta, \qquad \mu = q \cdot \beta - r \cdot \gamma, \qquad \nu = r \cdot \gamma - p \cdot \alpha.$$

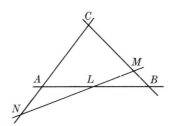

FIGURE 5–17

Proof.   "$\Leftarrow$": obvious, since $\lambda + \mu + \nu = o$. "$\Rightarrow$": Since L lies on AB, a coordinate vector λ of L can be written as $\lambda = p \cdot \alpha - q \cdot \beta$, for some p, q. Since M lies on BC, any coordinate vector of M is a linear combination of β and γ; by choice of a proper multiplier, we can write $\mu = q \cdot \beta - r \cdot \gamma$, for some r. Similarly, we can write $\nu = r \cdot \gamma - p' \cdot \alpha$, for some p'. Our problem, of course, is to show that $p' = p$. To do this, we make use of the hypothesis that L, M, N are collinear. Thus, there exist constants l, m, n, not all zero, such that

$$l \cdot \lambda + m \cdot \mu + n \cdot \nu = o,$$

that is,

$$l(p \cdot \alpha - q \cdot \beta) + m(q \cdot \beta - r \cdot \gamma) + n(r \cdot \gamma - p' \cdot \alpha) = o.$$

Rearranging terms we have

$$(lp - np')\alpha + (m - l)q \cdot \beta + (n - m)r \cdot \gamma = o.$$

Since α, β, γ are independent (why?), the coefficients $(lp - np')$, $(m - l)q$, $(n - m)r$ must each be zero. Since $q \neq 0$, $r \neq 0$ (why?), we conclude that $l = m = n$. Hence $p' = p$. This completes the proof of the lemma.

We proceed with a proof of the converse portion of Desargues' theorem. Since L, M, N are collinear points, one on each side of triangle A, B, C, it follows from Lemma 1 that it is possible to write their coordinate vectors as

$$\lambda = p \cdot \alpha - q \cdot \beta; \quad \mu = q \cdot \beta - r \cdot \gamma; \quad \nu = r \cdot \gamma - p \cdot \alpha.$$

Moreover, since L, M, N also lie one on each side of triangle $A'B'C'$, it is possible to write their coordinate vectors as

$$\lambda' = p' \cdot \alpha' - q' \cdot \beta', \quad \mu' = q' \cdot \beta' - r' \cdot \gamma', \quad \nu' = r' \cdot \gamma' - p' \cdot \alpha'.$$

Since λ and λ' are coordinate vectors of the same point, $\lambda = l \cdot \lambda'$, for some nonzero l. Likewise, $\mu = m \cdot \mu'$, $\nu = n \cdot \nu'$, for some nonzero m, n. Since $\lambda + \mu + \nu = o$ we conclude that $l \cdot \lambda' + m \cdot \mu' + n \cdot \nu' = o$; i.e., that

$$l(p' \cdot \alpha' - q' \cdot \beta') + m(q' \cdot \beta' - r' \cdot \gamma') + n(r' \cdot \gamma' - p' \cdot \alpha') = o.$$

By rearranging terms, we can write this equation as

$$(l - n)p' \cdot \alpha' + (m - l)q' \cdot \beta' + (n - m)r' \cdot \gamma' = o.$$

Since none of p', q', r' is zero, and since α', β', γ' are independent, we conclude that $l - n = 0$, $m - l = 0$, $n - m = 0$; in other words $l = m = n = k$, say. Then $\lambda = k \cdot \lambda'$ implies that

$$p \cdot \alpha - q \cdot \beta = k(p' \cdot \alpha' - q' \cdot \beta'), \quad \text{or} \quad p \cdot \alpha - kp' \cdot \alpha' = q \cdot \beta - kq' \cdot \beta'.$$

Likewise, $\mu = k \cdot \mu'$ leads to

$$q \cdot \beta - kq' \cdot \beta' = r \cdot \gamma - kr' \cdot \gamma'.$$

Now $p \cdot \alpha - kp' \cdot \alpha'$ is a coordinate vector of a point on the line AA': $q \cdot \beta - kq' \cdot \beta'$ is a coordinate vector of a point on BB'; $r \cdot \gamma - kr' \cdot \gamma'$ is a coordinate vector of a point on CC'. The equality of the vectors implies that the lines are concurrent.

We conclude this section with a lemma analogous to Lemma 1. It will be needed later.

Lemma 2. Let L, M, N be distinct points lying respectively on sides AB, BC, CA of triangle ABC (Fig. 5–18). Let coordinate vectors of A, B, C be respectively α, β, γ. Then AM, BN, CL concurrent $\Leftrightarrow$ coordinate

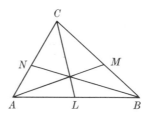

FIGURE 5–18

vectors λ, μ, ν of L, M, N can be chosen so that

$$\lambda = p \cdot \alpha + q \cdot \beta; \qquad \mu = q \cdot \beta + r \cdot \gamma; \qquad \nu = r \cdot \gamma + p \cdot \alpha.$$

Proof. "⇐": Consider the point P with coordinate vector $\pi = p \cdot \alpha + q \cdot \beta + r \cdot \gamma$. Since $\pi = p \cdot \alpha + 1 \cdot (q \cdot \beta + r \cdot \gamma)$, it is clear that P lies on AM. Likewise P lies on BN and on CL. Thus the three lines are concurrent.

"⇒": The situation is similar to that of the comparable portion of the proof of Lemma 1. We can write

$$\lambda = p \cdot \alpha + q \cdot \beta, \qquad \mu = q \cdot \beta + r \cdot \gamma, \qquad \nu = r \cdot \gamma + p' \cdot \alpha,$$

and must show that $p = p'$.

A coordinate vector π of P, the point of concurrence of AM, BN, and CL, can be written

$$\pi = h_1 \cdot (p \cdot \alpha + q \cdot \beta) + k_1 \cdot \gamma = h_2(q \cdot \beta + r \cdot \gamma) + k_2 \cdot \alpha$$

$$= h_3(r \cdot \gamma + p' \cdot \alpha) + k_3 \cdot \beta.$$

By rearranging terms and making use of the independence of α, β, γ, we readily conclude that $h_1 = h_2 = h_3$. From this equality, we deduce that $p' = p$.

PROBLEM SET 5–5

1. State the dual of Desargues' theorem to make it apparent that the theorem is self-dual.

2. (a) Give a geometrical proof of the converse portion of Desargues' theorem when ABC and $A'B'C'$ lie in different planes of extended Euclidean three-space.

(b) List the exceptional cases which must be considered in a statement of Desargues' theorem in ordinary (not extended) three-space.

(c) Complete the following geometrical proof of the converse portion of Desargues' theorem. In Fig. 5–16, consider the triangles BLB' and CNC'. The lines BC, LN, $B'C'$ are concurrent (at M). Hence, by the first portion of

Desargues' theorem, the points of intersection of corresponding sides of these triangles are collinear, that is, $\cdots$.

3. (a) State the duals in S_2, of Lemmas 1 and 2.

(b) Use the dual of Lemma 1 to prove Lemma 2. [*Hint:* Use the result of Problem 6(a) of Section 5–4.]

4. (a) Let A_1, A_2; B_1, B_2; C_1, C_2 be pairs of opposite vertices of a complete quadrilateral. Suppose that A_1A_2 and B_1B_2 meet at R, B_1B_2 and C_1C_2 at P, and C_1C_2 and A_1A_2 at Q. Show that the six lines A_1P, A_2P, B_1Q, B_2Q, C_1R, C_2R pass by threes through four points which are the vertices of a complete quadrangle. [It is clear that P, Q, R are the diagonal points of this quadrangle and that the complete configuration, consisting of 13 lines and 13 points, is self-dual.]

(b) What does the result of part (a) become if the S_2 is interpreted as the extended Euclidean plane and one of the sides of the quadrilateral is taken as the ideal line?

5. Use Desargues' theorem to give an easy solution of Problem 19 of Section 1–1.

CHAPTER 6

Introduction to Projectivities and Matrices

We will begin this chapter with a study of some of the properties of those transformations which we have called *projections* (Chapter 1). Initially our space will be the real, extended plane; we will consider projections from one line in this plane onto another line; and we will use familiar notions of distance in obtaining our results. Then we will turn to S_2, and, motivated by properties observed in the real extended plane, we will make some definitions and prove a basic theorem. Next, in S_n we will define projections in algebraic fashion to accord with this basic theorem. Finally, we will introduce matrices to express our conclusions more compactly and to obtain further results.

6–1 PROJECTION FROM ONE LINE ONTO A SECOND IN THE REAL, EXTENDED PLANE; CROSS RATIO IN TERMS OF DISTANCE

We return to the simple notion of projection described in Problem 1, Section 1–4, and pictured here again (Fig. 6–1).

In the extended plane we will have a one-to-one correspondence between the points of l and those of l' provided that O lies on neither l nor l'.

Clearly, not every one-to-one correspondence between the points of l and those of l' will be of the type illustrated by Fig. 6–1; for this sort of

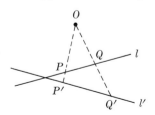

FIGURE 6–1

130

projection, it is obviously necessary and sufficient that the lines joining corresponding points be concurrent.

Definition 1. A one-to-one correspondence between the points of two lines in which the lines joining corresponding points are concurrent at point O is called a *perspectivity* with *center of perspective* O (alternatively worded: The lines are in perspective from O).

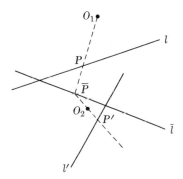

FIGURE 6–2

We extend this notion by considering correspondences of a more general type: If l and $\bar{l}$ are in perspective from O_1, and if $\bar{l}$ and l' are in perspective from O_2, then there is a one-to-one correspondence between the points of l and those of l' (Fig. 6–2). This is generally *not* a perspectivity. (Under what conditions *is* it a perspectivity?) (See Problem 7 of Section 6–3.) We can define a correspondence between the points of l and those of l' by a succession of more than two perspectivities. A correspondence defined by a succession of a finite number of perspectivities is termed a *projectivity* between the points of l and those of l'. Thus a single perspectivity is the simplest sort of projectivity. We will demonstrate later that any projectivity (determined, perhaps, as a succession of many perspectivities) is obtainable by a succession of at most *two* perspectivities.

What features of a configuration are preserved under a projectivity? Clearly not distance: $P'Q' \neq PQ$ in Fig. 6–3. Nor is it true that ratios of distances are preserved: $P'Q'/Q'R' \neq PQ/QR$. The Greeks knew, however, that "ratios of ratios" are preserved: for example,

$$\frac{R'P'/R'Q'}{S'P'/S'Q'} = \frac{RP/RQ}{SP/SQ}.$$

The distances under discussion are to be thought of as *directed*, as in Problem 4 of Section 1–2. Note that if the "ratios of ratios" can be shown to

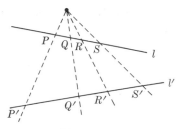

FIGURE 6–3

be equal for a general perspectivity, such as that of Fig. 6–3, it will follow immediately that they are also equal for a general projectivity.

The proof of the invariance under projection of the "ratio of ratios" will come in the next section (Theorem 6–1); we first choose a name and a notation, and then obtain an important result.

If A, B, C, D are four distinct collinear points in ordinary, real space, the cross ratio of A, B, C, D, denoted by (AB, CD), is the value of

$$\frac{CA/CB}{DA/DB} \left(= \frac{CA}{CB} \cdot \frac{DB}{DA} \right).$$

This definition has a meaning only if all four distances are defined. Hence, none of the four points may be ideal; this is why we restrict ourselves to "ordinary" space.

Now suppose that a homogeneous coordinate system is set up on the line $ABCD$, so that these four distinct points have, respectively, coordinate vectors $\alpha(a_0, a_1)$; $\beta(b_0, b_1)$; $\gamma(c_0, c_1)$; $\delta(d_0, d_1)$. We know that each of γ, δ can be expressed as a linear combination of α and β:

$$\gamma = h_1 \cdot \alpha + k_1 \cdot \beta, \qquad \delta = h_2 \cdot \alpha + k_2 \cdot \beta,$$

say. By straightforward analytic geometry (Problem 1 below), we can show that

$$\frac{CA}{CB} = -\frac{k_1}{h_1} \cdot \frac{b_0}{a_0};$$

similarly,

$$\frac{DA}{DB} = -\frac{k_2}{h_2} \cdot \frac{b_0}{a_0}.$$

Hence

$$(AB, CD) = \frac{k_1 h_2}{h_1 k_2}. \tag{1}$$

It is not hard to verify that the foregoing argument, leading to Eq. (1) for the cross ratio of four collinear points, is also valid when A, B, C, D are expressed in terms of two- or three-dimensional coordinates (Problem 2 below).

PROBLEM SET 6–1

1. Show that if A, B, C have coordinate vectors $\alpha(a_0, a_1)$, $\beta(b_0, b_1)$ and $\gamma = h_1\alpha + k_1\beta$, respectively, then $CA/CB = -(k_1/h_1) \cdot (b_0/a_0)$.

2. Obtain Eq. (1) in case the coordinates are two- or three-dimensional [i.e., in case $\alpha = (a_0, a_1, a_2)$ or $\alpha = (a_0, a_1, a_2, a_3)$, say].

3. Find (AB, CD) if nonhomogeneous coordinates of A, B, C, D are, respectively, $(1, 1)$, $(2, -1)$, $(\frac{3}{2}, 0)$, $(4, -5)$. Obtain the result in two ways: by considering lengths of line segments, and by using Eq. (1).

4. For the points of Problem 3, find the values of (BA, CD); (AB, DC); (BA, DC); (CD, AB); (AC, BD); (AC, DB); (AD, CB); (AD, BC).

5. For the points A, B, C of Problem 3, obtain the coordinates of X such that $(AB, CX) = \frac{1}{2}$; such that $(AB, CX) = -\frac{1}{2}$; such that $(AB, CX) = 2$. Can X be found so that $(AB, CX) = 0$? $= -1$?

6. (a) If collinear points are given in terms of homogeneous coordinates as follows: $P_1(3, 1, 2)$, $P_2(1, 0, -1)$, $P_4(1, 1, 4)$, and if $(P_1P_2, P_3P_4) = -\frac{3}{2}$, what are coordinates of P_3?

(b) In part (a), $(P_3P_4, P_2P_1) = ?$

7. If A, B, C, D are collinear points with $(AB, CD) = r$, express (CD, AB) and (AD, BC) in terms of r.

6–2 CROSS RATIOS IN S_1

Without reference to the notion of distance, we can use Eq. (1) of Section 6–1 to *define* cross ratio in S_1—a procedure which proves especially convenient.

Definition 2. Let A, B, C, D be four points in S_1. Relative to some coordinate frame in S_1, let coordinate vectors of A, B, C, D be, respectively, α, β, γ, δ, with $\gamma = h_1 \cdot \alpha + k_1 \cdot \beta$; $\delta = h_2 \cdot \alpha + k_2 \cdot \beta$. Then the cross ratio of A, B, C, D is defined by

$$(AB, CD) = \frac{k_1 h_2}{h_1 k_2}.$$

(Note the generality of this definition—remember that an S_1 does not have to be a straight line.)

It appears as though this may not be a satisfactory definition, for if $c_1\alpha$ replaces α as a coordinate vector for A, will not the cross ratio be changed? Moreover, if a new coordinate frame is chosen, what happens to the cross ratio? It turns out (Problem 1 below) that the cross ratio as given here is independent of the coordinate system and of particular constants of proportionality.

Unlike the definition in terms of distance mentioned in Section 6–1, Definition 2 assigns a value to the cross ratio of four collinear points even when one of the points is ideal—indeed, as is the case generally in projective geometry, no distinction is drawn between ordinary and ideal elements.

EXAMPLE 1. If A, B, C, D have, respectively, coordinate vectors $\alpha = (1, -1, 1)$, $\beta = (1, 1, 2)$, $\gamma = (0, 2, 1)$, $\delta = (3, -1, 4)$, then $\gamma = -\alpha + \beta$, $\delta = 2\alpha + \beta$. Hence $(AB, CD) = -1 \cdot 2 = -2$.

Since in S_2, the set of all lines through a point constitutes an S_1, Definition 2 is immediately applicable as the definition of the cross ratio of four coplanar, concurrent lines. This observation leads to an important lemma.

Lemma 1. In S_2, the cross ratio of four collinear points equals the cross ratio of the four lines obtained by joining the points to any fifth point, not on the line of the given four.

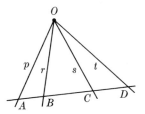

FIGURE 6-4

Proof. Let the collinear points A, B, C, D be joined to the point O, forming the lines p, r, s, t (Fig. 6-4). Let coordinate vectors in S_2, of A, B, C, D, respectively, be α, β, γ, δ; and let coordinate vectors, in Σ_2, of p, r, s, t, respectively, be π, ρ, σ, τ. If

$$\gamma = h_1 \cdot \alpha + k_1 \cdot \beta; \qquad \delta = h_2 \cdot \alpha + k_2 \cdot \beta,$$

then

$$\sigma = h_1 \cdot \pi + k_1 \cdot \rho; \qquad \tau = h_2 \cdot \pi + k_2 \cdot \rho,$$

by Theorem 5-10. Hence

$$(AB, CD) = \frac{k_1 h_2}{h_1 k_2} = (pr, st). \quad \square$$

The proof of Lemma 1 illustrates that, although the definitions of perspectivity and projectivity of Section 6-1 refer to the real, extended plane, they can be considered equally applicable to S_2, with the understanding that pictures, such as Figs. 6-1 and 6-2, are of no use in effecting proofs. An expression like "lines joining corresponding points are concurrent" is to be interpreted as "certain linear equations have a common solution"; we will often use the geometric language associated with the diagrams to abbreviate an algebraic argument, but not to replace it.

Theorem 6–1. Cross ratio is preserved in a projectivity from the points of one line to those of a second line.

Proof. Suppose that A_1, B_1, C_1, D_1 correspond respectively to A_2, B_2, C_2, D_2 in a perspectivity centered at P. Let us designate the lines A_1A_2, B_1B_2, C_1C_2, D_1D_2 by a, b, c, d, respectively. Then, by Lemma 1, $(A_1B_1, C_1D_1) = (ab, cd) = (A_2B_2, C_2D_2)$. Since a projectivity is a finite succession of perspectivities, the result follows.

Theorem 6–2, a converse of Theorem 6–1, follows after a lemma.

Lemma 2. If A, B, C, X, Y are collinear points such that $(AB, CX) = (AB, CY)$, then $X = Y$.

The proof is left as a problem (Problem 3 below).

Theorem 6–2. If A, B, C, ... on line l correspond to A', B', C', ... on line l', with the cross ratio of any four distinct points on l equal to the cross ratio of the corresponding four points on l', then there is a projectivity from l to l' which establishes the same correspondence.

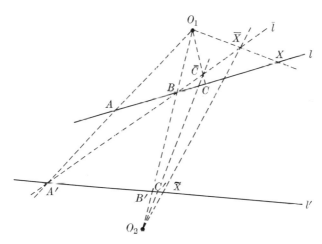

FIGURE 6–5

Proof. Let the line $A'B$ be called $\bar{l}$. Let AA' and BB' meet at O_1. Designate as $\overline{C}$ the intersection of $O_1 C$ with $\bar{l}$. Let $\overline{C}C'$ and BB' meet at O_2. Now, starting with an arbitrary point X of l, we let $\overline{X}$ be the point of $\bar{l}$ corresponding to X in the perspectivity from l to $\bar{l}$ centered at O_1, and we let $\widetilde{X}$ be the point of l' corresponding to $\overline{X}$ in the perspectivity from l to l' centered at O_2. We thus have a projectivity from l to l' (a succession of two perspectivities) in which A, B, C, X correspond, respectively, to A', B', C', $\widetilde{X}$ (verify). We will have succeeded in proving our theorem if we can show that $\widetilde{X}$ is the same point as X', the correspondent of X in the given cross-ratio-preserving transformation. This is done as follows: From the perspectivity centered at O_1, $(AB, CX) = (A'B, \overline{CX})$; and, from the perspectivity centered at O_2, $(A'B, \overline{CX}) = (A'B', C'\widetilde{X})$. Thus, $(AB, CX) = (A'B', C'\widetilde{X})$. (We might have obtained this result in one step by appealing to Theorem 6–1.) But, from the given transformation, $(AB, CX) = (A'B', C'X')$. Hence, from Lemma 2, we conclude that $\widetilde{X} = X'$.

Note that the construction involved in the proof of Theorem 6–2, together with Theorem 6–1, serves to justify the statement, following Definition 1, that a succession of any finite number of perspectivities is equivalent to a succession of at most two perspectivities.

PROBLEM SET 6–2

1. (a) Show that, if four collinear points have coordinate vectors $r_1\alpha$, $r_2\beta$, $r_3\gamma$, $r_4\delta$, the cross ratio, as given by Definition 2, is the same as though the coordinate vectors α, β, γ, δ were used for the points.

(b) Show that, if the coordinate frame is changed, so that collinear points with original coordinate vectors α, β, γ, δ have new coordinate vectors α, β', γ', δ', the cross ratio of the points, as given by Definition 2 is not changed. [*Hint:* Use the result of Example 1, Section 5–2.]

2. Definition 2 is meaningful for some cases where the points A, B, C, D are not all distinct. For what cases of coincidence of points is cross ratio defined?

3. Prove Lemma 2.

4. Write out the details of the proof that any projectivity is equivalent to a succession of at most two perspectivities.

*5. (a) State the duals of the definitions of perspectivity and projectivity, and draw the figures, in the ordinary plane, dual to Figs. 6–1 and 6–2, Section 6–1.

(b) State the duals of Theorems 6–1 and 6–2.

*6. (a) Show that for a rectangular coordinate system, Definition 2 reduces to the metric definition of cross ratio as a "ratio of ratios" of directed distances.

(b) Show that if D is the ideal point on the line ABC in the extended plane, then Definition 2 assigns a value to (AB, CD), viz., $(AB, CD) = CA/CB$.

7. In terms of two-dimensional homogeneous coordinates, let lines p, q, r have, respectively, the equations

$$x_0 - x_2 = 0, \qquad x_1 - x_2 = 0, \qquad x_0 - x_1 = 0.$$

Verify that they are concurrent; find an equation of line s so that $(pq, rs) = -1$; and find an equation of line t so that $(pr, qt) = -1$.

6–3 PROJECTIVITIES AND LINEAR TRANSFORMATIONS

Suppose that in S_2, we choose four arbitrary distinct points A, B, C, D on line l and try to require that they correspond, respectively, to four arbitrary distinct points A', B', C', D' on line l', in a *projectivity*. This is generally impossible, for the chances are that $(AB, CD) \neq (A'B', C'D')$. That is, there is no projectivity which will make four arbitrary points of l correspond to four arbitrary points of l'. If we become much more modest in our demands, we see that there are infinitely many projectivities (perspectivities, in fact) which make A on l correspond to A' on l'; that there is just one perspectivity which makes A, B of l correspond to A', B' of l'; and that there may be no perspectivity which makes A, B, C of l correspond to A', B', C' of l'. Is there perhaps a nonperspective projectivity which makes three arbitrary distinct points of l correspond to three arbitrary distinct points of l'? Figure 6–5 can be used again to give an affirmative answer to this question. If A, B, C are any three distinct points of l, and if A', B', C' are any three distinct points of l', then Fig. 6–5 shows how to set up a succession of two perspectivities (i.e., a projectivity between l and l') in which A, B, C correspond to A', B', C', respectively. Moreover, there is just one such projectivity; that is, just one such correspondence between the points of l and l', for if one projectivity takes A, B, C, X into A', B', C', X', respectively, and if another takes A, B, C, X into A', B', C', $\widetilde{X}$, then $(AB, CX) = (A'B', C'X')$ and $(AB, CX) = (A'B', C'\widetilde{X})$, by Theorem 6–1; whence $X' = \widetilde{X}$, by Lemma 2 of Section 6–2. In other words the transform of any point X is the same in one projectivity as in the other—the projectivities are the same. We have thus proved the following theorem.

Theorem 6–3. There is precisely one projectivity which makes three arbitrary distinct points of line l correspond to three arbitrary distinct points of l'. (Alternatively, a projectivity from one line to a second line is determined by three pairs of corresponding points.)

Note that the construction involved in the proof of Theorem 6–2 furnishes a method of locating geometrically in the ordinary plane the point X' corresponding to an arbitrary point X in the projectivity determined by three pairs of corresponding points.

Theorem 6–3 enables us to characterize perspectivities in a useful way. Consider the point M common to the lines l and l' (Fig. 6–6). In any perspectivity between l and l', M clearly is "self-corresponding," i.e., M as a point of l corresponds to M as a point of l' in the perspectivity. We can show that this property is characteristic of perspectivities.

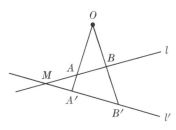

FIGURE 6–6

Theorem 6–4. In a projectivity between two lines, the common point is self-corresponding ⇔ the projectivity is a perspectivity.

Proof. "⇒" Call the given projectivity $\mathcal{P}$; let M be the common point of the two lines l and l'; let A, B be two points of l, both distinct from M; let A', B' be the two points of l' corresponding to A, B in the projectivity $\mathcal{P}$ (Fig. 6–6).

Let O be the point of intersection of AA' and BB', and call $\mathcal{P}'$ the perspectivity from l to l' centered at O. Then $\mathcal{P}$ carries M, A, B into M', A', B', respectively; so likewise does $\mathcal{P}'$. Hence, by Theorem 6–3, $\mathcal{P}$ is identical with $\mathcal{P}'$.

"⇐": This is trivial. □

Let us turn to some algebraic matters by considering projectivities in relation to linear transformations.

We first ask: If A, B, C are three fixed distinct points on l and A', B', C' are three fixed distinct points on l', for any X of l (distinct from A, B, C) can we find an X' of l' such that $(A'B', C'X') = (AB, CX)$? It is quite easy to establish that there is precisely one point X' corresponding to each X.

Let coordinate vectors of A, B, C, X be $\alpha, \beta, \gamma, \xi$ with $\gamma = h \cdot \alpha + k \cdot \beta$, $\xi = s \cdot \alpha + t \cdot \beta$; let coordinate vectors of A', B', C', X' be α', β', γ', ξ', with $\gamma' = h' \cdot \alpha' + k' \cdot \beta'$; $\xi' = s' \cdot \alpha' + t' \cdot \beta'$. The existence of s' and t' is in question. If the cross ratios are to be equal,

$$\frac{k'}{h'} \cdot \frac{s'}{t'} = \frac{k}{h} \cdot \frac{s}{t},$$

or

$$s':t' = h'ks:k'ht. \tag{1}$$

Thus, for given A, B, C, X, A', B', C', there is a unique ratio of s' to t' for the cross ratios to be equal; hence, X' is uniquely determined.

It will be useful to obtain an expression for the coordinates of X'. Suppose that in a one-dimensional coordinate system on l, $\alpha = (a_0, a_1)$, $\beta = (b_0, b_1)$, $\xi = (x_0, x_1)$, and that in a one-dimensional coordinate system on l', $\alpha' = (a'_0, a'_1)$, $\beta' = (b'_0, b'_1)$, $\xi' = (x'_0, x'_1)$.   It will not be necessary to deal explicitly with γ and γ'.

Since

$$\xi = s \cdot \alpha + t \cdot \beta,$$

we have

$$a_0 s + b_0 t = x_0, \qquad a_1 s + b_1 t = x_1.$$

Similarly, we have

$$a'_0 s' + b'_0 t' = x'_0, \qquad a'_1 s' + b'_1 t' = x'_1.$$

Solving these pairs of equations for s, t and s', t', and substituting into Eq. (1) leads to

$$(b'_1 x'_0 - b'_0 x'_1) : (a'_1 x'_0 - a'_0 x'_1) = h'k(b_1 x_0 - b_0 x_1) : k'h(a_1 x_0 - a_0 x_1),$$

or

$$\begin{aligned}
b'_1 x'_0 - b'_0 x'_1 &= mh'k(b_1 x_0 - b_0 x_1), \\
a'_1 x'_0 - a'_0 x'_1 &= mk'h(a_1 x_0 - a_0 x_1),
\end{aligned} \tag{2}$$

for a constant of proportionality $m \neq 0$.

Solving Eqs. (2) for x'_0, x'_1, and noting that h, k, h', k' are some functions of the coordinates of A, B, C, A', B', C', we finally obtain

$$\begin{aligned}
c \cdot x'_0 &= px_0 + qx_1, \\
& \qquad\qquad\qquad\qquad c \neq 0, \tag{3} \\
c \cdot x'_1 &= rx_0 + sx_1,
\end{aligned}$$

where p, q, r, s, c are somewhat involved functions of the coordinates of A, B, C, A', B', C'. Thus we have an expression for the coordinates of X' if $(A'B', C'X') = (AB, CX)$. We might have proceeded in reverse fashion to require the coordinates of X in terms of those of X'. This entire argument might have been carried out with this in view, and we would have obtained a unique point X corresponding to X'. This tells us, without our knowing explicit expressions for p, q, r, s, that Eqs. (3) can be solved for x_0, x_1 in terms of x'_0, x'_1; i.e., that $ps - qr \neq 0$.

A transformation, like that of Eqs. (3), in which the coordinates of X' are linear functions of the coordinates of X is called a *linear transformation*. We will presently study linear transformations in greater detail. The development culminating in Eqs. (3) constitutes a proof of the following theorem.

Theorem 6–5.   A cross-ratio-preserving transformation from the points of one line to the points of a second line is linear in the one-dimensional homogeneous coordinates of the points.

If we wish to interpret S_2 as the ordinary plane, and are willing to restrict our attention to ordinary points, we can divide the second of Eqs. (3) by the first, and, introducing the nonhomogeneous coordinates

$$x' = \frac{x'_1}{x'_0}, \qquad x = \frac{x_1}{x_0},$$

we obtain

$$x' = \frac{sx + r}{qx + p} \tag{4}$$

as the equation of our cross-ratio-preserving transformation. This transformation is not one-to-one without exception, of course.

It is important for our purpose to establish the converse of Theorem 6–5, i.e., that a one-to-one linear transformation from the points of one line to those of a second line preserves cross ratio. All we know from Theorem 6–5 is that under the linear transformation of Eqs. (3), the cross ratio of three *particular* points A, B, C and *any* fourth point X equals the cross ratio of the three *particular* points A', B', C' and the point X' corresponding to X. We don't yet know that the cross ratio of any four points on l equals the cross ratio of their correspondents as given by Eqs. (3). This can, however, be proved.

Theorem 6–6. If X, Y, Z, W are four points of line l, and if X', Y', Z', W' are corresponding points of line l', with the correspondence determined by Eqs. (3) with $ps - qr \neq 0$, then

$$(X'Y', Z'W') = (XY, ZW).$$

Proof. With obvious notation, we have

$$
\begin{aligned}
c_1 x'_0 &= p x_0 + q x_1, & c_2 y'_0 &= p y_0 + q y_1, \\
c_1 x'_1 &= r x_0 + s x_1; & c_2 y'_1 &= r y_0 + s y_1; \\
c_3 z'_0 &= p z_0 + q z_1, & c_4 w'_0 &= p w_0 + q w_1, \\
c_3 z'_1 &= r z_0 + s z_1; & c_4 w'_1 &= r w_0 + s w_1.
\end{aligned}
\tag{5}
$$

(As we observed earlier, the linear transformation which takes X into X' does not necessarily take ξ, a particular coordinate vector of X, into ξ', a particular coordinate vector of X', but rather into some multiple of ξ', say $c_1 \xi'$. The same linear transformation may take η, a coordinate vector of Y, into a different multiple, $c_2 \eta'$, of η', a coordinate vector of Y', etc.) Let ζ and ω, coordinate vectors of Z and W, have the following expressions as linear combinations of ξ and η:

$$\zeta = h_1 \xi + k_1 \eta; \qquad \omega = h_2 \xi + k_2 \eta.$$

Writing out these vector equations as algebraic equations in terms of the components of the vectors and substituting in Eqs. (5) gives

$$z_0' = \frac{h_1 c_1}{c_3} x_0' + \frac{k_1 c_2}{c_3} y_0'$$

and three similar expressions for z_1', w_0', w_1'. We thus obtain

$$\zeta' = \frac{h_1 c_1}{c_3} \xi' + \frac{k_1 c_2}{c_3} \eta', \qquad \omega' = \frac{h_2 c_1}{c_4} \xi' + \frac{k_2 c_2}{c_4} \eta'.$$

Hence

$$(XY, ZW) = \frac{k_1}{h_1} \cdot \frac{h_2}{k_2},$$

and

$$(X'Y', Z'W') = \frac{k_1 c_2/c_3}{h_1 c_1/c_3} \cdot \frac{h_2 c_1/c_4}{k_2 c_2/c_4} = \frac{k_1 h_2}{h_1 k_2}. \quad \square$$

The tedious algebra involved in the foregoing proof of the theorem that "linear transformations preserve cross ratio" will be materially abbreviated when we develop some matrix algebra.

In summary, we have the result that the following three types of transformations from the points of one line to those of a second line are equivalent to each other:

(1) projectivities,

(2) cross-ratio-preserving transformations,

(3) linear transformations:

$$c \cdot x_0' = p x_0 + q x_1,$$
$$ps - qr \neq 0; \quad c \neq 0.$$
$$c \cdot x_1' = r x_0 + s x_1,$$

We established the stated equivalence in four steps:

(a) transformations which are projectivities preserve cross ratio (Theorem 6–1);

(b) transformations which preserve cross ratio are projectivities (Theorem 6–2);

(c) transformations which preserve cross ratio are linear (Theorem 6–5);

(d) transformations which are linear preserve cross ratio (Theorem 6–6).

PROBLEM SET 6–3

1. Carry through the algebraic details leading to Eqs. (3).

2. Carry through the algebraic details of the proof of Theorem 6–6.

3. Find the equations of the linear transformation taking the points of l with one-dimensional coordinate vectors $(0, -1)$, $(2, 1)$, $(3, -1)$, respectively, into the points of l' with coordinate vectors $(2, 1)$, $(1, -1)$, $(1, 1)$.

4. (a) Find the equations of the linear transformation T taking the points of l with one-dimensional coordinate vectors $(1, 1)$, $(1, 0)$, $(1, -2)$, respectively, into the points of l' with coordinate vectors $(1, -1)$, $(-2, 1)$, $(8, -5)$.

(b) Find the inverse of T; i.e., solve your equations of part (a) for x_0, x_1 in terms of x_0', x_1'.

(c) Find coordinates of the point of l' into which the point $(0, 1)$ of l is mapped by T.

(d) Find coordinates of the point of l which is mapped by T into $(0, 1)$ of l'.

(e) Let ξ be a coordinate vector of a point of l, and ξ' a coordinate vector of the point on l' into which the former point is transformed by T. Find all points of l for which $\xi' = k\xi$, for some k.

5. In the extended Euclidean plane find equations of the projective transformation which carries the points with coordinates 0 and 1 and the point at infinity on l, respectively, into the point with coordinate 1, the point at infinity, and the point with coordinate 0 on l'. (Use homogeneous coordinates.)

6. (a) What are the equations of the linear transformation which takes the points of l with coordinates $(1, 2)$, $(1, -1)$, $(1, 0)$, respectively, into the points of l' with coordinates $(2, 1)$, $(0, 1)$, $(1, 3)$?

(b) What are the equations for transformation of coordinates so that the points of l with coordinates $(1, 2)$, $(1, -1)$, $(1, 0)$ assume, respectively, coordinates $(2, 1)$, $(0, 1)$, $(1, 3)$?

(c) In terms of the new coordinate frame of (b) for line l and the original coordinate frame of (a) for line l', what are the equations of the linear transformation of (a)?

7. Under what conditions is a succession of two perspectivities equivalent to a single perspectivity?

8. Draw two lines l and l', choose three arbitrary points on l and three arbitrary points on l', and locate geometrically the points of l' corresponding to various points of l in the projectivity determined by your chosen three pairs of points. Also, reverse the process by locating the points of l corresponding to several points of l' in this projectivity. In particular, if M is the point common to l and l', find the correspondent of M as a point of l; as a point of l'. Use alternatives to the method of Fig. 6–5 and verify that they lead to the same results.

9. The plane dual of Problem 8.

10. Consider the transformation T of S_1 to S_1', given by the equations $cx_0' = x_0$, $cx_1' = \bar{x}_1$, where $\bar{x}_1$ is the conjugate of x_1.

(a) Is T one-to-one without exception?

(b) What are coordinates of the transforms of $A = (1, 1)$, $B = (1, 0)$, $C = (1, i)$, $D = (1, -i)$?

(c) Is cross ratio preserved under T?

(d) Find equations of the projectivity which transforms A, B, C of part (b) just as T does.

(e) What are coordinates of the transform of D under this projectivity?

*11. State the plane duals of Theorems 6–3, 6–4, 6–5, and 6–6.

12. (a) Use the ideas of projectivity and perspectivity to solve Problem 25 of Section 1–1 and Problems 16(a) and (c) of Section 1–2.

(b) Make use of Problem 25 of Section 1–1 and duality to obtain a more complete statement of Problem 16(a) of Section 1–2.

(c) State the plane dual of the result of Problem 16(c) of Section 1–2.

6–4 PROJECTIVITIES IN n DIMENSIONS

An analysis similar to that of the preceding sections could be carried through to study the projectivities of planes onto planes, and the relationships of such projectivities to cross ratio and to linear transformations. It would be found that the situation is essentially the same as that of Sections 6–2 and 6–3, except that in the analogue of Theorem 6–2, for example, in addition to assuming that we are dealing with a point-to-point transformation, we would have to assume that collinear points are carried into collinear points in order that cross ratio may be preserved. We would obtain the following result. Projectivities from one plane onto another are equivalent to linear transformations:

$$cx_0' = a_{00}x_0 + a_{01}x_1 + a_{02}x_2,$$
$$cx_1' = a_{10}x_0 + a_{11}x_1 + a_{12}x_2,$$
$$cx_0' = a_{20}x_0 + a_{21}x_1 + a_{22}x_2.$$

Rather than examine the geometric details of projectivities or the arithmetic details of cross-ratio-preserving transformations, we will generally deal with the algebra of linear transformations. Remembering our experience with correspondences from the points of one line to those of another and what was stated in the preceding paragraph about correspondences from the points of one plane to those of another, we make the following definition.

Definition 3. If X is an arbitrary point with coordinates $(x_0, x_1, \ldots, x_n)$ in a certain coordinate frame of a projective space S_n and if X' is the point with coordinates $(x_0', x_1', \ldots, x_n')$ in a certain coordinate frame of a space S_n', then a projectivity from S_n to S_n' is a linear transformation:

$$cx_0' = a_{00}x_0 + a_{01}x_1 + \cdots + a_{0n}x_n,$$
$$cx_1' = a_{10}x_0 + a_{11}x_1 + \cdots + a_{1n}x_n, \quad (1)$$
$$\vdots$$
$$cx_n' = a_{n0}x_0 + a_{n1}x_1 + \cdots + a_{nn}x_n.$$

Note that Eqs. (1) define the projectivity in terms of specified coordinate frames in S_n and S'_n; if the coordinate frames were changed, the same projectivity (i.e., the same correspondence between points of S_n and those of S'_n) would be given by equations different from Eqs. (1).

Note also that there is no dependence, in the definition of a projectivity, on notions of distance; the coordinates of a point, it will be remembered, are quite independent of the idea of distance. Cross ratio is not mentioned in this definition of projectivity; it will appear later by explicit definition.

How may a projectivity be specified geometrically; how many pairs of points, $x_i \rightarrow x'_i$, determine a projectivity from S_n to S'_n? This is a basic question which we have answered for $n = 1$ in Theorem 6–3. The consideration of other values of n will be left until matrix notation has been introduced (Theorem 6–8).

The general linear transformation given by Eqs. (1) is not one-to-one without exception; there is no guarantee that the equations can be solved uniquely for each of the x_i in terms of the x'_i. But the projectivities which we considered in Chapter 1, as well as those so far discussed in this chapter, *have* been one-to-one correspondences. We are now widening the scope of our study to include what may be called "improper" projectivities, as well as the "proper" projectivities to which we have hitherto restricted our attention. We can obtain important information from a study of both types of projectivity.

It is instructive to picture an improper projectivity (Fig. 6–7). If we attempt a projection, in extended space, of plane π to plane π' from a center of projection O which lies in π, we observe that no point of π' corresponds to the point O of π; that the projection leads to all points of l, the line of intersection of π and π', and to no other points of π'; and that a point P' of l comes, not from a unique point P, but rather from any point on the line OP', except O.

In the language of *functions*, we may describe the situation as follows. The projectivity of Fig. 6–7 is a *function from π into π'*; the *domain* consists of all points of π except O; the *range* consists of all points of l; the *inverse relation* is not a function.

The preceding projectivity may be contrasted with a proper projectivity, in extended space, from π to π' from a center of projection O, which lies in neither π nor π' (Fig. 6–8). This (proper) projectivity is a *function from π onto π'*; the *domain* consists of all points of π; the *range* consists of all points of π'; the *inverse relation* is a function with π as range and π' as domain. The projectivity is, indeed, a one-to-one correspondence between the points of π and π'.

We turn now to the algebraic expression of the improper projectivity of Fig. 6–7. If plane π is considered to be an S_2, and line l an S_1, and if

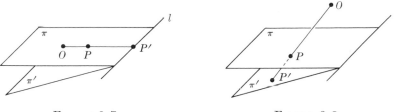

FIGURE 6–7   FIGURE 6–8

appropriate coordinate frames are chosen in each space, the point P of π will have coordinates (x_0, x_1, x_2), say, and the corresponding point P' will have coordinates (x_0', x_1'). Then the linear transformation has equations:

$$cx_0' = a_{00}x_0 + a_{01}x_1 + a_{02}x_2, \qquad cx_1' = a_{10}x_0 + a_{11}x_1 + a_{12}x_2. \quad (2)$$

Alternatively, we may think of l as part of π', an S_2, with a coordinate system which will give P' coordinates (x_0', x_1', x_2'), and hence lead to three equations rather than the two equations (2). But, since all points P' with which we will deal lie on l, a hyperplane in the S_2, there will be a linear relation of the type $l_0x_0' + l_1x_1' + l_2x_2' = 0$ to be satisfied. This is seen most simply by placing on l the points A_0 and A_1 of the triangle of reference in π', thus assigning to l the equation $x_2' = 0$. Then the equations of the projectivity are

$$
\begin{aligned}
cx_0' &= a_{00}x_0 + a_{01}x_1 + a_{02}x_2, \\
cx_1' &= a_{10}x_0 + a_{11}x_1 + a_{12}x_2, \\
cx_2' &= 0x_0 + 0x_1 + 0x_2.
\end{aligned}
\qquad (3)
$$

In general a projectivity, proper or improper, is a linear transformation from the points of S_n to the points of S_m', which is expressible, relative to chosen coordinate frames, as

$$
\begin{aligned}
cx_0' &= a_{00}x_0 + a_{01}x_1 + \cdots + a_{0n}x_n, \\
cx_1' &= a_{10}x_0 + a_{11}x_1 + \cdots + a_{1n}x_n, \qquad c \neq 0. \quad (4) \\
&\ \vdots \\
cx_m' &= a_{m0}x_0 + a_{m1}x_1 + \cdots + a_{mn}x_n.
\end{aligned}
$$

6–5 MATRICES: BASIC DEFINITIONS, OPERATIONS, AND PROPERTIES

It is time to introduce the theory of matrices to find a way through the algebraic jungle which faces us. Already in Chapter 2 we encountered sets of linear equations for which we had no systematic method of solution. These increased in numbers in Chapter 5, where we wished to find what points were common to a number of hyperplanes. Questions of linear dependence or independence of vectors likewise led to systems of linear equations. And now we have encountered linear transformations in three settings: in V_n, relating the coordinates of a vector with respect to two different bases (Eqs. (5) of Section 4–5), in S_n, relating coordinates of a point with respect to two different coordinate-frames (Eqs. (1) of Section 5–2), and finally, relating coordinates of a point in S_n to coordinates of the projected point in S'_m (Eqs. (4) of Section 6–4).

Matrix theory was developed in the 19th century to cope with all these problems. It furnished not only a convenient abbreviated symbolism for the expression of problems and results; but, studied as an abstract mathematical construct, it gave rise to theorems about matrices which have important implications for geometrical problems. On the other hand, easily obtained geometrical results were interpreted to furnish elegant proofs about matrices. Finally, in recent years, matrices have proved extraordinarily useful in the study of differential equations and other mathematical disciplines remote from the problems which inspired the theory originally. Matrix methods are likewise of advantage in physics and in some of the social sciences.

The theory will be carried further here than is strictly needed to solve geometrical problems, partly because of its intrinsic interest and partly to furnish a basis for some of its nongeometrical applications.

We have referred to many instances in which our earlier work has led us to sets of linear equations of the form:

$$
\begin{aligned}
y_1 &= a_{11}x_1 + a_{12}x_2 + \cdots + a_{1n}x_n, \\
y_2 &= a_{21}x_1 + a_{22}x_2 + \cdots + a_{2n}x_n, \\
&\vdots \\
y_m &= a_{m1}x_1 + a_{m2}x_2 + \cdots + a_{mn}x_n.
\end{aligned}
\tag{1}
$$

Clearly it is the set of coefficients of these equations which essentially determine them and which we need to manipulate. For this reason we turn to the consideration of arrays of elements which look like these sets of coefficients in their customary positions but with the rest of the equations erased. However, we study them now for themselves alone, giving them no specific interpretation.

Definition 4. The rectangular array

$$
\begin{bmatrix}
a_{11} & a_{12} & \cdots & a_{1n} \\
a_{21} & a_{22} & \cdots & a_{2n} \\
\vdots & \vdots & & \vdots \\
a_{m1} & a_{m2} & \cdots & a_{mn}
\end{bmatrix},
\tag{2}
$$

in which the a_{ij} are elements of a field $\mathfrak{F}$, is called a *matrix* over $\mathfrak{F}$. The matrix, which we shall denote by A, is said to have m *rows* and n *columns;* the a_{ij} are called its *elements*.

We shall customarily use capital letters to represent matrices.

A convenient abbreviated form of (2) is the following:

$$[a_{ij}], \quad i = 1, 2, \ldots, m; \quad j = 1, 2, \ldots, n. \tag{3}$$

If no misunderstanding is likely, the range of i and j may be omitted.

Definition 5. Two matrices are *equal* if their elements are respectively equal; i.e., if A represents $[a_{ij}]$ and B represents $[b_{ij}]$, then $A = B$ if and only if $a_{ij} = b_{ij}$ for $i = 1, 2, \ldots, m; j = 1, 2, \ldots, n$.

Clearly, then, two matrices cannot be equal if they do not have the same number of rows and the same number of columns.

Definition 6. The *sum* of two matrices is the matrix formed by adding corresponding elements. If $A = [a_{ij}]$ and $B = [b_{ij}]$, then

$$A + B = [a_{ij} + b_{ij}].$$

Note that the sum is not defined unless the two matrices have the same number of rows and the same number of columns.

Definition 7. The *product* of a matrix *by a scalar* is defined as follows: If $k \in \mathfrak{F}$, $A = [a_{ij}]$, then $k \cdot A = [ka_{ij}]$.

Definitions 5, 6, and 7 are similar to the corresponding ones for vectors. If we take $m = 1$ in (2), we get $[a_{11} \, a_{12} \ldots a_{1n}]$, called a *row matrix*, which looks very much like a vector. In fact it is clear that the set of all such row matrices, with equality, sum, and scalar product as just defined, constitute a system isomorphic to $V_n(\mathfrak{F})$. From this point of view, we may think of matrices as "generalized vectors." If we let α_i stand for the vector $(a_{11}, a_{12}, \ldots, a_{1n})$, we may represent the matrix of Eq. (2) as

$$A = \begin{bmatrix} \alpha_1 \\ \alpha_2 \\ \vdots \\ \alpha_m \end{bmatrix}. \tag{4}$$

We have thus written the matrix, originally thought of as a set of mn elements of $\mathfrak{F}$, as a set of m vectors, each with n components. The α_i

are called *row vectors* of A. We could condense this notation, if we wish, as $A = [\alpha_i]$, $i = 1, 2, \ldots, m$.

Likewise, if we take $n = 1$, we have the *column matrix*

$$\begin{bmatrix} a_{11} \\ a_{21} \\ \vdots \\ a_{m1} \end{bmatrix}.$$

The elements of each column matrix determine a vector $(a_{11}, a_{21}, \ldots, a_{m1})$, so that, recalling Definitions 5, 6, and 7, we see here again an isomorphism with $V_m(\mathfrak{F})$. Typographical convenience is the only reason for writing the ordered set of elements which constitute a vector in a horizontal line; they could just as well be written vertically, as in the column of a matrix. If we let $\tilde{\alpha}_j$ stand for the vector whose components are the elements of the jth column of A, that is, $\tilde{\alpha}_j = (a_{1j}, a_{2j}, \ldots, a_{mj})$, or if it is a visual aid to write it so:

$$\tilde{\alpha}_j = \begin{matrix} (a_{1j} \\ a_{2j} \\ \vdots \\ a_{mj}), \end{matrix}$$

then we have still another representation:

$$A = [\tilde{\alpha}_1, \tilde{\alpha}_2, \ldots, \tilde{\alpha}_n]. \tag{5}$$

The $\tilde{\alpha}_j$ are called *column vectors;* there are n of them, each with m components. This form could be condensed as $A = [\tilde{\alpha}_j]$, $j = 1, 2, \ldots, n$.

Except when $n = 1$ or $m = 1$, there can be no confusion between forms (4) and (5). However, for emphasis we shall occasionally use a Greek letter with the tilde ($\sim$) above it for a vector whose components occur in a column of the matrix under consideration; in particular, $[\alpha]$ will mean a row matrix, $[\tilde{\alpha}]$ a column matrix.

We have thus three representations for a matrix A: forms (2), (4), and (5), with a condensed form for each. The definitions of equality, sum, and scalar product, which were stated in terms of the elements, can be restated in terms of either of the other forms. For example, if

$$A = \begin{bmatrix} \alpha_1 \\ \alpha_2 \\ \vdots \\ \alpha_m \end{bmatrix} \quad \text{and} \quad B = \begin{bmatrix} \beta_1 \\ \beta_2 \\ \vdots \\ \beta_m \end{bmatrix},$$

then $A = B$ if and only if $\alpha_i = \beta_i$, $i = 1, 2, \ldots, m$;

$$A + B = \begin{bmatrix} \alpha_1 + \beta_1 \\ \alpha_2 + \beta_2 \\ \vdots \\ \alpha_m + \beta_m \end{bmatrix}, \qquad kA = \begin{bmatrix} k\alpha_1 \\ k\alpha_2 \\ \vdots \\ k\alpha_m \end{bmatrix}.$$

Likewise form (5) could be used in an analogous way.

For vectors, we defined not only sum, and product by a scalar, which we have defined similarly for matrices, but also inner product. It is natural to wonder whether there is an analogue for this concept also. Various reasons, the most cogent of which will appear later in our applications, lead us to make the following definition.

Definition 8. If

$$A = \begin{bmatrix} \alpha_1 \\ \alpha_2 \\ \vdots \\ \alpha_m \end{bmatrix} \qquad \text{and} \qquad B = [\tilde{\beta}_1 \quad \tilde{\beta}_2 \quad \ldots \quad \tilde{\beta}_p],$$

their *product* is

$$AB = [\alpha_i \cdot \tilde{\beta}_j], \qquad i = 1, 2, \ldots, m; \quad j = 1, 2, \ldots, p.$$

In words: The element in the ith row and jth column of the product matrix AB is the inner product of the ith row vector of A and the jth column vector of B. Expressed without vectors this reads: if A is an $m \times n$ and B an $n \times p$ matrix, then

$$AB = C = [c_{ij}],$$

where

$$c_{ij} = a_{i1}b_{1j} + a_{i2}b_{2j} + \cdots + a_{in}b_{nj}$$

$$= \sum_{k=1}^{n} a_{ik}b_{kj}, \qquad i = 1, 2, \ldots, m; \quad j = 1, 2, \ldots, p.$$

Thus C is an $m \times p$ matrix. We will write either $C = AB$, as above, or, if we choose, $C = A \cdot B$, just as with the products of elementary algebra.

Since $\alpha \cdot \beta$ is defined only if α and β have the same number of components, AB is defined only if the number of columns of A is the same as the number of rows of B. This means that we could not, for example, multiply together two row or two column matrices, but we can find the product of a row matrix by a column matrix with the same number of elements. If

$$[a_1 \quad a_2 \quad \ldots \quad a_n] = [\alpha]$$

and

$$\begin{bmatrix} b_1 \\ b_2 \\ \vdots \\ b_n \end{bmatrix} = [\tilde{\beta}],$$

we have $[\alpha] \cdot [\tilde{\beta}] = [\alpha \cdot \tilde{\beta}]$, a matrix with a single element, the inner product of α and β. So we can think of the matrix product as a sort of generalization of the vector inner product. Note that $[\tilde{\beta}] \cdot [\alpha]$ is not defined; in general the existence of AB does not imply the existence of BA.

It is perhaps worthwhile to write out an example in detail.

Let

$$A = \begin{bmatrix} a_{11} & a_{12} & a_{13} \\ a_{21} & a_{22} & a_{23} \\ a_{31} & a_{32} & a_{33} \\ a_{41} & a_{42} & a_{43} \end{bmatrix} = \begin{bmatrix} \alpha_1 \\ \alpha_2 \\ \alpha_3 \\ \alpha_4 \end{bmatrix}, \quad B = \begin{bmatrix} b_{11} & b_{12} \\ b_{21} & b_{22} \\ b_{31} & b_{32} \end{bmatrix} = [\tilde{\beta}_1 \quad \tilde{\beta}_2].$$

Then

$$AB = \begin{bmatrix} \alpha_1 \cdot \tilde{\beta}_1 & \alpha_1 \cdot \tilde{\beta}_2 \\ \alpha_2 \cdot \tilde{\beta}_1 & \alpha_2 \cdot \tilde{\beta}_2 \\ \alpha_3 \cdot \tilde{\beta}_1 & \alpha_3 \cdot \tilde{\beta}_2 \\ \alpha_4 \cdot \tilde{\beta}_1 & \alpha_4 \cdot \tilde{\beta}_2 \end{bmatrix}$$

$$= \begin{bmatrix} a_{11}b_{11} + a_{12}b_{21} + a_{13}b_{31} & a_{11}b_{12} + a_{12}b_{22} + a_{13}b_{32} \\ a_{21}b_{11} + a_{22}b_{21} + a_{23}b_{31} & a_{21}b_{12} + a_{22}b_{22} + a_{23}b_{32} \\ a_{31}b_{11} + a_{32}b_{21} + a_{33}b_{31} & a_{31}b_{12} + a_{32}b_{22} + a_{33}b_{32} \\ a_{41}b_{11} + a_{42}b_{21} + a_{43}b_{31} & a_{41}b_{12} + a_{42}b_{22} + a_{43}b_{32} \end{bmatrix}.$$

Note that if an $m \times n$ matrix A is multiplied on the left by a row matrix, say

$$R = [\rho] = [r_1 \quad r_2 \quad \ldots \quad r_m],$$

we get a row matrix:

$$RA = [\rho]A = [\rho \cdot \tilde{\alpha}_1 \quad \rho \cdot \tilde{\alpha}_2 \quad \ldots \quad \rho \cdot \tilde{\alpha}_n];$$

and, if we multiply on the right by a column matrix, say

$$X = [\tilde{\xi}] = \begin{bmatrix} x_1 \\ x_2 \\ \vdots \\ x_n \end{bmatrix},$$

we get a column matrix:

$$AX = A \cdot [\tilde{\xi}] = \begin{bmatrix} \alpha_1 \cdot \tilde{\xi} \\ \alpha_2 \cdot \tilde{\xi} \\ \vdots \\ \alpha_m \cdot \tilde{\xi} \end{bmatrix}.$$

In both these cases we can think of the vector which determines the row (column) matrix as "distributed" over the column (row) vectors of A to give the product, which is a row (column) matrix.

The usefulness of these notations will appear if we note that the set of Eqs. (1) can be written as $Y = AX$, where A and X have the meanings indicated above.

Observe, furthermore, another significant abbreviation. If $A = [a_{ij}]$ is an $m \times n$ matrix, $B = [b_{ij}]$ is an $n \times p$ matrix, and $C = [c_{ij}]$ is an $m \times p$ matrix such that $C = A \cdot B$, then we can also write

$$\begin{bmatrix} \gamma_1 \\ \gamma_2 \\ \vdots \\ \gamma_m \end{bmatrix} = \begin{bmatrix} a_{11} & \cdots & a_{1n} \\ a_{21} & \cdots & a_{2n} \\ \vdots & & \vdots \\ a_{m1} & \cdots & a_{mn} \end{bmatrix} \cdot \begin{bmatrix} \beta_1 \\ \beta_2 \\ \vdots \\ \beta_n \end{bmatrix}, \tag{6}$$

where the β's and the γ's are the respective row vectors of B and C. Then it is easy to check that

$$\gamma_1 = a_{11}\beta_1 + a_{12}\beta_2 + \cdots + a_{1n}\beta_n,$$
$$\gamma_2 = a_{21}\beta_1 + a_{22}\beta_2 + \cdots + a_{2n}\beta_n, \tag{7}$$
$$\vdots$$
$$\gamma_m = a_{m1}\beta_1 + a_{m2}\beta_2 + \cdots + a_{mn}\beta_n.$$

In other words, the definition of matrix multiplication has been so chosen that Eqs. (7) come from Eqs. (6) in the same way, formally, as though the γ's and the β's were scalars, i.e., as though

$$\begin{bmatrix} \gamma_1 \\ \vdots \\ \gamma_m \end{bmatrix} \quad \text{and} \quad \begin{bmatrix} \beta_1 \\ \vdots \\ \beta_n \end{bmatrix}$$

were column matrices.

The $m \times n$ matrix with every element the zero of $\mathfrak{F}$ is called a *zero matrix*, and is designated by O_{mn}, or simply by O if the indices are clear from the context.

A concept which is frequently useful follows.

Definition 9. The matrix obtained from A by interchanging rows and columns is called the *transpose* of A, denoted by A^t.

Thus, we have the following expressions for the transpose,

$$A^t = \begin{bmatrix} a_{11} & a_{21} & \cdots & a_{m1} \\ a_{12} & a_{22} & \cdots & a_{m2} \\ \vdots & & & \\ a_{1n} & a_{2n} & \cdots & a_{mn} \end{bmatrix} = [\alpha_1 \quad \alpha_2 \quad \cdots \quad \alpha_m] = \begin{bmatrix} \tilde{\alpha}_1 \\ \tilde{\alpha}_2 \\ \vdots \\ \tilde{\alpha}_n \end{bmatrix},$$

corresponding to the representations (2), (4), and (5) for A, where the α's and the $\tilde{\alpha}$'s are the same vectors as in Eqs. (4) and (5).

Note that for all A, $(A^t)^t = A$.

Every vector determines, of course, both a column matrix and a row matrix. We will simplify our notation considerably by omitting the square bracket from the symbol for such matrices. The apparent ambiguity will not be a real one; it will be clear from the context whether a Greek letter is to be interpreted as a vector in the old sense or as a matrix determined by that vector. Since we need column matrices more often than row matrices in the following discussion, we shall use α both for the vector $(a_1, a_2, \ldots, a_n)$ and for the *column* matrix

$$\begin{bmatrix} a_1 \\ a_2 \\ \vdots \\ a_n \end{bmatrix};$$

the row matrix $[a_1 \ a_2 \ \ldots \ a_n]$ will be denoted by α^t, the transpose of the column matrix α. To fix ideas, you should write out the following products:

$$\alpha\beta, \quad \alpha^t\beta, \quad \alpha\beta^t, \quad \alpha^tC, \quad D\alpha,$$

where $\alpha = (a_1, a_2, \ldots, a_n)$, $\beta = (b_1, b_2, \ldots, b_n)$ (or the corresponding column matrices), and

$$C = [c_{ij}], \qquad i = 1, 2, \ldots, n, \quad j = 1, 2, \ldots, m,$$
$$D = [d_{ij}], \qquad i = 1, 2, \ldots, m, \quad j = 1, 2, \ldots, n.$$

(Note that the first has meaning only if α and β are vectors in the old sense, and that reversing the order of factors in each of the last two gives undefined expressions for $m > 1$.)

If a matrix A over the field of complex numbers is *square* $(m = n)$, one can associate with the matrix a number $|A|$, or det A, the determinant of A (see Appendix 2). Note that the determinant of the sum of two matrices is *not* equal to the sum of their determinants

$$(|A + B| \neq |A| + |B|),$$

and the determinant of a scalar times a matrix is *not* equal to the scalar times the determinant of the matrix $(|kA| \neq k \cdot |A|)$; but the determinant of the product of two matrices *is* equal to the product of their determinants $(|A \cdot B| = |A| \cdot |B|)$.

We now use our matrix notation and definitions to abbreviate some of the expressions which we encountered in earlier chapters.

EXAMPLE 1. The linear equations of Example 5 of Section 2–2 may be written, in matrix form, as

$$\begin{bmatrix} 1 & -2 & -3 & 1 \\ 4 & -1 & -3 & 2 \\ 5 & -3 & -2 & -1 \end{bmatrix} \cdot \begin{bmatrix} x_0 \\ x_1 \\ x_2 \\ x_3 \end{bmatrix} = \begin{bmatrix} 0 \\ 0 \\ 0 \end{bmatrix},$$

or as

$$A \cdot \xi = o,$$

where A is the 3×4 matrix above, ξ is the vector (x_0, x_1, x_2, x_3), and o is the vector $(0, 0, 0)$.

EXAMPLE 2. Equations 5 of Section 4–5, expressing the relationship between the coordinates of a vector relative to two bases, may be written as

$$\begin{bmatrix} t_{11} & t_{21} & \cdots & t_{r1} \\ t_{12} & t_{22} & \cdots & t_{r2} \\ \vdots & & & \\ t_{1r} & t_{2r} & \cdots & t_{rr} \end{bmatrix} \cdot \begin{bmatrix} c_1 \\ c_2 \\ \vdots \\ c_r \end{bmatrix} = \begin{bmatrix} d_1 \\ d_2 \\ \vdots \\ d_r \end{bmatrix},$$

or

$$T^t \cdot \gamma = \delta,$$

where T is the matrix $[t_{ij}]$, $i = 1, \ldots, r$; $j = 1, \ldots, r$; γ is the vector $(c_1, c_2, \ldots, c_r)$, and δ is the vector $(d_1, d_2, \ldots, d_r)$.

EXAMPLE 3.   Note that each vector equation of the set of Eqs. (3) of Section 4–5 is itself equivalent to n ordinary algebraic equations. For example, if α_1 has components $a_{11}, a_{12}, \ldots, a_{1n}$, and if β_i has components $b_{i1}, b_{i2}, \ldots, b_{in}$, then the first equation of the set (3) of Section 4–5 is equivalent to the following equations:

$$a_{11} = t_{11}b_{11} + t_{12}b_{21} + \cdots + t_{1r}b_{r1},$$

$$a_{12} = t_{11}b_{12} + t_{12}b_{22} + \cdots + t_{1r}b_{r2},$$

$$\vdots$$

$$a_{1n} = t_{11}b_{1n} + t_{12}b_{2n} + \cdots + t_{1r}b_{rn}.$$

There will be n similar equations for each of the remaining $(r - 1)$ vector equations of Eqs. (3) of Section 4–5. These nr equations may be summarized as:

$$\begin{bmatrix} a_{11} & a_{12} & \cdots & a_{1n} \\ a_{21} & a_{22} & \cdots & a_{2n} \\ \vdots & & \vdots & \\ a_{r1} & a_{r2} & \cdots & a_{rn} \end{bmatrix} = \begin{bmatrix} t_{11} & t_{12} & \cdots & t_{1r} \\ t_{21} & t_{22} & \cdots & t_{2r} \\ \vdots & & \vdots & \\ t_{r1} & t_{r2} & \cdots & t_{rr} \end{bmatrix} \cdot \begin{bmatrix} b_{11} & b_{12} & \cdots & b_{1n} \\ b_{21} & b_{22} & \cdots & b_{2n} \\ \vdots & & \vdots & \\ b_{r1} & b_{r2} & \cdots & b_{rn} \end{bmatrix}$$

or $A = T \cdot B$, where T has the same significance as in Example 2. Alternatively, we may express the relationship as

$$\begin{bmatrix} \alpha_1 \\ \alpha_2 \\ \vdots \\ \alpha_r \end{bmatrix} = T \begin{bmatrix} \beta_1 \\ \beta_2 \\ \vdots \\ \beta_r \end{bmatrix}.$$

EXAMPLE 4.   Equations (1) of Section 5–2 may be written concisely as

$$r \cdot \eta = T \cdot \xi, \qquad r \neq 0,$$

where η is the vector $(y_0, \ldots, y_n)$, ξ is the vector $(x_0, \ldots, x_n)$ and T is the $(n + 1) \times (n + 1)$ matrix (t_{ij}), $i = 0, 1, \ldots, n$; $j = 0, 1, \ldots, n$.

The results embodied in the following theorem are immediate consequences of Definitions 4 through 9. The proof of the theorem is left to you.

Theorem 6–7

(a) $(A + B)^t = A^t + B^t$;

(b) $(k \cdot A)^t = k \cdot A^t$;

(c) $A \cdot (kB) = k \cdot (A \cdot B)$

(d) $A(B + C) = AB + AC$ (matrix multiplication is distributive over matrix addition).

EXAMPLE 5. Making use of Theorem 6–7, we can quickly dispose of Example 1, Section 5–2. Equations (2), (3), (4), and (5) of that example can be written as follows:

$$r_1 \cdot \alpha' = T \cdot \alpha; \quad r_2 \cdot \beta' = T \cdot \beta; \quad r_3 \cdot \gamma' = T \cdot \gamma, \quad \gamma = h \cdot \alpha + k \cdot \beta.$$

Hence,

$$r_3 \cdot \gamma' = T(h \cdot \alpha + k \cdot \beta) = hT \cdot \alpha + kT \cdot \beta = hr_1 \cdot \alpha' + kr_2 \cdot \beta'.$$

Therefore,

$$\gamma' = \frac{r_1}{r_3} h \cdot \alpha' + \frac{r_2}{r_3} k \cdot \beta'.$$

EXAMPLE 6. The proof of Theorem 6–6 assumes the following form in matrix notation. We know that

$$c_1 \xi' = T \cdot \xi; \quad c_2 \eta' = T \cdot \eta; \quad c_3 \zeta' = T \cdot \zeta; \quad c_4 \omega' = T \cdot \omega,$$

where

$$T = \begin{bmatrix} p & q \\ r & s \end{bmatrix}.$$

Also,

$$\zeta = h_1 \xi + k_1 \eta; \quad \omega = h_2 \xi + k_2 \eta.$$

Hence

$$c_3 \zeta' = T(h_1 \xi + k_1 \eta) = Th_1 \xi + Tk_1 \eta = h_1 T \xi + k_1 T \eta = h_1 c_1 \xi' + k_1 c_2 \eta'.$$

Therefore

$$\zeta' = \frac{h_1 c_1}{c_3} \xi' + \frac{k_1 c_2}{c_3} \eta'.$$

Similarly, we find that

$$\omega' = \frac{h_2 c_1}{c_4} \xi' + \frac{k_2 c_2}{c_4} \eta'.$$

The rest of the proof is unchanged.

EXAMPLE 7. The projectivity from the points of S_n to those of S'_m, as given by Eqs. (4) of Section 6-4, can be abbreviated as

$$c\xi' = A\xi,$$

where ξ' has components $x'_0, x'_1, \ldots, x'_m$, ξ has components $x_0, x_1, \ldots, x_n$, and A is the matrix $[a_{ij}]$, $i = 0, 1, \ldots, m; j = 0, 1, \ldots, n$.

Another projectivity, from the points of S'_m to those of S''_p, will be expressed by the linear transformation

$$d\xi'' = B\xi',$$

where ξ'' has components $x''_0, x''_1, \ldots, x''_p$ and B is a $(p+1) \times (m+1)$ matrix.

The first of these transformations followed by the second constitutes a transformation from the points of S_n to those of S''_p which is expressible as

$$d\xi'' = B \cdot \left(\frac{1}{c} A\xi\right). \tag{8}$$

We shall return to Eq. (8) in the next section.

With the amount of matrix notation now at our command, it is easy to establish a generalization of Theorem 6-3. We state the result for $n = 2$ and leave the general statement and its proof to you (Problem 12 below).

Theorem 6-8. There is precisely one projectivity which makes four distinct points of S_2, no three collinear, correspond, respectively, to four distinct points of S'_2, no three collinear. (Alternatively phrased: a projectivity from S_2 to S'_2 is determined by four pairs of corresponding points, no three points collinear in either set.)

Proof. We are clearly at liberty to choose coordinate frames so as to minimize the algebraic complexities of the proof. Let the vertices of the triangle of reference and the unit point of a coordinate frame in S_2 be chosen as A, B, C, and D, the four specified points of the statement of the theorem, with a similar choice in S'_2 relative to the corresponding points A', B', C', D'. With obvious notation we have

$$\alpha = (1, 0, 0) = \alpha';$$
$$\beta = (0, 1, 0) = \beta';$$
$$\gamma = (0, 0, 1) = \gamma';$$
$$\delta = (1, 1, 1) = \delta'.$$

We seek a matrix M such that

$$k_1\alpha' = M\alpha; \qquad k_2\beta' = M\beta;$$

$$k_3\gamma' = M\gamma; \qquad k_4\delta' = M\delta$$

for some k_1, k_2, k_3, k_4, none of them 0. It is easy to verify that all the k's must be equal (to k_1, say) and that M must be given by

$$M = \begin{bmatrix} k_1 & 0 & 0 \\ 0 & k_1 & 0 \\ 0 & 0 & k_1 \end{bmatrix} = k_1 \begin{bmatrix} 1 & 0 & 0 \\ 0 & 1 & 0 \\ 0 & 0 & 1 \end{bmatrix}.$$

Thus there is one, and only one projectivity satisfying the conditions. Moreover, the transformation is "invertible." The same argument will show that there is just one linear transformation taking A', B', C', D' into A, B, C, D. Thus each point of S_2' is the transform of some point of S_2, i.e., the projectivity is proper. $\square$

In studying conics and in other connections as well, we have occasion to deal with matrices which are "symmetric with respect to the main diagonal," or, briefly, "symmetric."

Definition 10. A square matrix M is *symmetric* if $M^t = M$.

Another way to characterize the symmetry of M is to note that $m_{ij} = m_{ji}$.

PROBLEM SET 6–5

*1. Let $A = [a_{ij}]$, $B = [b_{ij}]$ be $n \times n$ matrices with $a_{ij} = 0$ for $j \neq 1$ and $b_{ij} = 0$, $j = 1, 2, \ldots, n$. Express $A \cdot B$.

2. Prove Theorem 6–7.

*3. Formulate and prove a statement about the transpose of the product of two matrices in terms of a product of their transposes.

*4. Consider the set S of all $n \times n$ matrices, for fixed n, with elements from C, the field of complex numbers.

(a) With equality, addition, and multiplication by a scalar as given by Definitions 5, 6, and 7, show that S is isomorphic to $V_{n^2}(C)$.

(b) With equality, addition, and multiplication as given by Definitions 5, 6, and 8, is S a field?

5. Consider the set of all 2×2 matrices of the form

$$\begin{bmatrix} x & y \\ 0 & 1 \end{bmatrix}$$

where x, y are complex numbers. With equality, addition, and multiplication of matrices as defined in the text, which of the axioms of a field are not satisfied by this system? What restrictions on x and y will make this system satisfy at least Axioms M5 through M10 for a field? (See Section 3–3.)

6. Let U be the set of all 2×2 matrices of the form

$$\begin{bmatrix} x & -y \\ y & x \end{bmatrix},$$

where x and y are real numbers. Using equality, addition, and multiplication of matrices as defined in the text, verify that U is isomorphic to C, the field of complex numbers. *Hint:*

$$\begin{bmatrix} x & -y \\ y & x \end{bmatrix} \leftrightarrow x + iy.$$

*7. Find the set of all 2×2 idempotent matrices with elements from C (cf. Problem 12, Section 3–4).

*8. (a) Prove that if A is any square matrix, then the matrix $A \cdot A^t$ is symmetric.

(b) Prove that if M is symmetric, then so also is $N = A^t M A$.

*9. Are the following statements true?

(a) The sum of two symmetric matrices is symmetric.

(b) The product of two symmetric matrices is symmetric.

*10. Let α, β, γ be $n \times 1$ matrices. Verify that $(\alpha^t \cdot \beta)\gamma^t = \alpha^t(\beta \cdot \gamma^t)$.

11. Carry through the details of the proof of Theorem 6–8, culminating in the expression for M. Find the matrix of the inverse transformation, carrying A', B', C', D' into A, B, C, D.

12. Formulate and prove a statement on the number of pairs of points required to determine a projectivity from S_n to S'_n.

13. Let $X = [x_{ij}], Y = [y_{ij}]$ be $n \times n$ matrices with

$$x_{ij} = \begin{cases} 1, & i = j + 1, j = 1, \ldots, n - 1; \\ 1, & i = 1, j = n; \\ 0, & \text{otherwise.} \end{cases}$$

$$y_{ij} = \begin{cases} \omega^{i-1}, & j = i + 1, i = 1, \ldots, n - 1; \\ \omega^{n-1}, & i = n, j = 1; \\ 0, & \text{otherwise;} \end{cases}$$

where ω is an nth root of 1. Verify that $YX = \omega \cdot XY$.

6-6 FURTHER PROPERTIES OF MATRICES

Problem 4 of Section 6-5 raises a number of important points about $n \times n$ matrices.

(i) Multiplication of matrices is *not* commutative, for generally

$$\alpha_i \cdot \tilde{\beta}_j \neq \beta_i \cdot \tilde{\alpha}_j.$$

Consider, for example, $A \cdot B$ and $B \cdot A$ if

$$A = \begin{bmatrix} 1 & 0 \\ 2 & 0 \end{bmatrix} \quad \text{and} \quad B = \begin{bmatrix} 0 & 0 \\ 1 & 1 \end{bmatrix}.$$

Matrix multiplication constitutes a significant example of an operation which is not commutative.

(ii) Multiplication of matrices *is* associative, not only for square matrices, but for any "conformable" matrices, i.e., for any matrices with the proper numbers of rows and columns so that multiplication is defined. The proof of this fact furnishes practice in the use of the summation symbol.

Let $A = [a_{ij}]$ have m rows and n columns, $B = [b_{ij}]$ have n rows and p columns, $C = [c_{ij}]$ have p rows and q columns.

We wish to show that $A \cdot (B \cdot C) = (A \cdot B) \cdot C$. Let $D = [d_{ij}] = B \cdot C$, and $E = [e_{ij}] = A \cdot B$. Then we must show that $A \cdot D = E \cdot C$. The element in the ith row and jth column of $A \cdot D$ can be written as

$$\sum_{k=1}^{n} a_{ik}d_{kj} = \sum_{k=1}^{n} a_{ik} \left(\sum_{l=1}^{p} b_{kl}c_{lj} \right) = \sum_{k=1}^{n} \sum_{l=1}^{p} a_{ik}b_{kl}c_{lj}.$$

The element in the ith row and jth column of $E \cdot C$ can be written as

$$\sum_{l=1}^{p} e_{il}c_{lj} = \sum_{l=1}^{p} \left(\sum_{k=1}^{n} a_{ik}b_{kl} \right) c_{lj} = \sum_{l=1}^{p} \sum_{k=1}^{n} a_{jk}b_{kl}c_{lj}.$$

In obtaining these forms for the products, we have appealed to distributivity of multiplication over addition and to associativity of multiplication in the field $\mathfrak{F}$ of elements of the matrices. What properties of $\mathfrak{F}$ are used in concluding that

$$\sum_{k=1}^{n} \sum_{l=1}^{p} a_{ik}b_{kl}c_{lj} = \sum_{l=1}^{p} \sum_{k=1}^{n} a_{ik}b_{kl}c_{lj}?$$

EXAMPLE 1. With associativity of multiplication of matrices established, we have an alternative to the notation of Example 6 of Section 6-5 for the proof of Theorem 6–6:

$$\begin{bmatrix} \zeta \\ \omega \end{bmatrix} = \begin{bmatrix} h_1 & k_1 \\ h_2 & k_2 \end{bmatrix} \begin{bmatrix} \xi \\ \eta \end{bmatrix}.$$

$$\begin{bmatrix} c_3\zeta' \\ c_4\omega' \end{bmatrix} = \begin{bmatrix} \zeta \\ \omega \end{bmatrix} \cdot T^t = \left\{ \begin{bmatrix} h_1 & k_1 \\ h_2 & k_2 \end{bmatrix} \begin{bmatrix} \xi \\ \eta \end{bmatrix} \right\} T^t$$

$$= \begin{bmatrix} h_1 & k_1 \\ h_2 & k_2 \end{bmatrix} \left\{ \begin{bmatrix} \xi \\ \eta \end{bmatrix} T^t \right\} = \begin{bmatrix} h_1 & k_1 \\ h_2 & k_2 \end{bmatrix} \begin{bmatrix} c_1\xi' \\ c_2\eta' \end{bmatrix}.$$

Hence $c_3\zeta' = h_1c_1\xi' + k_1c_2\eta'$, etc.

We can return to Eq. (8) of Section 6–5 and obtain further information by writing it in the form

$$c \cdot d \cdot \xi'' = (B \cdot A) \cdot \xi. \tag{1}$$

We conclude that the transformation, consisting of the projectivity with matrix A followed by the projectivity with matrix B is a *projectivity*, with matrix $B \cdot A$.

(iii) It can readily be checked that the $n \times n$ matrix

$$I = \begin{bmatrix} 1 & 0 & 0 & \cdots & 0 \\ 0 & 1 & 0 & \cdots & 0 \\ & \vdots & & & \\ 0 & 0 & \cdots & 0 & 1 \end{bmatrix}$$

is a multiplicative identity: for all $n \times n$ matrices X, $I \cdot X = X = X \cdot I$. When it is necessary to emphasize that I is $n \times n$, it will be denoted by I_n.

There is a convenient standard notation which abbreviates the expression for I. The "Kronecker delta," δ_{ij}, is defined as follows: $\delta_{ij} = 1$, if $i = j$; $\delta_{ij} = 0$, otherwise. Then clearly $I = [\delta_{ij}]$.

Since the set of $n \times n$ matrices is not a field, we cannot appeal to Theorem 3–4 to argue the uniqueness of the multiplicative identity. But the suggested proof of Theorem 3–4 can be carried through for matrices (Problem 1 below) to establish the uniqueness.

(iv) When we come to discuss the multiplicative inverse, we must first distinguish, because of the noncommutativity of multiplication, between "left inverses" and "right inverses." If in the set of $n \times n$ matrices over C, $XA = I = AY$, then X is called a "left inverse" of A, and Y is called a "right inverse" of A. The following theorem is easy to prove (Problem 2 below).

Theorem 6–9. If a matrix has both a left inverse and a right inverse, then these inverses are equal.

This theorem still leaves open the question as to whether a given square matrix has either or both inverses. A direct argument presents problems. For instance, to find a right inverse, $Y = [y_{ij}]$, of a given square matrix, $A = [a_{ij}]$, would involve n^2 linear equations:

$$a_{11}y_{11} + a_{12}y_{21} + \cdots + a_{1n}y_{n1} = 1,$$

$$a_{11}y_{12} + a_{12}y_{22} + \cdots + a_{1n}y_{n2} = 0,$$

and so on. To consider this system of equations directly is much too formidable.

One might guess that every square matrix except O has a right inverse and a left inverse. If this were so, then $A \cdot B = O$ would imply that $A = O$ or $B = O$ (Problem 3 below). However, as was seen in Problem 1 of Section 6–5, this conclusion is *not* true. Hence there must be nonzero matrices without inverses.

Definition 11. A matrix which has a right inverse (left inverse) is called *right-nonsingular* (*left-nonsingular*). A matrix which is both right- and left-nonsingular is called *nonsingular*.

In the next chapter we shall find that a matrix which is right-nonsingular is also left-nonsingular and vice versa, so that we will be able to drop the adjectives "right" and "left," and speak of nonsingular matrices and their inverses. We shall also find that the inverse of a matrix is unique (see Problem 8 below).

Theorem 6–10. If A, B have, respectively, right inverses A^{-1}, B^{-1}, then $A \cdot B$ has a right inverse, $B^{-1} \cdot A^{-1}$.

The proof is straightforward (Problem 5 below). A similar result applies to left inverses, so that we may say, "The inverse of the product of matrices is the product of their inverses in reverse order." Note that the phrase "in reverse order" does not appear in Problem 15, Section 3–3, because the operations there are commutative.

PROBLEM SET 6–6

1. Show that in the set of $n \times n$ matrices, I_n is the only multiplicative identity.

2. Prove Theorem 6–9.

3. Prove that if every square matrix other than O has left and right inverses, then $A \cdot B = O$ implies that $A = O$ or $B = O$.

4. Let

$$B = \begin{bmatrix} 4 & 2 \\ -1 & 1 \end{bmatrix}.$$

Verify that B satisfies the equation $(X - 2I)(X - 3I) = O$, where

$$I = \begin{bmatrix} 1 & 0 \\ 0 & 1 \end{bmatrix} \quad \text{and} \quad O = \begin{bmatrix} 0 & 0 \\ 0 & 0 \end{bmatrix}.$$

Explain why you are not surprised that $B \neq 2I$, $B \neq 3I$.

5. Prove Theorem 6–10.

6. Is the sum of two right-nonsingular matrices also right-nonsingular?

7. If A^{-1} is a right inverse of A, give an expression for a right inverse of $k \cdot A$, $k \neq 0$.

*8. Show that if a matrix has both right and left inverses, then these inverses are unique.

9. (a) Consider matrices over a field $\mathfrak{F}$. Let $A = [a_{ij}]$ be an $m \times n$ matrix with $\sum_{j=1}^{n} a_{ij} = a$, for each i; and let $B = [b_{ij}]$ be an $n \times p$ matrix with $\sum_{j=1}^{p} b_{ij} = b$, for each i. Show that if $C = [c_{ij}] = A \cdot B$, then $\sum_{j=1}^{p} c_{ij} = a \cdot b$, for each i.

(b) As in part (a), show that if $\sum_{j=1}^{p} b_{ij} = b \neq 0$, for each i, and if $\sum_{j=1}^{p} c_{ij} = c$, for each i, then $\sum_{j=1}^{n} a_{ij} = c/b$, for each i.

(c) Show that if $A = [a_{ij}]$ is an $n \times n$ matrix with $\sum_{j=1}^{n} a_{ij} = a \neq 0$, for each i, and if A has a left inverse A^{-1}, then the sum of the elements of each row of A^{-1} is $1/a$.

(d) State and prove analogous theorems about matrices with constant column-sums.

*10. Consider the set, $\mathcal{S}$, of 2×2 matrices over C. Let

$$I = \begin{bmatrix} 1 & 0 \\ 0 & 1 \end{bmatrix}, \quad P = \begin{bmatrix} 0 & 1 \\ 1 & 0 \end{bmatrix}, \quad Q = \begin{bmatrix} 0 & -i \\ i & 0 \end{bmatrix}, \quad R = \begin{bmatrix} 1 & 0 \\ 0 & -1 \end{bmatrix}.$$

These are called "Pauli spin-matrices."

(a) Verify that $I^2 = I = P^2 = Q^2 = R^2$. (Note, then, the multiplicity of "square roots" of I.)

(b) Show that I, P, Q, R form a "basis" for the "space," $\mathcal{S}$; i.e., that any matrix

$$X = \begin{bmatrix} x_1 & x_2 \\ x_3 & x_4 \end{bmatrix}$$

of $\mathcal{S}$ can be expressed in precisely one way as a linear combination of I, P, Q, R.

(c) *Definition.* Two matrices A, B are said to *anticommute* if $AB + BA = 0$. Verify that P, Q, R anticommute in pairs.

(d) Prove that there are no nonzero 2×2 matrices which anticommute with each of P, Q, R.

11. If

$$D_1 = \begin{bmatrix} 0 & 0 & 0 \\ 0 & 0 & -1 \\ 0 & 1 & 0 \end{bmatrix}, \qquad D_2 = \begin{bmatrix} 0 & 0 & 1 \\ 0 & 0 & 0 \\ -1 & 0 & 0 \end{bmatrix}, \qquad D_3 = \begin{bmatrix} 0 & -1 & 0 \\ 1 & 0 & 0 \\ 0 & 0 & 0 \end{bmatrix},$$

verify that $[D_1, D_2] = D_3$, $[D_2, D_3] = D_1$, $[D_3, D_1] = D_2$, where $[D_1, D_2]$ is the commutator of D_1 and D_2 (cf. Problem 5, Section 3–5). (D_1, D_2, D_3 represent "infinitesimal rotations" about the x-, y-, and z-axes.)

12. Let X, Y, Z be $n \times n$ matrices with complex numbers as elements. Consider the set of equations

$$[X, Y] = iZ; \qquad [Y, Z] = iX; \qquad [Z, X] = iY; \tag{2}$$

where $[X, Y]$ is the commutator of X and Y (Problem 5, Section 3–5) and $i = \sqrt{-1}$.

(a) Verify that for $n = 2$ and P, Q, R as in Problem 10 above, $X = \frac{1}{2}P$, $Y = \frac{1}{2}Q$, $Z = \frac{1}{2}R$ is a solution of Eqs. (2).

(b) Verify that for $n = 3$,

$$X = \frac{\sqrt{2}}{2} \begin{bmatrix} 0 & 1 & 0 \\ 1 & 0 & 1 \\ 0 & 1 & 0 \end{bmatrix}, \qquad Y = \frac{i\sqrt{2}}{2} \begin{bmatrix} 0 & -1 & 0 \\ 1 & 0 & -1 \\ 0 & 1 & 0 \end{bmatrix}, \qquad Z = \begin{bmatrix} 1 & 0 & 0 \\ 0 & 0 & 0 \\ 0 & 0 & -1 \end{bmatrix},$$

is a solution of Eqs. (2).

(c) Verify that for $n = 4$,

$$X = \begin{bmatrix} 0 & \frac{1}{2}\sqrt{3} & 0 & 0 \\ \frac{1}{2}\sqrt{3} & 0 & 1 & 0 \\ 0 & 1 & 0 & \frac{1}{2}\sqrt{3} \\ 0 & 0 & \frac{1}{2}\sqrt{3} & 0 \end{bmatrix},$$

$$Y = i \begin{bmatrix} 0 & -\frac{1}{2}\sqrt{3} & 0 & 0 \\ \frac{1}{2}\sqrt{3} & 0 & -1 & 0 \\ 0 & 1 & 0 & -\frac{1}{2}\sqrt{3} \\ 0 & 0 & \frac{1}{2}\sqrt{3} & 0 \end{bmatrix},$$

$$Z = \frac{1}{2} \begin{bmatrix} 3 & 0 & 0 & 0 \\ 0 & 1 & 0 & 0 \\ 0 & 0 & -1 & 0 \\ 0 & 0 & 0 & -3 \end{bmatrix}$$

is a solution of Eqs. (2).

(d) Verify that if X, Y, Z is a solution of Eqs. (2) and if $U^2 = X^2 + Y^2 + Z^2$, then $[X, U^2] = O$.

(e) Show that if $X = A$, $Y = B$, $Z = C$ is a solution of Eqs. (2), then so also is $X = P^{-1}AP$, $Y = P^{-1}BP$, $Z = P^{-1}CP$.

(f) Find a solution of Eqs. (2) for general n. [*Hints:* Eliminate one of the indeterminates, say Y. Assume that one of the matrices, say Z, is in diagonal form; cf. (e) above.]

*13. Let X, Y be $n \times n$ matrices which commute under multiplication. Show that

$$(X + Y)(X^{k-1} - X^{k-2}Y + X^{k-3}Y^2 - \cdots + Y^{k-1}) = X^k + Y^k,$$

for k an odd positive integer, and

$$(X + Y)(X^{k-1} - X^{k-2}Y + X^{k-3}Y^2 - \cdots - Y^{k-1}) = X^k - Y^k,$$

for k an even positive integer.

14. Show that

$$E = \begin{bmatrix} 1 & 0 \\ 0 & 1 \end{bmatrix}, \qquad A = \begin{bmatrix} 0 & 1 \\ -1 & 0 \end{bmatrix},$$

$$B = \begin{bmatrix} -1 & 0 \\ 0 & -1 \end{bmatrix}, \qquad C = \begin{bmatrix} 0 & -1 \\ 1 & 0 \end{bmatrix}$$

form an Abelian group under multiplication. To which abstract group of order 4 is it isomorphic?

15. With multiplication as the operation, show that the set of all matrices

$$\begin{bmatrix} x & y \\ 0 & 1 \end{bmatrix}, \qquad x, y \text{ real}, \qquad x \neq 0,$$

is a group isomorphic to that of Problem 11, Section 3-6.

16. Find a real cube root of I_2; i.e., find a 2×2 matrix M with real elements such that $M^3 = I_2$.

17. If A_1, A_2, $\ldots$, A_p are symmetric $n \times n$ matrices with complex elements, and if $c_1, c_2, \ldots, c_p \in C$, is $B = \sum_1^p c_i A_i$ symmetric?

18. If $f(x)$ is the polynomial $a_0 x^n + a_1 x^{n-1} + \cdots + a_{n-1}x + a_n$, and if M is an $m \times m$ matrix, then $f(M)$ is the $m \times m$ matrix,

$$a_0 M^n + a_1 M^{n-1} + \cdots + a_{n-1}M + a_n \cdot I.$$

Is it true that $f(M^t) = [f(M)]^t$?

19. (a) Show that the set of all matrices

$$\begin{bmatrix} \cos \theta & -\sin \theta \\ \sin \theta & \cos \theta \end{bmatrix},$$

for all real θ, forms a group, the operation being multiplication.

(b) What is the inverse of the matrix given in part (a)?

(c) In terms of linear transformations of points of the ordinary Euclidean plane, give a geometric interpretation of the group of part (a).

20. Show that the product of two 3×3 matrices each of which is a magic square (sums of rows, columns, and diagonals constant) is a doubly symmetric matrix (symmetric with respect to both diagonals).   (G. P. Sturm, Jr.)

CHAPTER 7

Systems of Linear Equations; Rank of Matrices

The treatment of systems of linear equations is greatly facilitated by matrix methods. Although the development could be purely algebraic, we will find it illuminating to see its relation to the geometrical notion of linear transformation.

7–1 "EQUIVALENT" SYSTEMS OF LINEAR EQUATIONS; ELEMENTARY MATRICES

Consider the system of m linear homogeneous equations in n unknowns:

$$
\begin{aligned}
a_{11}x_1 + a_{12}x_2 + \cdots + a_{1n}x_n &= 0, \\
a_{21}x_1 + a_{22}x_2 + \cdots + a_{2n}x_n &= 0, \qquad a_{ij} \in C, \\
&\vdots \\
a_{m1}x_1 + a_{m2}x_2 + \cdots + a_{mn}x_n &= 0,
\end{aligned}
\tag{1}
$$

which may be abbreviated as

$$
A \cdot \xi = o,
\tag{2}
$$

where $A = [a_{ij}]$, $i = 1, \ldots, m; j = 1, \ldots, n$, and

$$
\xi = \begin{bmatrix} x_1 \\ x_2 \\ \vdots \\ x_n \end{bmatrix}.
$$

A solution of a system of linear equations may be expressible solely in terms of the coefficients in those equations, or it may have greater "freedom," being expressible also in terms of some parameters which may be assigned arbitrary values.

The "general solution" of Eqs. (1) [or (2)] is a set of explicit expressions for each of the x's, in terms of the coefficients a_{ij} and perhaps of some parameters, $u_1, u_2, \ldots, u_p$,

$$
\begin{aligned}
x_1 &= f_1(a_{11}, \ldots, a_{mn}, u_1, \ldots, u_p), \\
x_2 &= f_2(a_{11}, \ldots, a_{mn}, u_1, \ldots, u_p), \\
&\vdots \\
x_n &= f_n(a_{11}, \ldots, a_{mn}, u_1, \ldots, u_p),
\end{aligned}
\tag{3}
$$

with the following two properties.

(i) If the right-hand sides of Eqs. (3) are substituted for the respective x's in Eqs. (1), those equations will be identically satisfied.

(ii) Any set of x's which does satisfy Eqs. (1) is among those given by Eqs. (3).

Thus, in a sense, we replace the set of Eqs. (1) by a "simpler" set, Eqs. (3). We may visualize the situation in the following geometrical way.

Let us think of homogeneous coordinates in the intuitive fashion of Section 2–1, and consider the two straight lines (Fig. 7–1) with equations

$$
4x_0 - 2x_1 + x_2 = 0, \qquad 9x_0 - x_1 - 3x_2 = 0.
\tag{4}
$$

By multiplying the first of Eqs. (4) by 3 and adding to the second to "eliminate" x_2, and then by multiplying the second by 2 and subtracting from the first to "eliminate" x_1, we obtain

$$
21x_0 - 7x_1 = 0, \qquad -14x_0 + 7x_2 = 0.
\tag{5}
$$

In Eqs. (5), we set $x_0 = u$ and obtain $x_1 = 3u$, $x_2 = 2u$ to complete the solution.

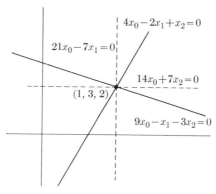

FIGURE 7–1

In analyzing our procedure, we may say that we have replaced the two lines given by Eqs. (4) by the two special lines (parallel to the coordinate axes) given by Eqs. (5), as shown in Fig. 7–1. We imply that Eqs. (4) and (5) are "equivalent" in the sense that any solution of either pair is a solution of the other.

The notion of equivalence of two systems of equations is very helpful. We make the following formal definition.

Definition 1. Two sets of equations are *equivalent* if every solution vector of either set is also a solution vector of the other.

(Verify that this is, indeed, an equivalence relation.)

To discuss the problem of determining useful forms for sets of equations equivalent to given sets, we abbreviate $a_{i1}x_1 + a_{i2}x_2 + \cdots + a_{in}x_n$ as g_i, thus writing Eqs. (1) as

$$
\begin{aligned}
g_1 &= 0, \\
g_2 &= 0, \\
&\vdots \\
g_{m-1} &= 0, \\
g_m &= 0.
\end{aligned}
\tag{6}
$$

Then we can prove a basic theorem.

Theorem 7–1. Each of the following operations on the set of Eqs. (6) gives rise to an equivalent set of equations:
(a) interchanging g_j and g_k, for any j, k;
(b) replacing g_j by $c \cdot g_j$, for any j and any $c \neq 0$;
(c) replacing g_j by $g_j + c \cdot g_k$, for any j, k, and any c.

Proof. (a) is immediate;
(b) follows from the fact that in a field,

$$(p \cdot q = 0) \Rightarrow (p = 0 \quad \text{or} \quad q = 0).$$

Thus $g_j = 0$ if and only if $c \cdot g_j = 0$, for $c \neq 0$;
(c) follows from the facts that

$$(g_j = 0 \text{ and } g_k = 0) \Rightarrow (g_j + c \cdot g_k = 0),$$

and

$$(g_k = 0 \text{ and } g_j + c \cdot g_k = 0) \Rightarrow (g_j = 0).$$

In Section 7–2 we shall apply Theorem 7–1 to obtain an algorithm (rule of procedure) for finding the solution of a system of equations.

But first we consider operations on matrices analogous to the operations on equations introduced in Theorem 7–1.

We define three types of *elementary row transformations* of a matrix.

(i) The interchange of two row vectors, i.e., the interchange of α_k and α_l, for any k, l;

(ii) the multiplication of a row vector by a nonzero scalar, i.e., the replacement of α_k by $c \cdot \alpha_k$, for any k and for any $c \neq 0$;

(iii) the addition to a row vector of a scalar multiple of a row vector, i.e., the replacement of α_k by $\alpha_k + c \cdot \alpha_l$, for any $k, l, k \neq l$, and any c.

Note that each of these transformations can be "undone" by another transformation of the same type: (i) is its own inverse; (ii) is undone by replacing the new kth row vector by $1/c$ times that vector; and the inverse of (iii) is the transformation in which $(-c \cdot \alpha_l)$ is added to the new kth row vector.

It is useful to consider the effect of elementary transformations on the identity matrix, I:

Definition 2. A matrix which is obtained from I by an elementary row transformation is called an *elementary matrix*.

Examples of elementary matrices obtained from I_5 by elementary row transformations of each of the three types are:

$$
\begin{bmatrix}
1 & 0 & 0 & 0 & 0 \\
0 & 0 & 1 & 0 & 0 \\
0 & 1 & 0 & 0 & 0 \\
0 & 0 & 0 & 1 & 0 \\
0 & 0 & 0 & 0 & 1
\end{bmatrix}
\quad
\begin{bmatrix}
1 & 0 & 0 & 0 & 0 \\
0 & 1 & 0 & 0 & 0 \\
0 & 0 & 1 & 0 & 0 \\
0 & 0 & 0 & c & 0 \\
0 & 0 & 0 & 0 & 1
\end{bmatrix}
\quad
\begin{bmatrix}
1 & 0 & 0 & 0 & 0 \\
0 & 1 & 0 & 0 & 0 \\
0 & 0 & 1 & 0 & c \\
0 & 0 & 0 & 1 & 0 \\
0 & 0 & 0 & 0 & 1
\end{bmatrix}
$$

$$\text{(i)} \qquad\qquad\qquad \text{(ii)} \qquad\qquad\qquad \text{(iii)}$$

The proof of the following theorem is simple.

Theorem 7–2. If an elementary row transformation T takes the matrices A, I, respectively, into A_T, I_T, then $A_T = I_T \cdot A$; or, in words, each elementary row transformation of a matrix can be effected by left-multiplying the matrix by the corresponding elementary matrix.

Because of the remarks above about "undoing" an elementary row transformation on a matrix, it is clear that an elementary matrix is left nonsingular. Moreover, it is easy to verify that a left inverse of an elementary matrix is also a right inverse of that matrix; hence, *an elementary matrix is nonsingular*.

PROBLEM SET 7–1

1. Prove the following generalization of Theorem 7–1(c). The system obtained from Eqs. (6) by replacing any g_j by $\sum_{i=1}^{n} c_i g_i$, $c_j \neq 0$ is equivalent to (6).

2. Demonstrate that the operations (a), (b), (c) of Theorem 7–1 are not independent by showing that (a) may be obtained as a result of combinations of operations of types (b) and (c).

3. Prove Theorem 7–2.

4. Write out the left inverses of each of the elementary matrices (i), (ii), (iii), and verify that each left inverse is also a right inverse.

*5. Define three elementary column transformations, write out the corresponding elementary matrices, and state the analogue of Theorem 7–2 for an elementary column transformation.

*6. Show that if a certain elementary transformation on rows is effected by left-multiplication by the elementary matrix E, then the analogous elementary transformation on columns is effected by right-multiplication by E^t.

7–2 SOLUTION OF SYSTEMS OF LINEAR EQUATIONS

We shall effect the solution of Eqs. (6), Section 7–1, in a sequence of steps, each of which will replace the system of equations by an equivalent, simpler system. It is suggested that, while studying the following description of the general process, you work these numerical examples:

$$
\begin{aligned}
3x_1 + 2x_2 - 4x_3 + x_4 &= 0, \\
x_1 - 2x_2 + x_3 \phantom{{}+ x_4} &= 0, \\
2x_1 - x_2 - x_3 + x_4 &= 0;
\end{aligned}
\tag{1a}
$$

$$
\begin{aligned}
5x_1 - x_2 + 6x_3 + 2x_4 &= 0, \\
-x_1 + 3x_2 - 3x_3 - x_4 &= 0, \\
2x_1 - x_2 + 3x_3 + x_4 &= 0.
\end{aligned}
\tag{1b}
$$

The method proceeds in two phases: phase 1 will replace the original system, $g_i = 0$, $i = 1, \ldots, m$, by an equivalent system

$$
g'_i = \sum_{j=1}^{n} a'_{ij} x_j = 0, \qquad i = 1, \ldots, n;
$$

and phase 2 will replace the system of phase 1 by an equivalent system

$$
g''_i = \sum_{j=1}^{n} a''_{ij} x_j, \qquad i = 1, \ldots, n.
$$

At the end of phase 1, we shall have a "triangular" system in which at least the last coefficient of g'_{m-1} is zero (i.e., at least $a'_{m-1,n} = 0$), at least the last two coefficients of g'_{m-2} are zero (i.e., at least $a'_{m-2,n} = 0 = a'_{m-2,n-1}$), ..., at least the last $m - 1$ coefficients of g'_1 are zero (i.e., at least $a'_{1n} = 0 = a'_{1,n-1} = \cdots = a'_{1,n-m+2}$). We obtain this triangular system as follows.

We may assume that some coefficient of x_n in Eqs. (6), Section 7–1, is not zero, for otherwise we would have at most $n - 1$ unknowns. By reordering, using operation (a) of Theorem 7–1, we may assume that $a_{mn} \neq 0$. By replacing g_1 by $g_1 - (a_{1n}/a_{mn})g_m$ (operation c), we obtain a new g_1 in which the coefficient of x_n is zero. Similarly, we can perform operations which will result in a system, equivalent to Eqs. (6), in which the coefficients of x_n in the second, third, ..., $(m - 1)$st equations are all zero. We now ignore g_m, and repeat the above procedure; start by making an interchange (if necessary) so that the coefficient of x_{n-1} in the $(m - 1)$st equation is not zero, and continue with operations of type (c) so that all the coefficients of x_{n-1} in the first $m - 2$ equations are zero. (Possibly, *all* the coefficients of x_{n-1} in the first $m - 1$ equations are already zero, in which case we proceed directly to operate on the coefficients of x_{n-2}.) Eventually we obtain a triangular system. If $m > n$, the first $m - n$ equations will have all coefficients zero. Hence, in the triangular system, the number of nonvanishing equations (not all coefficients zero) does not exceed the number of unknowns. If the number of equations is less than the number of unknowns, we may add vanishing equations so as to make a new system in which the number of equations equals the number of unknowns.

With Eqs. (1a) and (1b), for example, the most natural sequence of steps following the foregoing description leads to:

$$0x_1 \qquad\qquad\qquad = 0,$$

$$4x_1 - 3x_2 \qquad\qquad = 0, \qquad\qquad (2a)$$

$$x_1 - 2x_2 + x_3 \qquad = 0,$$

$$2x_1 - x_2 - x_3 + x_4 = 0;$$

$$0x_1 \qquad\qquad\qquad = 0,$$

$$x_1 + x_2 \qquad\qquad = 0, \qquad\qquad (2b)$$

$$x_1 + 2x_2 + 0x_3 \qquad = 0,$$

$$2x_1 - x_2 + 3x_3 + x_4 = 0.$$

The solution of (2a) can easily be obtained by "working down from the top," one equation at a time: $x_1 = u$ (arbitrary), $x_2 = \frac{4}{3}u$, $x_3 = \frac{5}{3}u$, $x_4 = u$; or, if we wish to dispense with fractions,

$$x_1 = 3v, \qquad x_2 = 4v,$$

$$x_3 = 5v, \qquad x_4 = 3v.$$

Thus, the solution space of (1a) is the one-dimensional vector space spanned by (3, 4, 5, 3). But this method applied to (2b) leads to difficulty: $x_1 = u$ (arbitrary), $x_2 = -u$, and then the next equation, far from assigning a value to x_3, shows that x_1 *cannot* be assigned an arbitrary value. We probably can, somehow, determine the solution of (2b), but we do not yet have the algorithm which we are seeking. This is the reason for going on to phase 2. You should apply the following procedure to Eqs. (2a) and (2b).

At the end of phase 1 we have a triangular system with n unknowns and n equations (designated as $g'_i = 0$, $i = 1, \ldots, n$), in which $a'_{ij} = 0$ for $i < j$. In phase 2 we shall obtain an equivalent system ($g''_i = 0$) in which (a) the "diagonal coefficients" (a''_{ii}, $i = 1, \ldots, n$) are 0 or 1, and (b) in case a diagonal coefficient is zero, all coefficients in that equation are zero. This is accomplished as follows.

Suppose that in the triangular system obtained in phase 1,

$$g'_l = a'_{l1}x_1 + a'_{l2}x_2 + \cdots + a'_{ll}x_l = 0$$

is the last equation such that the coefficient on the diagonal is zero; suppose further that the equation does not vanish identically, i.e., that there is at least one nonzero coefficient. Suppose that a'_{lk} is the last nonzero coefficient in this equation. If, in g'_k, $a'_{kk} = 0$, we can interchange the kth and lth equations to obtain a new triangular system in which the lth equation has one more zero coefficient to the right of its last nonzero coefficient than the old lth equation had. If, on the other hand, $a'_{kk} \neq 0$, we can add $-(a'_{lk}/a'_{kk})g'_k$ to g'_l, thus obtaining a new lth equation which has either all zero coefficients or one more zero coefficient than before to the right of its last nonzero coefficient. Proceeding in this way leads, in a finite number of steps, to a system in which any equation with diagonal coefficient zero has all coefficients zero. Finally, we can "normalize" by dividing through by any nonzero diagonal coefficient, and obtain the desired result—a system

$$g''_i = a''_{i1}x_1 + \cdots + a''_{in}x_n = 0$$

such that $a''_{ij} = 0$ for $i < j$; $a''_{ii} = 0$ or 1; and if $a''_{ii} = 0$, then $g''_i \equiv 0$.

This completes phase 2. Thus, for Eqs. (2a) and (2b), we obtain

$$
\begin{aligned}
0x_1 & & &= 0, \\
4x_1 - 3x_2 & & &= 0, \\
x_1 - 2x_2 + x_3 & & &= 0, \\
2x_1 - x_2 - x_3 + x_4 &= 0;
\end{aligned}
\tag{3a}
$$

$$
\begin{aligned}
x_1 & & &= 0, \\
x_1 + x_2 & & &= 0, \\
0x_1 + 0x_2 + 0x_3 & & &= 0, \\
2x_1 - x_2 + 3x_3 + x_4 &= 0.
\end{aligned}
\tag{3b}
$$

Working down from the top in (3b), one equation at a time, leads to $x_1 = 0$, $x_2 = 0$, $x_3 = u$ (arbitrary), $x_4 = -3u$. Thus, the solution space of Eqs. (1b) is the one-dimensional vector space spanned by $(0, 0, 1, -3)$.

Let us use the term "complete triangulation procedure" for the process described in phases 1 and 2 and the notation introduced there.

If as a result of this procedure,

$$a''_{ii} = 0 \qquad \text{for} \qquad i = k_1, k_2, \ldots, k_{n-r},$$

we set

$$x_{k_1} = u_1, \qquad x_{k_2} = u_2, \ldots, x_{k_{n-r}} = u_{n-r},$$

and we find that each of the other x's is expressible as a linear combination of these. Indeed, we have the following theorem.

Theorem 7–3. If the complete triangulation procedure applied to the matrix A with n columns leads to $n - r$ rows of zeros, then the system of equations $A \cdot \xi = o$ has a solution space of dimension $n - r$.

The proof is left as a problem (Problem 14 below). Note that the triangulation procedure must be *complete* for the validity of this theorem. Just because there are two zeros on the main diagonal in Eqs. (2b) does *not* mean that the solution space has dimension two. In fact, the complete process leads to Eqs. (3b) with one vanishing equation, and the solution space has dimension one.

The solution of the nonhomogeneous system

$$
\begin{aligned}
a_{11}x_1 + a_{12}x_2 + \cdots + a_{1n}x_n &= b_1, \\
a_{21}x_1 + a_{22}x_2 + \cdots + a_{2n}x_n &= b_2, \\
&\ \vdots \\
a_{m1}x_1 + a_{m2}x_2 + \cdots + a_{mn}x_n &= b_m,
\end{aligned}
\tag{4}
$$

or, in abbreviated form,

$$A \xi = \beta, \tag{5}$$

is now easily discussed. We simply write the homogeneous system

$$b_1 x_0 + a_{11} x_1 + a_{12} x_2 + \cdots + a_{1n} x_n = 0,$$
$$b_2 x_0 + a_{21} x_1 + a_{22} x_2 + \cdots + a_{2n} x_n = 0, \tag{6}$$
$$\vdots$$
$$b_m x_0 + a_{m1} x_1 + a_{m2} x_2 + \cdots + a_{mn} x_n = 0,$$

and observe that the solutions of Eqs. (4) are precisely those solutions of Eqs. (6) for which $x_0 = -1$.

EXAMPLE 1. Let us take the pair of nonhomogeneous equations

$$a_1 x + b_1 y = c_1,$$
$$a_2 x + b_2 y = c_2. \tag{7}$$

As we did above, we write the homogeneous equations

$$c_1 z + a_1 x + b_1 y = 0,$$
$$c_2 z + a_2 x + b_2 y = 0, \tag{8}$$

and we seek those solutions of Eqs. (8) for which $z = -1$.

Case (i)
$$b_2 \neq 0, \qquad a_1 b_2 - a_2 b_1 \neq 0.$$

Equations (8) are equivalent to the triangular system

$$0z \qquad\qquad\qquad\qquad = 0,$$
$$(b_2 c_1 - c_2 b_1) z + (b_2 a_1 - a_2 b_1) x \qquad = 0,$$
$$c_2 z \qquad + \qquad a_2 x \qquad + b_2 y = 0,$$

of which the solution is

$$z = u, \qquad x = \frac{b_2 c_1 - c_2 b_1}{a_2 b_1 - b_2 a_1} u, \qquad y = \frac{c_1 a_2 - a_1 c_2}{a_2 b_1 - b_2 a_1} u.$$

Hence, in this case, the solution of Eqs. (7) is

$$x = \frac{c_1 b_2 - c_2 b_1}{a_1 b_2 - a_2 b_1}, \qquad y = \frac{a_1 c_2 - a_2 c_1}{a_1 b_2 - a_2 b_1}.$$

Case (ii)
$$b_2 \neq 0, \qquad a_1 b_2 - a_2 b_1 = 0, \qquad b_1 c_2 - b_2 c_1 \neq 0.$$

Equations (8) are equivalent to the system

$$(b_1c_2 - b_2c_1)z = 0,$$
$$0z + 0x = 0,$$
$$c_2z + a_2x + b_2y = 0,$$

of which the solution is

$$z = 0, \qquad x = u, \qquad y = -\frac{a_2}{b_2}u.$$

Hence, in this case Eqs. (7) have no solution.

Case (iii)

$$b_2 \neq 0, \qquad a_1b_2 - a_2b_1 = 0, \qquad b_1c_2 - b_2c_1 = 0.$$

Equations (8) are equivalent to

$$0z = 0,$$
$$0z + 0x = 0,$$
$$c_2z + a_2x + b_2y = 0,$$

for which the solution is

$$z = u, \qquad x = v, \qquad y = -\frac{c_2}{b_2}u - \frac{a_2}{b_2}v.$$

Hence, in this case, Eqs. (7) have the infinite set of solutions, $x = v$, $y = (c_2/b_2) - (a_y/b_2)v$.

The consideration of other cases is left as a problem (Prob. 7(c) below).

We have now an algorithm for solving either a homogeneous or a non-homogeneous system —an algorithm, moreover, of practical significance in numerical analysis (the Gaussian procedure). But, without carrying out the steps of the method, we cannot yet predict how many solutions there will be. The study of the rank of a matrix (Section 7–3) will enable us to solve this problem.

PROBLEM SET 7-2

In Problems 1 through 5, solve the given systems by changing each to a triangular system. In each case interpret the result, both in terms of intersections of hyperplanes and in terms of dependence or independence of vectors.

1. (a) Same as Eqs. (1a) with the additional equation

$$6x_1 - x_2 - 4x_3 + 2x_4 = 0.$$

(b) Same as (a), with the additional equation

$$5x_2 - 4x_3 = 0.$$

2. (a)
$$-x_1 - x_2 + x_4 + x_5 = 0,$$
$$-3x_2 - x_3 + 2x_4 + 2x_5 = 0,$$
$$-3x_1 + x_3 + x_4 + x_5 = 0.$$

(b) Same as (a), with the additional equation

$$x_1 + x_2 - x_3 + 2x_4 + x_5 = 0.$$

(c) Same as (b), with the additional equation

$$x_3 - 3x_4 - 2x_5 = 0.$$

(d) Same as (c), with the additional equation

$$2x_1 - x_2 + 2x_4 + x_5 = 0.$$

3. (a) $-x_1 + 2x_3 + x_4 = 0,\ x_1 - x_2 + 4x_3 + 2x_4 = 0.$
(b) Same as (a), with the additional equation

$$3x_1 - 2x_2 + 6x_3 + 3x_4 = 0.$$

(c) Same as (b), with the additional equation

$$5x_1 - 2x_2 + 2x_3 - x_4 = 0.$$

4.
$$x_1 + x_2 - x_3 = 0,$$
$$x_1 + 2x_3 = 0,$$
$$2x_1 + x_2 + x_3 = 0,$$
$$x_1 + 3x_3 - 2x_4 + x_5 = 0,$$
$$x_2 - x_3 - x_4 + 5x_5 = 0.$$

5.
$$2x_1 - x_2 - 3x_3 + 5x_4 = 0,$$
$$x_1 + 2x_2 - 4x_3 - 5x_4 = 0,$$
$$3x_1 + 2x_2 - 8x_3 - 3x_4 = 0.$$

*6. Show that if Eqs. (1) of Section 7-1 are equivalent to a triangular system in which all the diagonal coefficients are 1, then o is the only solution vector.

7. With reference to Example 1,
(a) verify the algebraic details of each of the cases discussed.
(b) Give a geometrical interpretation of each of the cases discussed.
(c) Consider the cases not discussed; i.e., $b_2 = 0$, etc.

8. Solve the following systems of nonhomogeneous equations by the method of the text.
(a) $3x_1 + 2x_2 - x_3 = 6,\ x_1 - x_2 + 4x_3 = -4.$
(b) Same as (a) with the additional equation

$$4x_1 - x_2 - 2x_3 = 5.$$

(c) Same as (a) with the additional equation

$$6x_1 - x_2 + 11x_3 = 8.$$

(d) Same as (b) with the additional equation of (c).

9. Solve the following set of nonhomogeneous equations by the method of the text.

$$4x_1 + 2x_3 - 2x_4 + 2x_5 = 0,$$
$$x_1 + 7x_2 + 3x_3 + 2x_4 + x_5 = 1,$$
$$2x_2 + x_3 + x_4 = 1,$$
$$x_1 - 4x_2 - x_3 - 3x_4 + x_5 = -1.$$

10. Using the "triangulation" procedure, find the most general expression for the vector $(5, 3, 0)$ as a linear combination of the vectors $(1, 1, 1)$, $(3, 2, 0)$, $(2, 1, -1)$, and $(7, 5, 2)$.

*11. (a) Show that if ϕ is a solution vector of the nonhomogeneous system $A \cdot \xi = \beta$, and if ψ is a solution vector of the associated homogeneous system, $A \cdot \xi = o$, then $\phi + \psi$ is also a solution vector of $A \cdot \xi = \beta$.

(b) Show, conversely, that if γ is a *fixed* solution vector of $A \cdot \xi = \beta$, then *any* solution vector ρ of $A \cdot \xi = \beta$ can be written as $\rho = \gamma + \sigma$, where σ is some solution vector of $A \cdot \xi = o$.

*12. Prove Theorem 7–3.

7–3 ROW RANK AND COLUMN RANK OF A MATRIX

The algebraic properties of a matrix, such as the existence of an inverse and similar matters, are often illuminated by the study of the transformation which the matrix determines.

First, we note that the set of row vectors of a matrix spans a certain vector space; this space is called the *row space of the matrix*. Likewise the column vectors span a (generally different) vector space, called the *column space of the matrix*.

Definition 3. The *row rank of a matrix* is the dimension of its row space. The *column rank of a matrix* is the dimension of its column space.

In other words, the row rank (column rank) of a matrix equals the maximum number of independent vectors among its row (column) vectors.

A major theorem to come later (Theorem 7–14) is that the row and column ranks of a matrix are equal. We now develop some results about row rank of matrices; it should be clear what the analogous statements about column rank are.

Theorem 7–4. If $A \cdot B = C$, then the row space of C is a subspace of the row space of B.

Proof. Suppose that $A = [a_{ij}]$, $i = 1, \ldots, m$; $j = 1, \ldots, n$; that

$$B = \begin{bmatrix} \beta_1 \\ \vdots \\ \beta_n \end{bmatrix}; \quad \text{and that} \quad C = \begin{bmatrix} \gamma_1 \\ \vdots \\ \gamma_n \end{bmatrix}.$$

Then $\gamma_k = \sum_{l=1}^{n} a_{kl}\beta_l$, $k = 1, \ldots, m$. In other words, each vector of the set spanning the row space of C can be written as a linear combination of the vectors spanning the row space of B. $\square$

The following theorem is an immediate consequence of this theorem.

Theorem 7–5. If $A \cdot B = C$, then the row rank of C is less than or equal to the row rank of B.

In case A is left nonsingular (and hence square), then a stronger statement than the preceding one can be made.

Theorem 7–6. If $A \cdot B = C$, and if A is left nonsingular, then the row rank of C equals the row rank of B.

Proof. If we designate a left inverse of A by A^{-1}, we can write $A^{-1} \cdot C = B$. Hence, the row rank of B is less than or equal to the row rank of C. Putting this statement together with that of Theorem 7–5 gives the desired result.

In view of Theorem 7–2 and the comments immediately following that theorem, we can deduce a result about equality of row ranks.

Theorem 7–7. If A_T is obtained from A by an elementary row transformation, or by a succession of such transformations, then the row rank of A_T equals the row rank of A.

This, in turn, leads us to one of the theorems that we shall need in proving (later) that row rank equals column rank.

Theorem 7–8. If the triangulation procedure applied to a matrix A with n columns leads to $n - r$ rows of zeros, then the row rank of A equals r.

Proof. First we must verify that A_T, in triangular form with $n - r$ rows of zeros, has precisely r linearly independent row vectors. (Problem 3 below.) Then we appeal to Theorem 7–7 to conclude that A has row rank r.

We introduce some convenient terminology before developing other properties of matrices. Earlier we used the term "main diagonal" to describe the set of elements a_{ii}, $i = 1, 2, \ldots, n$ of an $n \times n$ matrix; hereafter, unless otherwise stated, "diagonal" will mean "main diagonal."

Definition 4. The square matrix A is called *lower triangular* if every element above the diagonal is zero, i.e., if $a_{ij} = 0$ for $i < j$.

Definition 5. A matrix H is a *Hermite matrix* if it has the following properties:

(i) H is lower triangular, with every diagonal element 0 or 1.
(ii) If the diagonal element of a certain row is zero, every element of that row is zero.
(iii) If the diagonal element of a certain column is 1, every other element of that column is zero.

Theorem 7–9. If A is a square matrix, there exists a matrix E which is a product of elementary matrices, such that $EA = H$, where H is a Hermite matrix.

Proof. The reduction to the stated triangular form is effected by a succession of elementary row transformations, or, what we know to be the same thing (Theorem 7–2), by a succession of left-multiplications by elementary matrices. Since the elementary matrices are left-nonsingular, their product E will likewise be left-nonsingular.

The process of obtaining the triangular form fulfilling parts (i) and (ii) of this theorem is precisely like the corresponding process for equations, described in Section 7–2. We now go one step farther than we chose to go in discussing equations to establish part (iii) of this theorem: if $a_{kk} = 1$, $a_{lk} \neq 0$ for some $l > k$, we add $-a_{lk} \cdot \alpha_k$ to α_l, where α_k, α_l are row vectors.

Thus, by a succession of elementary row transformations (or, by left-multiplying by a left-nonsingular matrix which is the product of elementary matrices) we can reduce A to the prescribed form.

It can be shown that the Hermite matrix H of Theorem 7–9 is unique, for given A. By Theorem 7–7 its row rank equals the row rank of A.

PROBLEM SET 7–3

1. Observe the similarity of the argument of Theorem 7–6 to the following demonstration that the degree of an algebraic plane curve is not changed by a rotation of axes: "It is known that the formula for rotation of axes is of the form, $x = ax' + by'$, $y = cx' + dy'$. Hence the degree of an equation clearly cannot be *raised* by a rotation. Suppose, on the other hand, that it were *lowered*. Then the inverse rotation, applied to the new equation, would give $\ldots$". Complete the argument.

*2. (a) State the analogues of Theorems 7–4 through 7–8 for column rank.

(b) State the analogue of Theorem 7–9 for "upper triangular" form.

*3. In V_n, let $\alpha_i = (a_{i1}, a_{i2}, \ldots, a_{ii}, 0, \ldots, 0)$, $i = 1, 2, \ldots, s$. Show that if $a_{ii} \neq 0$ for $i = 1, \ldots, s$, then the s α's form an independent set.

4. Find the Hermite matrix corresponding to

$$A = \begin{bmatrix} 0 & 1 & 7 \\ 1 & 2 & 4 \\ 2 & 3 & 1 \end{bmatrix}$$

in accordance with Theorem 7–9. Use two different sets of elementary transformations to accomplish the result, and observe that the Hermite matrices are indeed the same. Find the matrices E and E^* which are the left-multipliers of A for the two reductions.

*5. Let $S = [s_{ij}]$ and $T = [t_{ij}]$ be lower triangular $n \times n$ matrices. Show that (a) $R = ST$ is likewise lower triangular, and $r_{ii} = s_{ii} \cdot t_{ii}$; (b) if, in S, all the elements on the principal diagonal and on the $p - 1$ parallels immediately "below" the diagonal are zero, and if a similar situation exists in T for the principal diagonal and the $q - 1$ parallels immediately below the diagonal, then the same situation obtains in ST for the principal diagonal and the $p + q - 1$ parallels immediately below the diagonal.

Corollary 1. If all the elements of the principal diagonal of S are zero, then (i) $S^n = O$, and (ii) $(I + S)^{-1} = I - S + S^2 - \cdots \pm S^{n-1}$. [*Hint:* For (ii), use Problem 13, Section 6–6, and the result of (i) above.]

Corollary 2. If $t_{ii} = 1$, $i = 1, \ldots, n$ and if $T^{-1} = V = [v_{ij}]$, then $v_{ii} = 1$ and $v_{i,i-1} = - t_{i,i-1}$, $i = 1, \ldots, n$.

[These results are significant for computer solutions of matrix problems and for the proof that the Jordan form of a matrix is essentially unique (Chapter 12).]

7–4 RANK AND NULLITY

In Chapter 6 we defined projectivities as linear transformations from the points of one projective space to those of another. It is fruitful also to consider linear transformations of the vectors of a vector space.

If $\xi = (x_1, \ldots, x_n)$ is a vector of V_n, and if $A = [a_{ij}]$, $i = 1, \ldots, m$; $j = 1, \ldots, n$, then $A \cdot \xi$ is the result of the linear transformation of ξ by the matrix A. Actually, $A \cdot \xi = \xi'$, where $\xi' = (x_1', \ldots, x_m')$ is some vector of V_m'.

Thus, the matrix A maps the space V_n into the space V_m'. It will be convenient to introduce a notation reminiscent of familiar functional notation. Just as we use $f(x)$ to designate the number into which x is carried by the function f, so we shall use $A(V_n)$ as a designation for the set of vectors which are the transforms of all the vectors of V_n under the transformation with matrix A. [If we wish, we can also write $A(\xi) = \xi'$, but we already have a perfectly adequate symbolism in $A \cdot \xi = \xi'$.]

As noted above, if A is an $m \times n$ matrix, $A(V_n) \subseteq V'_m$. Under what circumstances is equality achieved; what are the properties of A which make it map V_n *onto* V'_m? It turns out that the question is tied to a related question on linear equations: under what circumstances are there solutions, other than the null vector, of the system $A \cdot \xi = o$? We already have *an* answer to the latter question (Theorem 7–3), and we shall now investigate the relationship between the two questions.

It is a straightforward problem to show that the image of V_n under a linear transformation is a vector space (Problem 8 below). The dimension of this space is equal to the column rank of the matrix of the transformation.

Theorem 7–10. The image of V_n under a linear transformation with an $m \times n$ matrix A is a subspace, V'_k, of V'_m, where k is the column rank of A.

Proof. We shall assume that you have established the image as a subspace and will establish the dimension. Let $\xi = (x_1, \ldots, x_n)$ be an arbitrary vector of V_n, and let $\epsilon_1, \epsilon_2, \ldots, \epsilon_n$ be the unit vectors of V_n. Then $\xi = \sum_1^n x_i \cdot \epsilon_i$. Hence

$$A \cdot \xi = A \cdot \left(\sum_1^n x_i \epsilon_i \right) = \sum_1^n A \cdot (x_i \epsilon_i) = \sum_1^n x_i (A \cdot \epsilon_i) = \sum_1^n x_i \cdot \tilde{\alpha}_i,$$

where $\tilde{\alpha}_1, \ldots, \tilde{\alpha}_n$ are the column vectors of A. In other words, any vector in the image of V_n can be written as a linear combination of the α's. Thus, the image of V_n is the column space of A, whose dimension is, by definition, the column rank of A.

As we know from Theorem 4–1, the set of vectors of V_n carried into the null vector of V'_m by a linear transformation is a subspace of V_n.

Definition 6. The subspace of V_n carried into the null vector of V'_m by the linear transformation with matrix A is called the *null space V_l* of A. The dimension l of V_l is called the *nullity* of A.

We shall prove that the column rank plus the nullity of a matrix equals the number of columns of the matrix. First we must prove a preliminary result.

Theorem 7–11. If $\phi_1, \phi_2, \ldots, \phi_q$ form a set of independent vectors, all lying in a subspace of V_n complementary to the null space of a matrix A, then $A \cdot \phi_1, A \cdot \phi_2, \ldots, A \cdot \phi_q$ form a set of independent vectors.

Proof. We use an indirect argument. Suppose that $A \cdot \phi_1, \ldots, A\phi_q$ are linearly dependent, so that there are scalars $f_1, \ldots, f_q$, not all zero, such that $\sum_1^q f_i(A \cdot \phi_i) = o$. Then $A \cdot \sum_1^q f_i \phi_i = o$. This last equation implies that the vector $\sum_1^q f_i \phi_i$ belongs to the null space of A. This contradicts the hypothesis that the ϕ's lie in a subspace complementary to the null space of A, unless $\sum_1^q f_i \phi_i = o$. This, in turn, is impossible because of the assumed independence of the ϕ's.

Theorem 7–12. If A, an $m \times n$ matrix, has column rank k and nullity l, then $k + l = n$.

Proof. Suppose that $\beta_1, \beta_2, \ldots, \beta_l$ form a basis of the null space, V_l. Then, by Theorem 4–8, there is a basis of V_n of the form $\beta_1, \ldots, \beta_l$, $\gamma_1, \ldots, \gamma_{n-l}$. As in the proof of Theorem 4–10, we know that $\gamma_1, \ldots, \gamma_{n-l}$ lie in a complement of V_l. Hence, by Theorem 7–11, the vectors $A \cdot \gamma_1, \ldots, A \cdot \gamma_{n-l}$ are independent. We proceed to show that these vectors span $A(V_n)$. Let ξ be an arbitrary vector of V_n. Then ξ can be written as

$$ \xi = \sum_1^l f_i \beta_i + \sum_1^{n-l} g_i \gamma_i. $$

Hence

$$ A \cdot \xi = A \cdot \left(\sum_1^l f_i \beta_i + \sum_1^{n-l} g_i \gamma_i \right) = \sum_1^l f_i(A \cdot \beta_i) + \sum_1^{n-l} g_i(A \cdot \gamma_i). $$

But since each $\beta_i \in V_l$, $A \cdot \beta_i = o$. Thus

$$ A \cdot \xi = \sum_1^{n-l} g_i(A \cdot \gamma_i). $$

Hence $A \cdot \gamma_1, \ldots, A \cdot \gamma_{n-l}$ span $A(V_n)$, the image of V_n. Because we noted that these vectors are independent, we know that they form a basis of $A(V_n)$. Hence, k, the dimension of $A(V_n)$ (see Theorem 7–10) equals $n - l$, or $k + l = n$.

The proof makes it clear that the foregoing theorem has the equivalent formulation that follows.

Theorem 7–13. Let V_q be a complement, in V_n, of V_l, the null space of a linear transformation A. Then $A(V_q) = V_q'$.

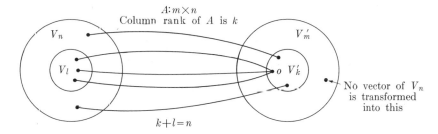

FIGURE 7–2

Figure 7–2 may be helpful in summarizing our results so far.

EXAMPLE.   Consider the transformation

$$\begin{bmatrix} x_1' \\ x_2' \end{bmatrix} = \begin{bmatrix} 1 & 2 & 3 \\ 2 & -1 & 1 \end{bmatrix} \cdot \begin{bmatrix} x_1 \\ x_2 \\ x_3 \end{bmatrix}.$$

The first two column vectors of the transformation matrix are clearly independent, but the third is a linear combination of the first two. (Verify.) Hence $k = 2$. If we solve the pair of equations

$$x_1 + 2x_2 + 3x_3 = 0,$$
$$2x_1 - x_2 + x_3 = 0,$$

we obtain $x_1 = u$, $x_2 = u$, $x_3 = -u$. Hence, the null space of this transformation is the one-dimensional subspace of V_3 spanned by $(1, 1, -1)$. Thus $l = 1$, and n, of course, equals 3.

Theorem 7–12 has the following interpretation in terms of solutions of equations.

Since the solution vectors of

$$A \cdot \xi = o \tag{1}$$

constitute V_l, the null space of A, there are $n - k$ independent solution vectors of Eq. (1) which form a basis for V_l, all solution vectors of Eq. (1) being expressible as linear combinations of these basis vectors.

Now compare this statement with our earlier results. Theorems 7–3 and 7–8 show that the solution space of Eqs. (1) has dimension $n - r$, where r is the row rank of A. Hence $n - k = n - r$, or $k = r$. We have thus proved the following basic theorem.

Theorem 7–14.   The column rank of a matrix equals its row rank.

Definition 7.   The *rank* of a matrix is the common value of its column rank and its row rank.

Clearly, the rank of an $m \times n$ matrix is not greater than the smaller of the numbers m and n. In symbols, rank $\leq \min(m, n)$. We lump together several results of our work above.

Theorem 7–15. If A is an $m \times n$ matrix, then

(a) the dimension of $A(V_n) \leq \min(m, n)$;
(b) the dimension of $A(V_n)$ equals $n \Leftrightarrow A \cdot \phi = o$ implies $\phi = o$;
(c) if $m < n$, then $l > 0$;
(d) $A(V_n) = V'_m \Leftrightarrow l = n - m$.

The proof is left as a problem (Problem 9 below).

Another consequence of Theorem 7–14 is the following theorem, whose proof is also left as a problem (Problem 10 below).

Theorem 7–16. The rank of the product of two matrices does not exceed the rank of either factor.

PROBLEM SET 7–4

In each of the Problems 1 through 7 below, compute independently the column rank, the row rank, and the nullity.

1. $\begin{bmatrix} 2 & 1 & 3 & 0 \\ 1 & 0 & -1 & 1 \\ 0 & 1 & 5 & -2 \end{bmatrix}$
2. $\begin{bmatrix} 1 & 3 & -2 \\ 2 & 0 & 1 \\ 3 & 3 & -1 \\ 0 & 6 & -3 \end{bmatrix}$

3. The matrix of coefficients of Problems 1(a) and (b) of Section 7–2.

4. Same as Problem 3 above, for Problems 2(a), (b), (c), and (d) of Section 7–2.

5. Same as Problem 3 above, for Problems 3(a), (b), and (c) of Section 7–2.

6. Same as Problem 3 above, for Problem 4 of Section 7–2.

7. Same as Problem 3 above, for Problem 5 of Section 7–2.

8. If A is an $m \times n$ matrix, show that $A(V_n)$ is a vector space.

9. Prove Theorem 7–15.

10. Prove Theorem 7–16. [*Hint:* See Theorem 7–5 and Problem 2, Section 7–3.]

11. Designate by M the matrix of the coefficients of the system of linear equations of Problem 4, Section 7–2. What is the rank of M? If $M(V_5) = V'_p$, what is the value of p? What is the dimension of the null space of M? In V_5, let S be a complement of the null space of M. Find a basis for S, and verify that the transforms, by M, of these basis vectors form a basis for V'_p.

7–5 SYLVESTER'S LAW OF NULLITY*

The general methods of Section 7–4 can be used to prove a theorem of considerable depth. We first prove a lemma on the dimension of the image of what might be called a "relative complement" of a null space, which is analogous to Theorem 7–13.

Lemma. Let T be the matrix of a linear transformation from V_n to V_m'. Let V_p be a subspace of V_n, and let V_q be the subspace of V_p carried into the null vector by T. Suppose that V_r is a complement of V_q in V_p, i.e., that $V_q + V_r = V_p$, $V_q \cap V_r = \{o\}$. Then $T(V_r) = V_r'$.

Proof. The proof is essentially the same as that of Theorem 7–12. Let $\beta_1, \ldots, \beta_q$ be a basis for V_q, and $\beta_1, \ldots, \beta_q, \gamma_1, \ldots, \gamma_r$ be a basis for V_p. Let $\gamma_i' = T \cdot \gamma_i$, $i = 1, \ldots, r$. Then by Theorem 7–11, $\gamma_1', \ldots, \gamma_r'$ form a basis for V_r'.

Theorem 7–17. *Sylvester's Law of Nullity.* Let A, B be $n \times n$ matrices with nullities l_A, l_B, respectively. Let l_{AB} be the nullity of the product AB. Then $\max(l_A, l_B) \le l_{AB} \le l_A + l_B$. "The nullity of a product is at least as great as the nullity of each factor and is not greater than the sum of the nullities of the factors."

Proof. That $l_{AB} \ge l_A$; $l_{AB} \ge l_B$ follows directly from Theorems 7–12 and 7–16. The other half of the theorem is more complicated.

Let V_{l_B}, $V_{l_{AB}}$ be the null spaces of B, AB, respectively. Then $B(V_{l_B}) = \{o\}$; $AB(V_{l_{AB}}) = \{o\}$. Clearly, $V_{l_B} \subseteq V_{l_{AB}}$. Suppose that V_r is a complement of V_{l_B} in $V_{l_{AB}}$. Then $r = l_{AB} - l_B$. By the Lemma, $B(V_r) = V_r'$. Hence $AB(V_r) = A(V_r')$. But $AB(V_r) = \{o\}$. Hence $V_r' \subseteq V_{l_A}$. Therefore

$$l_A \ge r = l_{AB} - l_B, \quad \text{or} \quad l_{AB} \le l_A + l_B. \quad \square$$

PROBLEM SET 7–5

1. Give an example to show that in Theorem 7–17, the equal signs can be attained.

2. If A, B are $n \times n$ matrices with ranks r, s, respectively, prove that the rank of AB cannot be less than $r + s - n$.

* J. J. Sylvester, a 19th century British mathematician, was one of the developers of matrix theory.

7–6 NONSINGULAR MATRICES

We are now in a position to complete the discussion of nonsingular matrices, begun in Chapter 6, by proving that a left-nonsingular matrix is also right-nonsingular. We shall exploit the transformation theory to derive this result. As related results, we shall prove that the set of $n \times n$ nonsingular matrices forms a group, and we shall obtain an algorithm for finding the inverse of a matrix.

Theorem 7–18. Let A be a linear transformation from V_n to V'_m. The transform of any vector of V_n is determined by the transforms of a set of basis vectors of V_n.

Proof. Suppose that $\beta_1, \ldots, \beta_n$ form a basis of V_n, and that $\beta'_i = A \cdot \beta_i$, $i = 1, \ldots, n$. Then any vector ξ of V_n can be written as $\xi = \sum_1^n c_i \beta_i$. Hence $\xi' = A \cdot \xi = \sum_1^n c_i (A \cdot \beta_i) = \sum_1^n c_i \beta'_i$.

The next theorem is an immediate corollary of the preceding theorem.

Theorem 7–19. Let A be a linear transformation of V_n to itself which leaves fixed each vector of a basis. Then $A = I$.

Theorem 7–20. Let A be an $n \times n$ left-nonsingular matrix, transforming V_n into V'_n. Then A is also right-nonsingular.

Proof. Let B be a left inverse of A: $BA = I$. Let $\phi_1, \ldots, \phi_n$ be a basis for V_n, and let $\phi'_i = A \cdot \phi_i$, $i = 1, \ldots, n$. Note that $B \cdot \phi'_i = \phi_i$, $i = 1, \ldots, n$. We shall show that the ϕ'_i form an independent set. We proceed as follows.

Let us suppose that they do not; i.e., suppose that there are scalars, c_i, not all zero such that $\sum_1^n c_i \phi_i = o$. Then

$$B \cdot \sum_1^n c_i \phi_i = B \cdot o = o.$$

That is,

$$\sum_1^n c_i B \cdot \phi_i = o \qquad \text{or} \qquad \sum_1^n c_i \phi_i = o.$$

But this contradicts the independence of the ϕ_i. Thus A maps V_n onto V'_n, and $\phi'_1, \ldots, \phi'_n$ constitute a basis of V'_n. Consider AB. Since $B \cdot \phi'_i = \phi_i$,

$$AB \cdot \phi'_i = \phi'_i, \qquad i = 1, \ldots, n.$$

Hence, by Theorem 7–19, $AB = I$. In other words B, a left inverse of A, is also a right inverse of A.

Thus, as we predicted in Section 6–6, we can drop the adjectives "left" and "right," and refer to matrices as being singular or nonsingular.

Theorem 7–21. The set of all $n \times n$ nonsingular matrices is a group under multiplication.

Proof. We must verify that the axioms of a group are satisfied.

(i) The product of two nonsingular matrices is known to be non-singular (Theorem 6–10).
(ii) Multiplication of matrices is associative.
(iii) The matrix I is a (two-sided) identity.
(iv) A nonsingular matrix A has a (two-sided) inverse B, which is nonsingular because A is its inverse.

As was noted in the proof of Theorem 7–20, a nonsingular $n \times n$ matrix maps V_n onto V_n'; hence the rank of the matrix is n. Thus, by left-multiplication of A by an appropriate matrix E, a product of elementary matrices, we obtain a Hermite matrix (Theorem 7–9) which must be I, because its rank is also n. But this means that E is the inverse of A. We have, then, an algorithm for finding the inverse of a given nonsingular matrix, A.

Perform in succession the same elementary row transformations on I which are used to transform A to a Hermite matrix. The matrix E, thus obtained from I, is the inverse of A.

PROBLEM SET 7–6

1. Find the inverse of each of the following matrices:

(a) $\begin{bmatrix} 1 & 0 & -1 \\ 2 & 1 & 1 \\ 3 & 1 & 2 \end{bmatrix}$ (b) $\begin{bmatrix} 2 & 0 & 0 & 1 \\ -1 & 1 & 0 & 2 \\ 1 & 1 & 0 & 0 \\ 2 & 2 & 1 & 1 \end{bmatrix}$ (c) $\begin{bmatrix} 3 & 0 & 1 \\ -4 & -1 & 1 \\ 0 & -1 & 2 \end{bmatrix}.$

2. Obtain the inverses of the matrices of Problem 1 by performing elementary column transformations.

*3. Show that if A is nonsingular, A^t is also nonsingular, and that $(A^t)^{-1} = (A^{-1})^t$.

4. If the $n \times n$ matrix A is nonsingular, show that, for any $n \times n$ matrix B, the matrices AB, B, and BA all have the same rank.

5. Establish the truth or falsity of each of the following statements.
(a) If $BA = I$ and A is symmetric, then B is symmetric.
(b) If $BA = c \cdot I$, for some scalar c, and A is symmetric, then B is symmetric.
(c) If $BA = C$, and if A and C are symmetric, then B is symmetric.

6. Show, in several ways, that

$$\begin{bmatrix} 1 & 2 & -2 \\ -1 & 3 & 0 \\ 0 & -2 & 1 \end{bmatrix}$$

is nonsingular.

7. Given the matrices

$$A = \begin{bmatrix} 2 & -1 \\ 0 & 1 \end{bmatrix} \quad \text{and} \quad B = \begin{bmatrix} 1 & 0 \\ -1 & -1 \end{bmatrix},$$

find a matrix X such that $XA = B$, and a matrix Y such that $AY = B$.

8. If $AB = O$ show that $A = O$ or $B = O$ or both A and B are singular.

7–7 RATIONAL EQUIVALENCE OF MATRICES

Up to this point we have performed *either* row transformations *or* column transformations on a matrix. If we perform *both* types on a given matrix, we can reduce the matrix to diagonal form.

Theorem 7–22. An $n \times n$ matrix of rank $r > 0$ can be reduced by row *and* column transformations to the matrix

$$\overbrace{(n - r) \text{ columns}}$$

$$(n - r) \text{ rows} \begin{cases} \\ \\ \\ \\ \end{cases} \begin{bmatrix} & & & 0 & \dots & 0 \\ I_r & & & & & \\ & & & 0 & \dots & 0 \\ 0 & \dots & 0 & 0 & & 0 \\ \vdots & & & & & \\ 0 & \dots & 0 & 0 & & 0 \end{bmatrix},$$

abbreviated

$$\begin{bmatrix} I_r & 0 \\ 0 & 0 \end{bmatrix},$$

where I_r is the $r \times r$ identity matrix.

Proof. By row transformations the given matrix can be changed into a Hermite matrix. Column transformations can be used on the Hermite matrix to eliminate all nonzero terms below the principal diagonal. Rearrangement of rows and columns (effected by further elementary transformations) leads to the desired form.

We know that performing elementary row transformations on a matrix A has the same effect as left-multiplying A by a certain nonsingular matrix, and performing elementary column transformations on A has the same effect as right-multiplying A by a certain nonsingular matrix. Hence, we have the following alternative form of Theorem 7–22.

Theorem 7–23.   If A is an $n \times n$ matrix of rank $r > 0$, there are nonsingular $n \times n$ matrices, P and Q, such that

$$PAQ = \begin{bmatrix} I_r & 0 \\ 0 & 0 \end{bmatrix}.$$

Definition 8.   The matrix X is said to be *rationally equivalent* to the matrix Y if there exist nonsingular matrices M, N such that $X = MYN$.

Theorem 7–24.   "Rational equivalence" is an equivalence relation between matrices.

The proof is left as a problem (Problem 1 below). Because of Theorem 7–24, we are justified in replacing the statement "X is rationally equivalent to Y" by the statement "X and Y are rationally equivalent."

Theorem 7–25.   Two $n \times n$ matrices are rationally equivalent $\Leftrightarrow$ they have the same rank.

Proof.   "$\Rightarrow$." Use the definition of rational equivalence, Theorem 7–6, and Problem 2(a) of Section 7–3.

"$\Leftarrow$." If A and B have the same rank r, then each is rationally equivalent to the same matrix

$$\begin{bmatrix} I_r & 0 \\ 0 & 0 \end{bmatrix}.$$

Hence, by Theorem 7–24, A and B are rationally equivalent.

A transformation which is defined as a succession of elementary row and column transformations is called an *equivalence transformation*. Thus, if X and Y are any two rationally equivalent matrices, either can be transformed into the other by an equivalence transformation.

The $n \times n$ matrices

$$
\begin{bmatrix} 0 & \cdots & 0 \\ & & \\ \vdots & & \vdots \\ & & \\ 0 & \cdots & 0 \end{bmatrix}, \quad
\begin{bmatrix} 1 & 0 & \cdots & 0 \\ 0 & 0 & \cdots & 0 \\ \vdots & & & \vdots \\ 0 & \cdots & & 0 \end{bmatrix},
$$

$$
\begin{bmatrix} 1 & 0 & 0 & \cdots & 0 \\ 0 & 1 & 0 & \cdots & 0 \\ 0 & 0 & 0 & \cdots & 0 \\ \vdots & & & & \vdots \\ 0 & & \cdots & & 0 \end{bmatrix} \cdots
\begin{bmatrix} 1 & 0 & 0 & \cdots & 0 \\ 0 & 1 & 0 & \cdots & 0 \\ 0 & 0 & 1 & \cdots & 0 \\ \vdots & & & \ddots & \vdots \\ 0 & & \cdots & & 1 \end{bmatrix}
$$

are *canonical forms under equivalence transformations* in the sense that any given $n \times n$ matrix can be reduced to one, and to only one, of these matrices by equivalence transformations. Under equivalence transformations, the matrix

$$
\begin{bmatrix} I_r & 0 \\ 0 & 0 \end{bmatrix}
$$

is a representative of the set of all $n \times n$ matrices of rank r, just as, under congruence modulo 5, the number 2 is a representative of the set $\{2, 7, 12, 17, \ldots\}$.

PROBLEM SET 7–7

1. Prove Theorem 7–24. [*Hint:* Can you find M, N, such that $X = MXN$? If $X = PYQ$, then $Y = ? \ldots$.]

2. Reduce

$$
A = \begin{bmatrix} 4 & 3 & 2 \\ 6 & 0 & 1 \\ 2 & 6 & 3 \end{bmatrix}
$$

to canonical form by equivalence transformation. Find P, Q such that

$$
PAQ = \begin{bmatrix} I_r & 0 \\ 0 & 0 \end{bmatrix}.
$$

Are P and Q unique?

3. Find the most general matrix which commutes under multiplication with all $n \times n$ matrices; i.e., what is the most general form of A if $AX = XA$ for all X?

4. Let A be an $n \times n$ matrix whose elements are integers. Let elementary row and column transformations be

(i) an interchange of two rows, or of two columns;

(ii) a multiplication of a row, or column, by -1;

(iii) addition of one row, or column, to another (different) row, or column.

Prove that A can be reduced by these transformations to a matrix with nonnegative integers (not necessarily 1's) along the principal diagonal, and zeros elsewhere. Prove further that this reduction can be carried out so that each diagonal term divides the next.

5. (a) If A is an $n \times n$ matrix, list as many statements as you can, each of which is logically equivalent to the statement, "The row rank of A is r."

(b) Same as (a) for, "The row rank of A is n."

7-8 SOLUTION OF A SYSTEM OF NONHOMOGENEOUS LINEAR EQUATIONS

We have satisfactorily completed the analysis of solutions of systems of homogeneous linear equations. If $A \cdot \xi = o$, where A is an $m \times n$ matrix of rank r, then the values of some $(n - r)$ of the x's can be assigned arbitrarily, and the remaining r of the x's will be uniquely determined in terms of the arbitrary ones. Moreover, we have a procedure (reduction of A to a Hermite matrix) to obtain an explicit expression for the solutions.

For nonhomogeneous equations, we have a procedure, as described on p. 174, to find solutions, but we do not yet have a theorem which tells us, in terms of the rank of a matrix, whether solutions exist. We can easily obtain such a theorem.

Remember that, on p. 174, we analyzed

$$A \cdot \xi = \beta \tag{1}$$

by considering instead

$$
\begin{bmatrix}
b_1 & a_{11} & \cdots & a_{1n} \\
b_2 & a_{21} & \cdots & a_{2n} \\
\vdots & & & \vdots \\
b_m & a_{m1} & \cdots & a_{mn}
\end{bmatrix}
\cdot
\begin{bmatrix}
x_0 \\
x_1 \\
\vdots \\
x_n
\end{bmatrix}
=
\begin{bmatrix}
0 \\
0 \\
\vdots \\
0
\end{bmatrix},
\tag{2}
$$

and we sought the solutions of Eqs. (2) for which $x_0 = -1$.

In standard terminology, A is called the *coefficient matrix* of Eq. (1) and

$$\begin{bmatrix} b_1 & a_{11} & \cdots & a_{1n} \\ b_2 & a_{21} & \cdots & a_{2n} \\ \vdots & & & \vdots \\ b_m & a_{m1} & \cdots & a_{mn} \end{bmatrix}$$

is called the *augmented matrix*.

Now, if there *is* a solution of Eqs. (2) of the required type, then $\beta = x_1 \cdot \tilde{\alpha}_1 + x_2 \cdot \tilde{\alpha}_2 + \cdots + x_n \cdot \tilde{\alpha}_n$, where $\beta = (b_1, \ldots, b_m)$ and $\tilde{\alpha}_i$ is the ith column vector of A. In other words, β is linearly dependent on the $\tilde{\alpha}$'s. Thus, if a solution of Eqs. (2) exists, the rank of the augmented matrix equals the rank of A.

Conversely, if the rank of the augmented matrix equals the rank of A, then β lies in the vector space spanned by the column vectors of A. Hence β can be written as a linear combination of the $\tilde{\alpha}$'s, which implies the existence of a solution of Eqs. (2) of the required type. Thus, we have proved the following theorem.

Theorem 7–26. A necessary and sufficient condition for the existence of a solution of a system of nonhomogeneous linear equations is that the rank of the augmented matrix equal the rank of the coefficient matrix.

We can prove (Problem 2 below) that if the common value of the rank in Theorem 7–26 is r, there are $(n - r + 1)$ linearly independent solutions of the nonhomogeneous system.

PROBLEM SET 7–8

1. Solve

$$\begin{aligned} x_1 - 2x_2 + x_3 &= 1, \\ x_1 \qquad - x_3 + 3x_4 &= -1, \\ 2x_2 - 2x_3 + 3x_4 &= -2, \\ 3x_1 - 4x_2 + x_3 + 3x_4 &= 1, \end{aligned}$$

and verify that there are $n - r + 1$ linearly independent solutions.

2. Prove that $A \cdot \xi = \beta$ has $n - r + 1$ linearly independent solutions if the rank of the augmented matrix equals r. [*Hint:* Use Problem 11, Section 7–2.]

3. Prove that if H is a Hermite matrix, $H^2 = H$.

4. (a) A matrix M such that $AMA = A$ is called a "pseudo-inverse of A." (If A is nonsingular, clearly $M = A^{-1}$.) Show that the matrix E of Theorem 7–9 is a pseudo-inverse of A. [*Hint:* Use Problem 3 above.]

(b) If $A\xi = \beta$ is a consistent system of linear equations, and M is a pseudo-inverse of A, show that $M\beta$ is a solution vector of the set of equations.

(c) If $A\xi = o$ has a nontrivial solution, and if M is a pseudo-inverse of A, show that $\xi = (I - MA)\beta$, β arbitrary, is a solution. (R. D. Sheffield, *Amer. Math. Monthly*, 1958.)

7-9 A GENERAL DEFINITION OF LINEAR TRANSFORMATIONS

In Section 4-9 mention was made of a definition for a vector space more general than the definition involving ordered n-tuples. Likewise, we may define a linear transformation (of one projective space to a second, or of one vector space to a second) more generally than by means of a system of linear equations, or equivalently, in terms of a matrix.

We know that if α, β are any two vectors of $V_n(\mathfrak{F})$, and if M is an $m \times n$ matrix over $\mathfrak{F}$, then

$$M \cdot (c_1\alpha + c_2\beta) = c_1 M \cdot \alpha + c_2 M \cdot \beta,$$

for all scalars c_1, c_2. Alternatively, using the notation of Section 7-4, we can write

$$M(c_1\alpha + c_2\beta) = c_1 M(\alpha) + c_2 M(\beta). \tag{1}$$

We can use Eq. (1) to *define* a linear transformation of $V_n(\mathfrak{F})$ into $V_m(\mathfrak{F})$. It turns out that the same happy state of affairs exists here as was true in Section 1-9: Just as the "more general" vector spaces of n dimensions are isomorphic to our $V_n(\mathfrak{F})$, so likewise the set of "more general" linear transformations just defined can be put into one-to-one correspondence with the set of $m \times n$ matrices over $\mathfrak{F}$. Thus, in studying matrices we are studying "all" linear transformations from one vector space to another.

PROBLEM SET 7-9

1. Show that the defining equation (1) is equivalent to the following two equations characterizing linear transformations.

(a) For all ξ, η, $T(\xi + \eta) = T(\xi) + T(\eta)$
(b) For all ξ, c, $T(c \cdot \xi) = cT(\xi)$

2. Let S be a transformation from $V_n(C)$ to itself, and let $S^2(\alpha)$ be an abbreviation for $S[S(\alpha)]$. Suppose that S has the following properties:

(a) for all ξ, η, $S(\xi + \eta) = S(\xi) + S(\eta)$;
(b) for all ξ, k, $S(k \cdot \xi) = \bar{k} \cdot S(\xi)$, where $\bar{k}$ is the conjugate of k; and
(c) for all ξ, $S^2(\xi) = \xi$.

Show that there exist n linearly independent vectors $\gamma_1, \gamma_2, \ldots, \gamma_n$ in $V_n(C)$ such that $S(\gamma_i) = \gamma_i$, $i = 1, 2, \ldots, n$.

7–10 THE ADJOINT OF A MATRIX

In Section 7–6, we learned how to obtain the inverse of a given non-singular matrix. It is useful to approach the same problem differently; i.e., by way of the adjoint of a matrix. The adjoint will *not* lead us to a more effective way of computing the inverse of a given matrix, but it has important theoretical uses. Moreover, the adjoint of A exists even when A is singular.

The terms *minor* of an element of a matrix and *cofactor* of an element of a matrix are introduced in Appendix 3.

Definition 9. If $A = [a_{ij}]$ is an $n \times n$ matrix, and if A_{ij} is the co-factor of a_{ij}, then the *adjoint* of A is the $n \times n$ matrix which has A_{ji} as the element in its ith row and jth column,

$$A_{\mathrm{adj}} = [A_{ji}].$$

As is shown in Appendix 2, $\sum_{k=1}^{n} a_{ik}A_{ik} = \det A$, for each i, and $\sum_{k=1}^{n} a_{ik}A_{jk} = 0$, for $i \neq j$. For short, we can write

$$\sum_{k=1}^{n} a_{ik}A_{jk} = (\det A) \cdot \delta_{ij}.$$

Hence

$$A \cdot A_{\mathrm{adj}} = [\det A \cdot \delta_{ij}] = \det A \cdot [\delta_{ij}] = (\det A)I.$$

Likewise,

$$\sum_{k=1}^{n} a_{kj}A_{ki} = (\det A) \cdot \delta_{ji},$$

so that

$$A_{\mathrm{adj}} \cdot A = (\det A)I.$$

Thus, if A is nonsingular,

$$\frac{1}{\det A} A_{\mathrm{adj}} = A^{-1}.$$

EXAMPLE.   If

$$M = \begin{bmatrix} p & q \\ r & s \end{bmatrix}, \quad \text{then} \quad M_{\mathrm{adj}} = \begin{bmatrix} s & -q \\ -r & p \end{bmatrix}.$$

$$M \cdot M_{\mathrm{adj}} = \begin{bmatrix} ps - qr & 0 \\ 0 & ps - qr \end{bmatrix} = (ps - qr)I = \Delta I,$$

where $\Delta = \det M$.

PROBLEM SET 7–10

*1. (a) Show that if A and B are 2×2 matrices,

$$(hA + kB)_{\text{adj}} = hA_{\text{adj}} + kB_{\text{adj}},$$

for any scalars h, k.

(b) Show by an example that the equality of part (a) does not hold for all $n > 2$.

2. Let A, B be 3×3 matrices, with $\det A = \Delta_1$, $\det B = \Delta_2$.

(a) Show that for all scalars h, k, $(hA + kB)_{\text{adj}} = h^2 A_{\text{adj}} + hkC + k^2 B_{\text{adj}}$, and that $(hA_{\text{adj}} + kB_{\text{adj}})_{\text{adj}} = h^2 \Delta_1 A + hk\, D + k^2 \Delta_2 B$, for some matrices C, D.

(b) Find C, D of part (a) if $A = I$ and

$$B = \begin{bmatrix} b_0 & 0 & 0 \\ 0 & b_1 & 0 \\ 0 & 0 & b_2 \end{bmatrix}.$$

(c) Find C of part (a) if

$$A = \begin{bmatrix} a_0 & 0 & 0 \\ 0 & a_1 & 0 \\ 0 & 0 & a_2 \end{bmatrix} \quad \text{and} \quad B = \begin{bmatrix} 0 & b_2 & b_1 \\ b_2 & 0 & b_0 \\ b_1 & b_0 & 0 \end{bmatrix}.$$

Verify in this case that $A \cdot C + B \cdot A_{\text{adj}} = O$. (This problem appears in the study of invariants of pairs of conics.)

*3. *Definition.* A square matrix M is *skew-symmetric* if $M^t = -M$.

It is clear from this definition that all the elements of the main diagonal of a skew-symmetric matrix are zero.

Prove that any square matrix can be written as the sum of a symmetric matrix and a skew symmetric matrix. [*Hint:* If the given matrix A is to be written as $A = X + Y$, where X is symmetric and Y is skew-symmetric, then $A^t = \ldots$.] Indeed, you will see that the representation is unique.

4. Let M be an $n \times n$ skew-symmetric matrix.

(a) Prove that M is singular if n is odd.

(b) Prove that M_{adj} is symmetric if n is odd.

(c) Prove that M_{adj} is skew-symmetric if n is even and M is nonsingular (this is easy).

(d) Prove that M_{adj} is skew-symmetric if n is even (whether or not M is singular).

[*Hint:* If $M = [m_{ij}]$, define $M(x) = [m_{ij}(x)]$ as follows.

$$m_{21}(x) = m_{21} + x; \qquad m_{12}(x) = m_{12} - x; \qquad m_{ij}(x) = m_{ij}$$

for all other i, j. Then $M(x)$ is skew-symmetric. For all sufficiently large x, $M(x)$ is nonsingular. Hence, by (c), for all sufficiently large x, $M(x)_{\text{adj}}$ is skew-symmetric . . . .]

CHAPTER 8

Projective Geometry in One and Two Dimensions

The introduction to projectivities contained in Chapter 6 will now be developed for one-dimensional projectivities, that is, projectivities of an S_1 to an S_1'. In some cases it will be necessary that the S_1 and the S_1' be embedded in an S_2; in some other cases the S_1' will be the same as the S_1, that is, the projectivities will be from an S_1 to itself. Often it will be natural to formulate the discussion immediately in terms of S_n's. Occasionally attention will be focused upon the closely related concept of cross ratio, rather than upon projectivities as such.

We must remember that because of the abstract nature of a linear projective space, figures can play no essential role in proof; we rely entirely on algebraic methods. Although matrix notation is not really much help in the one-dimensional case, we shall use it here in preparation for the projective geometry of higher dimensions where it, or some such condensed notation, is essential.

8–1 DEFINITIONS AND NOTATION

(i) A proper projectivity from S_1 to S_1' in which the points A, B, C, ... of S_1 correspond respectively to the points A', B', C', ... of S_1' may be designated as

$$(A, B, C, \ldots) \wedge (A', B', C', \ldots).$$

(ii) If the S_1, S_1' of (i) are lines l, l', respectively, each line is sometimes called a *range of points*, and the projectivity of (i) may be denoted as $l \wedge l'$.

(iii) If the projectivity of (i) is a perspectivity, with center of perspective O, the following symbolism is sometimes used:

$$(A, B, C, \ldots) \overset{O}{\wedge} (A', B', C', \ldots),$$

or

$$l \overset{O}{\wedge} l'.$$

(iv) If the lines VA, VB, ... of the pencil with vertex V correspond in a projectivity with the lines $V'A'$, $V'B'$, ... of the pencil with vertex V', we write $V(A, B, \ldots) \wedge V'(A', B', \ldots)$.

If two projective pencils are perspective (Problem 5(a), Section 6–2), the line on which corresponding lines of the two pencils meet is called the *axis of perspective*.

(v) If the two pencils of (iv) are perspective, with axis of perspective p, we may write $V(A, B, \ldots) \overset{p}{\wedge} V'(A', B', \ldots)$, or more briefly, $V \overset{p}{\wedge} V'$.

We may speak of *perspectivity* in an intuitive sense, without using a precise definition. For example, in Fig. 5–16, of two triangles in the relationship of Desargues, mathematicians sometimes refer to triangles ABC and $A'B'C'$ as being *in perspective from the point X*, or alternatively, to the triangles with sides AB, BC, CA, and $A'B'$, $B'C'$, $C'A'$ as being *in perspective from the line LMN*.

(vi) We may have a projectivity (i.e., a linear transformation) relating the *points* of a range to the *lines* of a pencil.

For example, in Fig. 8–1, there is clearly a one-to-one, cross-ratio-preserving transformation which takes A, B, C, D, ... into PA, PB, PC, PD, ... We can symbolize this projectivity as

$$(A, B, C, D, \ldots) \wedge P(A, B, C, D, \ldots).$$

A particularly important type of projectivity from several points of view is that in which the range of the transformation coincides with its

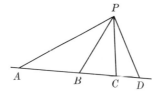

FIGURE 8–1

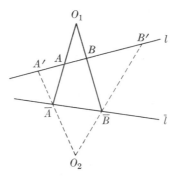

FIGURE 8–2

domain, i.e., a projectivity of the points of S_n onto the points of the same S_n. Such a projectivity is called a *collineation* of the S_n.

We can visualize a collineation of a line l as a succession of two perspectivities: $l \overset{O_1}{\wedge} \bar{l} \overset{O_2}{\wedge} l$ (Fig. 8–2). This process entails the embedding of l into an S_2. But the collineation may be expressed algebraically without reference to an S_2: if we choose a coordinate system on l, then the correspondent of any point (x_0, x_1) is the point (x_0', x_1') where

$$ k \begin{bmatrix} x_0' \\ x_1' \end{bmatrix} = A \begin{bmatrix} x_0 \\ x_1 \end{bmatrix}, \tag{1} $$

A being a nonsingular 2×2 matrix.

Literally the word "collineation" refers to a transformation which takes collinear points into collinear points, and this is true of any proper projectivity of the points of S_n to those of S_n'. Some authors thus use the term "collineation" as a synonym for "proper projectivity," but we shall reserve "collineation" for those projectivities in which $S_n' = S_n$. Note that if $S_m \subset S_n$, a collineation of S_n is *not* necessarily also a collineation of S_m.

Collineations are to be contrasted with *correlations*. A correlation is a proper projectivity of the *points* of S_n to the hyperplanes of the same S_n. If ξ, with components $x_0, \ldots, x_n$, is the coordinate vector of a point of S_n, and if ω, with components $w_0, \ldots, w_n$, is the coordinate vector of a related hyperplane, then the equation of a correlation is $k\omega = B \cdot \xi$, where B is an $(n + 1) \times (n + 1)$ matrix. We shall have occasion to study collineations and correlations in some detail in subsequent chapters, but a little more must be said now.

A collineation of S_n, defined as a transformation of points, incidentally carries hyperplanes into hyperplanes. However, the matrix which expresses the point transformation is different from that which expresses the hyperplane transformation. The relation between the matrices is an important one.

Suppose that, relative to a certain coordinate frame, a collineation in S_n is characterized as the point transformation

$$k\xi' = A \cdot \xi.$$

If the point with coordinate vector ξ lies in the hyperplane with coordinate vector π, so that $\pi^t \cdot \xi = o$ (remember that π may be interpreted either as a vector or as a column matrix), then the transformed point, with coordinate vector ξ', will lie in the transformed hyperplane, with coordinate vector π', so that $(\pi')^t \cdot \xi' = o$. Thus

$$(\pi')^t \cdot \left(\frac{1}{k} A \cdot \xi\right) = o \quad \text{or} \quad \left[(\pi')^t \frac{1}{k} A\right] \cdot \xi = o.$$

Hence $\pi^t = k'(\pi')^t A$, or $k'(\pi')^t = \pi^t \cdot A^{-1}$. Here π^t and $(\pi')^t$ are row matrices; in terms of column matrices, the last equation becomes

$$k'\pi' = (A^{-1})^t \cdot \pi. \tag{2}$$

Similar remarks apply to correlations. If, relative to a certain coordinate frame, a correlation transforms a point with coordinate vector ξ into a hyperplane with coordinate vector ω according to the formula

$$k\omega = B\xi, \tag{3}$$

then an argument quite like the preceding one shows that the correlation carries the hyperplane with coordinate vector α into the point with coordinate vector η according to the formula

$$k'\eta = (B^{-1})^t \cdot \alpha. \tag{4}$$

It is useful to think of the correlation as a transformation T which carries points *and* hyperplanes into hyperplanes *and* points. With this viewpoint one can think of T as being a transformation of a certain set (points and hyperplanes onto itself). We shall return to this concept in Problem 16 of Section 8–8.

PROBLEM SET 8–1

1. (a) Given points A, B of line l corresponding in a perspectivity with A', B' of l'. Show how to find geometrically the point X' of l' corresponding to an arbitrary point X of l.
(b) The dual of (a).

2. (a) For the set of all lines of a plane, consider the relation of projective correspondence between the points of any pair of them. Is this an equivalence relation?

(b) Same for perspective correspondence.

3. (a) Let $A(1, 2)$, $B(-1, 1)$, $M(0, 1)$ of line l correspond, respectively, to $A'(1, 0)$, $B'(1, 1)$, $M(2, 1)$ of line l'. Find the matrix of the perspectivity determined by this correspondence.

(b) In S_2, let four points have the following coordinates: $A(1, 1, -2)$, $B(1, 0, 1)$, $A'(0, 1, 1)$, $B'(2, 1, 4)$. The correspondence $A \leftrightarrow A'$, $B \leftrightarrow B'$ determines a perspectivity between the ranges AB, $A'B'$. Find in three ways the coordinates of C' on line $A'B'$ corresponding, in this perspectivity, to $C(2, 1, -1)$ of AB:

(i) by finding the center of perspective;

(ii) by expressing the coordinate vector of C as a linear combination of the coordinate vectors of A and B;

(iii) by finding the point D common to the ranges AB and $A'B'$, and then setting $(AB, CD) = (A'B', C'D)$.

*4. A point which corresponds to itself in a collineation is called a *fixed point of the collineation.*

(a) Prove that if a collineation in S_1 has more than two fixed points, then it is the identity transformation. [*Hint:* Use Theorem 6-3.]

(b) Find, geometrically, the fixed points of the collineation of l shown in Fig. 8-2.

(c) Use Eq. (1) to decide under what circumstances a collineation in S_1 has two fixed points; one fixed point; no fixed points.

5. (a) Formulate a statement analogous to that of Problem 4(a) above about the number of fixed points of a collineation in S_2 (cf. Theorem 6-8).

(b) For the collineation

$$kx'_0 = x_0, \quad kx'_1 = 2x_1, \quad kx'_2 = x_1 + x_2,$$

find the transforms of $(1, 0, 0)$, $(0, 1, 0)$, $(0, 0, 1)$, $(1, 0, 1)$, $(2, 0, 1)$, $(0, 1, 1)$, and $(0, 2, 1)$.

(c) With (or without) the help of your answer to (b), list all the fixed points of the collineation in (b).

(d) Is your answer to (c) in harmony with the statement you formulated in (a)?

8-2 PAPPUS' THEOREM

We can now prove a theorem of fundamental importance, due to Pappus of Alexandria, 4th century A.D. (cf. Problem 15(a), Section 1-2).

Theorem 8-1. If the points of two ranges in a plane are projectively related, then the points of intersection of lines joining pairs of corresponding points crosswise are collinear; i.e., if

$$(A, B, C, \ldots) \wedge (A', B', C', \ldots),$$

then the points of intersection of AB' and $A'B$, of AC' and $A'C$, $\ldots$, of BC' and $B'C$, $\ldots$ are collinear.

[*Note:* The line on which these points lie is called the *Pappus line* or the *cross axis* of the projectivity.]

It will be instructive to consider two proofs of this theorem.

Proof 1.   Consider the pencils AA', AB', AC', $\ldots$ and $A'A$, $A'B$, $A'C$, $\ldots$. These pencils are projective, for

$$A(A', B', C', \ldots) \wedge (A', B', C', \ldots) \wedge (A, B, C, \ldots) \wedge A'(A, B, C, \ldots).$$

Moreover, the pencils are perspective, for the common line AA' is self-corresponding (Problem 11, Section 6–3). Hence, the points of intersection of corresponding lines are collinear; i.e., AB' and $A'B$, AC' and $A'C$, $\ldots$, meet in collinear points. Likewise, the similar pencils with vertices B and B' are perspective, so that BA' and $B'A$, BC' and $B'C$, $\ldots$ meet in collinear points. It is our problem to show that the two lines so determined (i.e., the axis of perspective of the pencils with vertices A and A', and the axis of perspective of the pencils with vertices B and B') are the same line, the desired cross axis of the projectivity. To do this, we distinguish two cases.

Case 1.   If the given projectivity is *not* a perspectivity, then the point of intersection of the two ranges, l: A, B, C, $\ldots$, and l': A', B', C', $\ldots$, is *not* self-corresponding. Suppose that the common point, thought of as a point of l, is called M, with a corresponding point M' on l' while the same common point, thought of as a point of l' is called N', with a correspondent N on l. The axis of perspective of the pencils with vertices A, A' goes

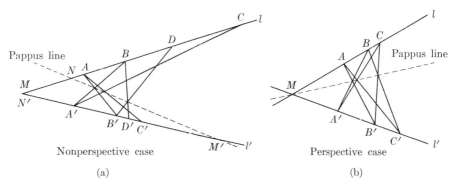

Nonperspective case   Perspective case

(a)   (b)

FIGURE 8–3

through M' and N; likewise for the pencils with vertices B, B' or, indeed, with any pair of corresponding points of the given projectivity as vertices. Since two points determine a line, we have the desired result.

Case 2.   If the given projectivity *is* a perspectivity, then the axis of perspective of the pencils with vertices A, A' passes through the following two points: the point of intersection of l and l', and the point of intersection of AB' and $A'B$. Likewise, the axis of perspective of the pencils with vertices B, B' passes through the same two points. This completes the first proof.

Proof 2.   Let A, B, C on l correspond, respectively, to A', B', C' on l'. Choose a two-dimensional coordinate system for the plane and designate coordinate vectors by α, β, γ; α', β', γ'. Since C is collinear with A and B, γ is a linear combination of α and β; choose α and β so that $\gamma = \alpha + \beta$. Likewise, choose α' and β' so that $\gamma' = \alpha' + \beta'$. The equation of AB' can be written in terms of a determinant as

$$\begin{vmatrix} x_0 & a_0 & b'_0 \\ x_1 & a_1 & b'_1 \\ x_2 & a_2 & b'_2 \end{vmatrix} = 0, \tag{1}$$

which we shall abbreviate as $|\xi\alpha\beta'| = 0$.

Using similar abbreviations, we can write the equation of $A'B$ as

$$|\xi\alpha'\beta| = 0; \tag{2}$$

the equation of AC' as

$$|\xi\alpha\alpha'| + |\xi\alpha\beta'| = 0; \tag{3}$$

the equation of $A'C$ as

$$|\xi\alpha'\alpha| + |\xi\alpha'\beta| = 0; \tag{4}$$

the equation of BC' as

$$|\xi\beta\alpha'| + |\xi\beta\beta'| = 0; \tag{5}$$

the equation of $B'C$ as

$$|\xi\beta'\alpha| + |\xi\beta'\beta| = 0. \tag{6}$$

Suppose that $A'B$ and AB' meet at L, with coordinate vector λ. Then λ satisfies Eqs. (1) and (2). Likewise, if $A'C$ and AC' meet at M, with coordinate vector μ, then μ satisfies Eqs. (3) and (4); and, if $B'C$ and BC' meet at N, with coordinate vector ν, then ν satisfies Eqs. (5) and (6).

We are to show that L, M, N are collinear. If we add (1) and (2), or (3) and (4), or (5) and (6), we get

$$|\xi\alpha\beta'| + |\xi\alpha'\beta| = 0. \tag{7}$$

Each of λ, μ, ν satisfies (7). Thus (7) is the equation of the Pappus line.

From Proof 1 we see that in the nonperspective case, we can characterize the cross axis as the line joining the two points corresponding to the common point of the two ranges. We shall shortly prove that in the perspective case, the cross axis can be characterized in terms of a certain cross ratio (Problem 10, Section 8–3).

PROBLEM SET 8–2

1. Fill in the missing details of Proof 2.

2. Use Pappus' theorem to obtain an alternative solution of Problem 8, Section 6–3.

3. (a) State the plane dual of Pappus' theorem.

(b) Use the dual to obtain an alternative solution of Problem 9, Section 6–3.

(c) Use the dual to prove that if for triangles ABC and DEF, AD, BE, CF are concurrent and also AE, BF, CD are concurrent, then AF, BD, CE are concurrent; i.e., that "two triangles which are doubly perspective are triply perspective."

4. (a) Given three points A, B, C on line l, and three other points A', B', C' on l', how many different one-to-one correspondences are possible involving these two sets of three points?

(b) Each of the correspondences of part (a) gives rise to a Pappus line. Draw a figure picturing all the Pappus lines which can arise from two sets of three collinear points; then formulate and prove a statement about these lines. [*Hint:* For the proof, use the method of Proof 2.]

8–3 CROSS RATIO AND HARMONIC DIVISION

To make further use of the concept of cross ratio, we first derive an expression for the cross ratio of four collinear points, each of which is expressed as a linear combination of two particular points.

Suppose that the collinear points A, B, C, D, E, F have coordinate vectors α, β, γ, δ, ϵ, ϕ, respectively, with $\gamma = h_1\alpha + k_1\beta$, $\delta = h_2\alpha + k_2\beta$, $\epsilon = h_3\alpha + k_3\beta$, and $\phi = h_4\alpha + k_4\beta$. Then, from Definition 1 of Section 6–2, we can obtain (Problem 1 below):

$$(CD, EF) = \frac{\begin{vmatrix} h_3 & h_1 \\ k_3 & k_1 \end{vmatrix}}{\begin{vmatrix} h_3 & h_2 \\ k_3 & k_2 \end{vmatrix}} \cdot \frac{\begin{vmatrix} h_4 & h_2 \\ k_4 & k_2 \end{vmatrix}}{\begin{vmatrix} h_4 & h_1 \\ k_4 & k_1 \end{vmatrix}}. \tag{1}$$

It follows directly from Eq. (1) that

$$(CD, EF) = (DC, FE) = (EF, CD) = (FE, DC). \tag{2}$$

Among the $4! = 24$ permutations of 4 elements, there are, then, at most, 6 distinct cross ratios (cf. Problem 4 of Section 6–1). Using the definition of cross ratio, we find that if $(XY, ZW) = r$, then $(XY, WZ) = 1/r$; $(XZ, YW) = 1 - r$; $(XZ, WY) = 1/(1 - r)$; $(XW, YZ) = 1 - (1/r)$; and $(XW, ZY) = r/(r - 1)$.

It is possible that there may be fewer than 6 distinct numbers in this set.

(a) If $r = 1/r$, then $r = \pm 1$.

(i) If $r = 1$, then the only other value among the cross ratios is 0. (Two of the expressions are undefined in this case.) This will happen if and only if two of the four elements coincide.

(ii) If $r = -1$, the only other values of the cross ratio are 2 and $\frac{1}{2}$. In this case, $(XY, ZW) = (XY, WZ)$. Standard terminology is "Z and W divide X and Y harmonically" or "X, Y, Z, W form a harmonic set" or "W is the fourth harmonic element of the set X, Y, Z" or "W is the harmonic conjugate of Z with respect to X and Y." Clearly, if Z and W divide X and Y harmonically, then W and Z also divide X and Y harmonically; and furthermore, X and Y (and Y and X) divide Z and W harmonically.

(b) If $r = 1/(1 - r)$, then r is an imaginary cube root of -1, and the only other value among the cross ratios is the other imaginary cube root of -1. In this case, $X, Y, Z,$ and W are said to form an *equianharmonic set*.

The significance of harmonic sets will be illustrated geometrically now; equianharmonic sets also have a geometric interpretation, which we shall not study here.*

The concept of harmonic division is related fundamentally to the complete quadrangle and the complete quadrilateral in the following manner. Let A, B, C, D be the vertices of a complete quadrangle, with diagonal points P, Q, R (see Fig. 8–4). Suppose that PR meets AB in S. Then it can be shown that S is the harmonic conjugate of Q with respect to A and B, i.e., $(AB, QS) = -1$.

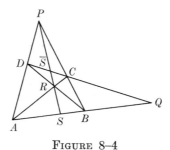

FIGURE 8–4

---

* See Todd, *Projective and Analytical Geometry*, listed in Bibliography.

We shall derive this result in two ways.

(1) Suppose that PR meets CD in $\bar{S}$. Then $(A, B, Q, S) \overset{P}{\wedge} (D, C, Q, \bar{S})$ $\overset{R}{\wedge} (B, A, Q, S)$. Hence $(AB, QS) = (BA, QS)$. Since the elements are distinct, this implies that $(AB, QS) = -1$.

(2) Let α, β, γ, δ be coordinate vectors of A, B, C, D in a two-dimensional coordinate frame. These vectors form a linearly dependent set:

$$k_1\alpha + k_2\beta + k_3\gamma + k_4\delta = o.$$

Since no three of the points are collinear, none of the k's is zero. For simplicity, we may choose new coordinate vectors for A, B, C, D:

$$\alpha' = k_1\alpha, \qquad \beta' = k_2\beta, \qquad \gamma' = k_3\gamma, \qquad \delta' = k_4\delta,$$

so that we have

$$\alpha' + \beta' + \gamma' + \delta' = o.$$

The equation $\alpha' + \beta' = -(\gamma' + \delta')$ states that a certain linear combination of the coordinates of A and B equals a certain linear combination of the coordinates of C and D. This means that Q has coordinates $\alpha' + \beta'$ [or, alternatively, $-(\gamma' + \delta')$]. Likewise, $\alpha' + \delta' = -(\beta' + \gamma')$ implies that P has coordinates $\alpha' + \delta'$ or, $-(\beta' + \gamma')$. Finally, $\beta' + \delta' = -(\alpha' + \gamma')$ implies that R has coordinates $\beta' + \delta'$ or, $-(\alpha' + \gamma')$. Let us use $\alpha' + \beta'$ as coordinate vector of Q; $\alpha' + \delta'$, of P; and $\beta' + \delta'$, of R. Since S lies on PR, its coordinates must be expressible as a linear combination of those of P and R; i.e., for some k, l,

$$\sigma = k(\alpha' + \delta') + l(\beta' + \delta') = k\alpha' + l\beta' + (k + l)\delta'.$$

But S also lies on AB; hence σ must be expressible as a linear combination of α' and β' alone. Thus we must have $k + l = 0$, so that $\sigma = k\alpha' - k\beta'$. From the definition of cross ratio, we have $(AB, QS) = -1$.

We have thus given two proofs of the following theorem.

Theorem 8-2. Two vertices of a complete quadrangle are separated harmonically by the diagonal point on their side and the point in which their side is met by the line joining the other two diagonal points.

As a consequence of this theorem, we see that the lines PA, PB, PQ, and PS (Fig. 8-4) form a harmonic set. Hence, we have another theorem.

Theorem 8-3. Two opposite sides of a complete quadrangle are separated harmonically by the lines joining their point of intersection to the other two diagonal points.

From Theorem 8–3, we observe still another result—that R and Q are separated harmonically by the points in which RQ meets AD and BC. Thus we have a third theorem.

Theorem 8–4. Two diagonal points of a complete quadrangle are separated harmonically by the points in which their line is met by the sides of the quadrangle passing through the third diagonal point.

PROBLEM SET 8–3

1. Obtain Eq. (1) for the cross ratio of four elements in a given order.

2. Obtain Eqs. (2).

3. Verify that the six possible values of the cross ratio of four elements are r, $1/r$, $1 - r$, $1/(1 - r)$, $1 - (1/r)$, $r/(r - 1)$.

4. Show that the value 1 will appear as a cross ratio if and only if two of the four elements coincide.

5. Verify the first sentence of (b) of this section.

6. Show that if A_0, A_1, D, X have, respectively, coordinates $(1, 0)$, $(0, 1)$, $(1, 1)$, (x_0, x_1), then $(A_0A_1, XD) = x_1/x_0$.

7. Let X, Y, Z, and W have, respectively, the one-dimensional coordinates (x_0, x_1), (y_0, y_1), (z_0, z_1), (w_0, w_1); show that

$$(XY, ZW) = \frac{\begin{vmatrix} z_0 & x_0 \\ z_1 & x_1 \end{vmatrix} \begin{vmatrix} w_0 & y_0 \\ w_1 & y_1 \end{vmatrix}}{\begin{vmatrix} z_0 & y_0 \\ z_1 & x_1 \end{vmatrix} \begin{vmatrix} w_0 & x_0 \\ w_1 & x_1 \end{vmatrix}}.$$

[*Hint:* To apply Eq. (1) most simply, express the coordinate vectors of each of X, Y, Z, and W as linear combinations of ?.]

*8. (a) Let the collinear points A, B, C, and D have coordinate vectors α, β, $\gamma = \alpha + k\beta$, $\delta = \alpha + k'\beta$, and show that $(AB, CD) = k/k'$.

(b) Show that if $(AB, CD) = g$, with coordinate vectors of A, B, and D being α, β, $h\alpha + k\beta$, then a coordinate vector of C can be written $\gamma = h\alpha + gk\beta$.

(c) Show that a necessary and sufficient condition that the point with coordinate vector δ be the fourth harmonic element of the set of points with coordinate vectors α, β, $h\alpha + k\beta$ is that δ can be written as $h\alpha - k\beta$.

*9. Dualize Theorems 8–2, 8–3, and 8–4 to theorems about complete quadrilaterals. Draw a figure to illustrate the results.

*10. Show that in a perspectivity between l and l', the Pappus line is the harmonic conjugate, with respect to l and l', of MC, where M is the point common to l and l', and C is the center of perspective.

*11. (a) What is the *metric* interpretation of a harmonic set of four points?

(b) For various positions of X on the line AB, describe, in metric terms, the position of the harmonic conjugate of X with respect to A and B.

12. Define an operation "$\bigcirc$" as follows:

$$f(x) \; \bigcirc \; g(x) \; = \; f[g(x)].$$

Write out the 6×6 table for this operation for the functions r, $1/r$, $1 - r$, $1/(1 - r)$, $1 - (1/r)$, $r/(r - 1)$ [cf. Example, Section 3–6].

*13. Prove that the diagonal points of a complete quadrangle are not collinear. [*Hint:* Use the notation of Proof 2 of Theorem 8–2.]

*14. (a) Given three collinear points, use Theorem 8–2 to describe how to construct the fourth harmonic element by using a straight edge. (Note that there will be some freedom in the construction.)

(b) Dualize the construction of (a).

15. Show that a complete quadrangle is uniquely determined by its diagonal triangle and one vertex. Perform the demonstration in two ways:

(a) purely geometrically, making use of the harmonic properties of the complete quadrangle; and

(b) partly algebraically, choosing the diagonal triangle as the triangle of reference and the given vertex as the unit point, and establishing that the coordinates of the four vertices will then be $(1, \pm1, \pm1)$.

16. In the extended Euclidean plane, find the fourth harmonic element to the three given ones and describe the configuration in metric terms:

(a) the collinear points $(1, 2, 1)$, $(2, 0, -2)$, $(0, 2, 2)$;

(b) the concurrent lines $x_0 - x_2 = 0$, $x_0 - x_1 = 0$, $x_1 - x_2 = 0$;

(c) the concurrent lines $a_0 x_0 + a_1 x_1 + a_2 x_2 = 0$, $a_0' x_0 + a_1 x_1 + a_2 x_2 = 0$, $x_0 = 0$.

17. (a) Prove the following theorem: Let A, B, and C be distinct points on a line h, and let l, m, and n be distinct lines, l through A, m through B, and n through C. For an arbitrary point P on n, let AP meet m at D, and let BP meet l at E. Let DE meet h at C'. Then C' is the harmonic conjugate of C with respect to A and B.

(b) State the dual of the theorem of part (a).

8–4 SOME THEOREMS ON THE TRIANGLE

Making use of Lemmas 1 and 2 of Section 5–5, we can obtain a pair of theorems which are generalizations of results that we have encountered earlier.

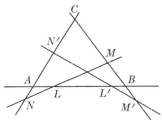

FIGURE 8–5

Theorem 8–5. Let L, M, and N be three collinear points, one on each side of triangle ABC, and let L', M', N' be three other points, one on each side of the triangle (Fig. 8–5). Suppose that $(AB, L'L) = k_1$; $(BC, M'M) = k_2$; $(CA, N'N) = k_3$. Then a necessary and sufficient condition that L', M', and N' be collinear is that $k_1 k_2 k_3 = 1$.

Proof. In accordance with Lemma 1 of Section 5–5, coordinate vectors of L, M, and N can be written

$$\lambda = p\alpha - q\beta, \qquad \mu = q\beta - r\gamma, \qquad \nu = r\gamma - p\alpha.$$

Then, using Problem 8(b) of Section 8–3, we can conclude that coordinate vectors of L', M', and N' can be written

$$\lambda' = p\alpha - k_1 q\beta, \qquad \mu' = q\beta - k_2 r\gamma, \qquad \nu' = r\gamma - k_3 p\alpha.$$

If the points L', M', and N' are collinear, then there exist h_1, h_2, and h_3, not all zero, such that

$$h_1 \lambda' + h_2 \mu' + h_3 \nu' = o,$$

or

$$h_1(p\alpha - k_1 q\beta) + h_2(q\beta - k_2 r\gamma) + h_3(r\gamma - k_3 p\alpha) = o.$$

Because of the independence of α, β, γ, we can conclude that $h_1 = h_3 k_3$, $h_2 = h_1 k_1$, $h_3 = h_2 k_2$. These equations imply that $k_1 k_2 k_3 = 1$. Conversely, if $k_1 k_2 k_3 = 1$, then

$$\lambda' + k_1 \mu' + k_1 k_2 \nu' = o. \qquad \square$$

Theorem 8–6. Let L, M, N be three collinear points, one on each side of triangle ABC, and let $\overline{L}$, $\overline{M}$, $\overline{N}$ be three other points, also one on each side of the triangle. Suppose that $(AB, \overline{L}L) = k_1$; $(BC, \overline{M}M) = k_2$; $(CA, \overline{N}N) = k_3$. Then a necessary and sufficient condition that $A\overline{M}$, $B\overline{N}$, $C\overline{L}$ be concurrent is that $k_1 k_2 k_3 = -1$.

The proof is left as a problem (Problem 1 below).

Corollary 1. Let L, M, N be three collinear points, one on each side of triangle ABC. Let $\overline{L}$ be the harmonic conjugate of L with respect to A and B; $\overline{M}$, of M with respect to B and C; $\overline{N}$, of N with respect to C and A. Then $A\overline{M}$, $B\overline{N}$, $C\overline{L}$ are concurrent.

In the extended plane of the complex domain, Theorems 8–5 and 8–6 have some interesting metric consequences.

By choosing the line LMN to be the ideal line of the plane and by using the result of Problem 6(b), Section 6–2, we obtain the following corollaries of Theorems 8–5 and 8–6.

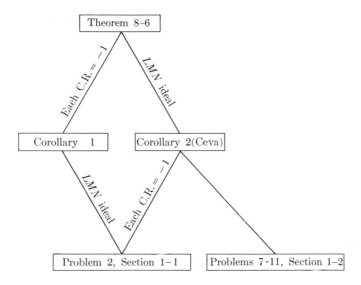

FIGURE 8-6

Corollary 2.   Three points L', M', and N', one on each side of triangle ABC, are collinear if and only if the product of the algebraic ratios in which they divide the sides AB, BC, CA is 1.

Corollary 3.   If $\overline{L}$, $\overline{M}$, $\overline{N}$ are three points, one on each side of triangle ABC, then $A\overline{M}$, $B\overline{N}$, $C\overline{L}$ are concurrent if and only if the product of the algebraic ratios in which the points divide the sides AB, BC, CA is -1.

Corollaries 2 and 3 will be recognized as the theorems of Menelaus and Ceva (Problems 3 through 6, Section 1–2).

Thus, we have a hierarchy of results, some of which may be pictured schematically (Fig. 8–6).

PROBLEM SET 8–4

1. Prove Theorem 8–6.

2. (a) State the plane duals of Theorem 8–5, Theorem 8–6, and Corollary 1.

(b) Reword the two theorems and the corollary so that they become self-dual statements.

3. Given triangle $A_1A_2A_3$ with P_1, Q_1, R_1, S_1 on A_2A_3; P_2, Q_2, R_2, S_2 on A_3A_1; P_3, Q_3, R_3, S_3 on A_1A_2. Suppose that A_1P_1, A_2P_2, A_3P_3 are concurrent and that Q_i is the harmonic conjugate of P_i with respect to the vertices of the triangle on the side on which they lie, $i = 1$, 2, 3. (Then Q_1, Q_2, Q_3 are collinear, by the dual of Corollary 1.) Suppose further that $(P_iQ_i, R_iS_i) =$

-1, $i = 1$, 2, 3. Show that if R_1, R_2, R_3 are collinear, then S_1, S_2, S_3 are collinear, and if A_1R_1, A_2R_2, A_3R_3 are concurrent, then A_1S_1, A_2S_2, A_3S_3 are concurrent.

8–5 CHANGE OF COORDINATE SYSTEM; REDUCTION TO CANONICAL FORM

In ordinary analytic geometry we often attempt to reduce the algebraic complexities of a problem in either of two ways: (1) we perform a rigid motion of the points of the space, leaving the coordinate axes fixed, *or* (2) we shift the axes, leaving the points of space fixed. For example, in the case illustrated in Fig. 8–7, we can obtain a simpler form for the equation of the ellipse by transforming each point P of the plane into the point P' by means of a clockwise rotation of angle θ about O (thus transforming $\mathcal{C}$ into $\mathcal{C}'$ by this rigid motion), *or* by leaving the plane (and hence the curve $\mathcal{C}$) fixed and replacing the xy-coordinate frame by the $x'y'$-frame.

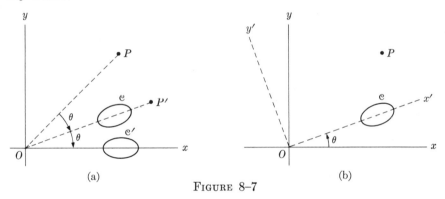

FIGURE 8–7

The equivalence of these transformations can be seen algebraically. If, relative to the xy-frame of Fig. 8–7(a), P has coordinates (x, y) and P' has coordinates (x', y'), then

$$\begin{bmatrix} x' \\ y' \end{bmatrix} = \begin{bmatrix} \cos\theta & \sin\theta \\ -\sin\theta & \cos\theta \end{bmatrix} \cdot \begin{bmatrix} x \\ y \end{bmatrix} \tag{1}$$

is an equation which also expresses the relationship between the coordinates of a fixed point P relative to the two frames of Fig. 8–7(b). Thus Eq. (1) admits of two interpretations. It may be thought of as signifying either a rotation of the *plane* (through angle θ, clockwise), or as a rotation of *axes* (through angle θ, counterclockwise). These interpretations are sometimes called, respectively, an *active transformation* and a *passive trans-*

formation; or, alternatively, an *alibi* ("I was somewhere else") and an *alias* ("I've changed my name").

The same two interpretations are to be found in S_n. The equation

$$\xi' = T \cdot \xi \tag{2}$$

may be thought of as a collineation of S_n (in which a point P is moved to "somewhere else") or as a change of coordinate frame (in which each point is "renamed").

The following question is a natural one: Given a collineation defined by Eq. (2) relative to a certain coordinate frame, how may the coordinate frame be changed so as to simplify the equation of the collineation?

It will be convenient in the following discussion to express the relationship between the "old" coordinates and the "new" by solving for the former in terms of the latter. Thus, suppose that we make the change of coordinate frame characterized by

$$\xi = A \cdot \eta,$$

where ξ is a coordinate vector of a point P relative to the old coordinate system, and η is a coordinate vector of P relative to a new coordinate system. Then, if the collineation of Eq. (2) transforms P into P', with coordinate vectors ξ', η', relative to the old and new frames, respectively, we also have

$$\xi' = A \cdot \eta',$$

so that Eq. (2) becomes

$$A \cdot \eta' = TA \cdot \eta,$$

or

$$\eta' = A^{-1}TA \cdot \eta;$$

that is, relative to the new coordinate frame, the collineation has the matrix $A^{-1}TA$. Our question, then, may be put as follows: Given a matrix T, how can a matrix A be chosen so as to make $A^{-1}TA$ as simple as possible?

We answer the question now for $n = 1$ and consider the general case later. It turns out that the solution depends upon finding the fixed points of the collineation, i.e., those points of S_1 which are carried into themselves by the transformation.

If a certain point, with coordinate vector $\xi = (x_0, x_1)$ of S_1 is to be carried into itself, it is necessary and sufficient that ξ' be the vector with coordinates (kx_0, kx_1) for some $k \neq 0$. So, the problem of finding the fixed points is equivalent to that of solving for ξ the equation $k\xi = T \cdot \xi$.

This may be written as

$$(T - kI) \cdot \xi = o.$$

Here we have two homogeneous linear equations in two unknowns, x_0 and x_1; a nontrivial solution exists if and only if the rank of $T - kI$ is less than 2. Thus, a necessary and sufficient condition for a solution is that the determinant, $|T - kI|$, equal zero. We have, then, a quadratic equation in k, with two roots, k_1, k_2, say. We distinguish two cases.

Case 1. $k_1 \neq k_2$. In this case, the rank of $T - k_1I$ is 1; likewise, the rank of $T - k_2I$. (Problem 1 below.) Hence, the pair of equations $(T - k_1I) \cdot \xi = o$ has one solution, (u_0, u_1), say; and the pair of equations $(T - k_2I) \cdot \xi = o$ has one solution, (v_0, v_1), say. In other words

$$T\begin{bmatrix} u_0 \\ u_1 \end{bmatrix} = \begin{bmatrix} k_1 & u_0 \\ k_1 & u_1 \end{bmatrix} \quad \text{and} \quad T\begin{bmatrix} v_0 \\ v_1 \end{bmatrix} = \begin{bmatrix} k_2 & v_0 \\ k_2 & v_1 \end{bmatrix}.$$

Now (u_0, u_1) and (v_0, v_1) are linearly independent (Problem 2 below). Hence the matrix,

$$A = \begin{bmatrix} u_0 & v_0 \\ u_1 & v_1 \end{bmatrix},$$

is nonsingular. Consider the change of coordinate system defined by $\sigma = A \cdot \tau$. It is easy to verify that

$$\text{if} \quad \sigma = \begin{bmatrix} u_0 \\ u_1 \end{bmatrix}, \quad \text{then} \quad \tau = \begin{bmatrix} 1 \\ 0 \end{bmatrix},$$

and

$$\text{if} \quad \sigma = \begin{bmatrix} v_0 \\ v_1 \end{bmatrix}, \quad \text{then} \quad \tau = \begin{bmatrix} 0 \\ 1 \end{bmatrix}.$$

In other words, the *fixed points of the transformation are the fundamental points of the new coordinate system*. Relative to the new coordinate system, the transformation takes $(1, 0)$ into $(k_1, 0)$, and $(0, 1)$ into $(0, k_2)$. Hence, the matrix of this transformation must be

$$\begin{bmatrix} k_1 & 0 \\ 0 & k_2 \end{bmatrix}$$

(Problem 3 below).

Before summarizing the foregoing development, it is convenient to introduce some standard terminology. Although we have been dealing with 2×2 matrices, the following definition applies to square matrices of any size.

Definition 1. The equation $|T - kI| = 0$ is called the *characteristic equation* of the matrix T. The roots of this equation are called the *characteristic roots* of T. A nonzero vector ξ such that $T \cdot \xi = k \cdot \xi$ for some k is called a *characteristic vector* of T.

We have encountered the characteristic equation and its associated concepts in simplifying the matrix of a collineation, but, like most of matrix theory, there are many nongeometrical applications also. (See Section 8–6.) Characteristic vectors and characteristic roots play important roles in quantum mechanics, for example, where they are sometimes called *proper states* and *proper values*, or *eigenstates* and *eigenvalues*.

Using the terms of Definition 1, we can state a result of simplifying the matrix of a collineation.

Theorem 8–7. Relative to a certain coordinate frame in S_1, suppose that a collineation has the form $\xi' = T \cdot \xi$, where T has distinct characteristic roots k_1, k_2, and characteristic vectors (u_0, u_1) and (v_0, v_1). Then the change of coordinate system $\xi = A \cdot \eta$, where

$$A = \begin{bmatrix} u_0 & v_0 \\ u_1 & v_1 \end{bmatrix},$$

makes the collineation take, relative to the new coordinate system, the form, $\eta' = T'_1 \cdot \eta$, where

$$T'_1 = A^{-1}TA = \begin{bmatrix} k_1 & 0 \\ 0 & k_2 \end{bmatrix}.$$

We now turn to the second case.

Case 2. $k_1 = k_2 = k_0$, say. In this case, the rank of $T - k_0 I$ may be either 0 or 1. If the rank is 0, T is a multiple of I (Problem 4 below), and the transformation is uninteresting. If the rank is 1, there is one fixed point F, say, with coordinate vector $\phi = (f_0, f_1)$; that is, $T \cdot \phi = k_0\phi$. As in Case 1, we will make a change of coordinate system so that F is one of the fundamental points of the new coordinate frame, but there is no obvious choice for the second fundamental point. It turns out that some arbitrariness is feasible. Let $P(p_0, p_1)$ be an arbitrary point other than F, and let $T(P) = P'$, with coordinate vector (p'_0, p'_1). Then P' is distinct both from P and from F (Problem 5 below). Hence there are nonzero scalars c_1, c_2, such that

$$\begin{bmatrix} p'_0 \\ p'_1 \end{bmatrix} = c_1 \begin{bmatrix} f_0 \\ f_1 \end{bmatrix} + c_2 \begin{bmatrix} p_0 \\ p_1 \end{bmatrix}.$$

Now choose the change of coordinate system determined by $\sigma = A \cdot \tau$

where σ is the coordinate vector of a point in the old system; τ, in the new; and

$$A = \begin{bmatrix} p_0/c_1 & f_0 \\ p_1/c_1 & f_1 \end{bmatrix}.$$

It is easy to verify that in the new coordinate frame, F has coordinates $(0, 1)$, P has coordinates $(c_1, 0)$, $T(F)$ has coordinates $(0, k_0)$, and $P' = T(P)$ has coordinates $(c_1 c_2, c_1)$. Hence, the collineation which appears relative to the old frame as $\xi' = T \cdot \xi$ has the equation, relative to the new frame, $\eta' = A^{-1} T A \cdot \eta$ or $\eta' = T_1 \cdot \eta$, where

$$T_1 = \begin{bmatrix} c_2 & 0 \\ 1 & k_0 \end{bmatrix}$$

(Problem 6 below).

To discover that T_1 is even simpler than it appears to be, we introduce a new term and two theorems. Note that the following definition, like the last one, applies to square matrices of any size.

Definition 2.   The matrix X is *similar* to the matrix Y if there exists a matrix A such that $X = A^{-1} Y A$.

It is easy to verify that similarity is an equivalence relation (Problem 7 below), so that it is meaningful to use the expression, "X and Y are similar" rather than "X is similar to Y."

Theorem 8-8.   If X and Y are similar, so are $X - kI$ and $Y - kI$, and conversely.

Proof.   If $X = A^{-1} Y A$, then

$$X - kI = A^{-1} Y A - kI = A^{-1} Y A - A^{-1} k I A = A^{-1}(Y - kI)A.$$

The proof of the converse proceeds equally easily.   □

Theorem 8-9.   If X and Y are similar, they have the same characteristic equation.

Proof.   If

$$X - kI = A^{-1}(Y - kI)A,$$

then

$$|X - kI| = |A^{-1}| \cdot |Y - kI| \cdot |A| = |Y - kI|.$$

We return now to Case 2. We had obtained T, with the (repeated) characteristic root k_0, similar to T_1, whose characteristic equation is $(c_2 - k)(k_0 - k) = 0$. Hence, appealing to Theorem 8–9, we conclude that $c_2 = k_0$. Thus

$$T_1 = \begin{bmatrix} k_0 & 0 \\ 1 & k_0 \end{bmatrix}.$$

We summarize our result in the following theorem, companion to Theorem 8–7.

Theorem 8–10. Relative to a certain coordinate frame in S_1, suppose that a collineation has the form $\xi' = T \cdot \xi$, where T has the repeated characteristic root k_0, and the characteristic vector (f_0, f_1). Let $P(p_0, p_1)$ be an arbitrary point of S_1 other than F, and let $T(P) = P'$, with coordinates (p_0', p_1'). Let

$$\begin{bmatrix} p_0' \\ p_1' \end{bmatrix} = c_1 \begin{bmatrix} f_0 \\ f_1 \end{bmatrix} + c_2 \begin{bmatrix} p_0 \\ p_1 \end{bmatrix}.$$

Then the change of coordinate system $\xi = A \cdot \eta$, where

$$A = \begin{bmatrix} p_0/c_1 & f_0 \\ p_1/c_1 & f_1 \end{bmatrix},$$

makes the collineation take the form, relative to the new coordinate system,

$$\eta' = T_1 \cdot \eta,$$

where

$$T_1 = A^{-1}TA = \begin{bmatrix} k_0 & 0 \\ 1 & k_0 \end{bmatrix}.$$

We have introduced the notion of similarity of matrices to simplify the matrix of a collineation. But our discussion makes it clear that we can state the following strong result.

Two $(n + 1) \times (n + 1)$ matrices, T_1, T_2 represent the same collineation of S_n, relative to possibly different coordinate frames, if and only if T_1 and T_2 are similar.

Thus, in S_1, we have two canonical forms for the matrices of collineations:

$$\begin{bmatrix} k_1 & 0 \\ 0 & k_2 \end{bmatrix} \quad \text{and} \quad \begin{bmatrix} k_0 & 0 \\ 1 & k_0 \end{bmatrix};$$

by appropriate choice of coordinate frame, the matrix of every collineation of S_1 can be put into one or the other of these forms.

It is convenient to refer to a collineation in S_1 with a single fixed point as "parabolic," and to one with two fixed points as "nonparabolic." The nonparabolic collineations may be further classified as "elliptic" if the fixed points are imaginary and "hyperbolic" if the fixed points are real. (Compare the classification of conics into parabolas, ellipses, hyperbolas according as they have one real, no real, two real points in common with the ideal line of the real extended plane.)

In terms of nonhomogeneous coordinates,

$$y = y_1/y_0, \qquad y' = y_1'/y_0',$$

the canonical form of a nonparabolic collineation may be written as

$$y' = cy,$$

where $c = k_2/k_1$, while the canonical form of a parabolic collineation may be written as

$$y' = y + a,$$

where $a = 1/k_0$. Thus, in the descriptive language of ordinary geometry, we may say that appropriate changes of coordinate systems make each one-dimensional collineation with two fixed points appear as a "stretch" (or a "compression"), and each one-dimensional collineation with a single fixed point appear as a "translation."

Later similar analyses will be made for S_2, and general statements about S_n will be derived.

PROBLEM SET 8–5

1. Show that if the 2×2 matrix T has distinct characteristic roots, k_1, k_2, then each of $T - k_1 I$, $T - k_2 I$ is of rank 1.

2. Show that if $U(u_0, u_1)$, $V(v_0, v_1)$ are the two fixed points of a collineation, then (u_0, u_1), (v_0, v_1) are linearly independent.

3. Show that if T_1 transforms $(1, 0)$ into $(k_1, 0)$, and $(0, 1)$ into $(0, k_2)$, then

$$T_1 = \begin{bmatrix} k_1 & 0 \\ 0 & k_2 \end{bmatrix}.$$

4. Show that if $T - k_0 I$ has rank zero, then T is a multiple of I.

5. Show that if F is the unique fixed point of the collineation with matrix T, and if P is a point distinct from F, then $P' = T(P)$ is distinct from both F and P.

6. Verify that if

$$T_1 \begin{bmatrix} 0 \\ 1 \end{bmatrix} = \begin{bmatrix} 0 \\ k_0 \end{bmatrix} \quad \text{and if} \quad T_1 \begin{bmatrix} c_1 \\ 0 \end{bmatrix} = \begin{bmatrix} c_1 c_2 \\ c_1 \end{bmatrix},$$

then

$$T_1 = \begin{bmatrix} c_2 & 0 \\ 1 & k_0 \end{bmatrix}.$$

7. Show that similarity is an equivalence relation among matrices.

8. Carry through the reductions which led to Theorem 8-7 (or to Theorem 8-10) for each of the following transformations.

(a) $T = \begin{bmatrix} 4 & 2 \\ -1 & 1 \end{bmatrix}$ (c) $T = \begin{bmatrix} 4 & 2 \\ -3 & -1 \end{bmatrix}$

(b) $T = \begin{bmatrix} -3 & -1 \\ 1 & -1 \end{bmatrix}$ (d) $T = \begin{bmatrix} 2 & 1 \\ -3 & -2 \end{bmatrix}$

*9. (a) The characteristic equation of the matrix T of Problem 8(a) is $k^2 - 5k + 6 = 0$. Verify that T satisfies the matrix equation $X^2 - 5X + 6I = 0$. (We shall see later that "every matrix satisfies its characteristic equation.")

(b), (c), (d) Verify that the matrix of the corresponding part of Problem 8 above "satisfies its characteristic equation."

10. Let P be a square matrix with the property that the sum of the elements of each row is c. Show that c is a characteristic root of P.

11. Find the characteristic roots and characteristic vectors of

$$M = \begin{bmatrix} e^{\theta} & e^{-\theta} \\ e^{-\theta} & e^{\theta} \end{bmatrix}.$$

(This problem arises in the study of the structure of crystal lattices.)

12. Find the characteristic roots of the matrices X and Y of Problem 13, Section 6-5.

13. (a) Show that the characteristic roots of

$$M = \begin{bmatrix} 1 + yz & z(2 + yz) \\ y & 1 + yz \end{bmatrix}, \quad y, z \text{ complex,}$$

are $e^{\pm\phi}$, where $\cosh \phi = 1 + yz$.

(b) Show that for $n = 1, 2, \ldots,$

$$M^n = \begin{bmatrix} \cosh n\phi & z_0 \sinh n\phi \\ \dfrac{1}{z_0} \sinh n\phi & \cosh n\phi \end{bmatrix}, \quad \text{where } z_0 = \frac{\sinh \phi}{y}.$$

(This problem appears in the analysis of filters in electrical circuit theory.)

(c) If

$$M_\phi = \begin{bmatrix} \cosh \phi & z_0 \sinh \phi \\ \dfrac{1}{z_0} \sinh \phi & \cosh \phi \end{bmatrix},$$

show that the characteristic roots of $M_\phi \cdot M_\psi$ are $e^{\pm\theta}$, where

$$\cosh \theta = 2 \cosh \phi \cosh \psi = 1.$$

*14. Find an expression for M^n, n a positive integer, if M equals

(a) $\begin{bmatrix} k_1 & 0 \\ 0 & k_2 \end{bmatrix}$,   (b) $\begin{bmatrix} k_0 & 0 \\ 1 & k_0 \end{bmatrix}$.

15. Show that if r is a characteristic root of the matrix M, then $1 + r$ is a characteristic root of $I + M$ (Brenner).

16. The matrix

$$M = \begin{bmatrix} a+b & -a & -b \\ -a & 2a & -a \\ -b & -a & a+b \end{bmatrix}$$

appears in the analysis of small vibrations of a triatomic molecule. Show quickly that one of the characteristic roots of M is 0, and determine the other characteristic roots. Also find the characteristic vector corresponding to each characteristic root.

17. Find the canonical form of the collineation which takes $(0, 2)$ into $(-2, -3)$, $(2, 1)$ into $(0, 2)$, and $(1, 2)$ into $(-3, -4)$.

18. Let A, B, C be nonsingular $n \times n$ matrices. Show that
(a) ABC, BCA, CAB are similar;
(b) there exists T such that $AC = TBT$. [Hint: Set $T = SB^{-1}$, and try to determine the existence of S.] (Brenner, Amer. Math. Monthly, Feb., 1962.)

*19. For an $n \times n$ matrix $A = [a_{ij}]$, the trace of A is defined as

$$Tr(A) = \sum_{i=n}^{n} a_{ii}.$$

(a) Show that if A and B are $n \times n$ matrices over a field, $Tr(AB) = Tr(BA)$.
(b) Hence show that $Tr(A_1A_2 \cdots A_k) = Tr(A_lA_{l+1} \cdots A_kA_1 \cdots A_{l-1})$; i.e., the trace of a product of matrices is unchanged under cyclic permutation.
(c) Hence show that $Tr(P^{-1}AP) = Tr(A)$; i.e., that the traces of similar matrices are equal.

20. (Refer to Problem 19 for definition and helpful results.)
For square matrices of order n over the field C, prove that any matrix M
(a) has zero trace if $MQ = -QM$, for some nonsingular Q,
(b) can be written as a matrix of zero trace plus a multiple of I. (R. G. Winter, Am. Math. Monthly, Nov., 1961.)

*21. Let M be a nonsingular matrix with complex numbers as elements. Prove that

(a) none of the characteristic roots of M is zero,

(b) the characteristic roots of M^t are the same as those of M,

(c) the characteristic roots of M^{-1} are the reciprocals of the characteristic roots of M. [*Hint:* Suppose that $\det (M - k_0 I) = 0$. Now $M - k_0 I = (-k_0 M)(M^{-1} - (1/k_0)I)$. Hence ...].

*22. Let M be an upper (or lower) triangular matrix. Show that the characteristic roots of M are the elements on the main diagonal.

8-6 REDUCTION TO CANONICAL FORM APPLIED TO AN ALGEBRAIC PROBLEM

We digress from a consideration of the projective geometry which motivated the development of Section 8–5 to illustrate the application of the results of that section to the solution of a nongeometrical problem.

Suppose that a sequence of complex numbers $\{a_n\}$ is defined recursively as follows:

$$a_0 = a,$$

$$a_1 = b,$$

$$a_{n+2} = p \cdot a_{n+1} + q \cdot a_n, \qquad n \geq 0,$$

where a, b, p, q are complex numbers. What is an explicit expression for a_n in terms of a, b, p, q, and n?

We note that

$$\begin{bmatrix} a_{n+1} \\ a_n \end{bmatrix} = \begin{bmatrix} p & q \\ 1 & 0 \end{bmatrix}\begin{bmatrix} a_n \\ a_{n-1} \end{bmatrix} = \begin{bmatrix} p & q \\ 1 & 0 \end{bmatrix}^2 \begin{bmatrix} a_{n-1} \\ a_{n-2} \end{bmatrix} = \cdots = \begin{bmatrix} p & q \\ 1 & 0 \end{bmatrix}^n \begin{bmatrix} b \\ a \end{bmatrix}.$$

Let

$$R = \begin{bmatrix} p & q \\ 1 & 0 \end{bmatrix}.$$

The characteristic equation of R is

$$k^2 - pk - q = 0.$$

Case 1. $p^2 + 4q \neq 0$. In this case R has two distinct characteristic roots, k_1, k_2, say. Then there exists a matrix A such that

$$A^{-1}RA = \begin{bmatrix} k_1 & 0 \\ 0 & k_2 \end{bmatrix}.$$

It is clear that $(A^{-1}RA)^n = A^{-1}R^nA$. Hence,

$$A^{-1}R^nA = \begin{bmatrix} k_1 & 0 \\ 0 & k_2 \end{bmatrix}^n = \begin{bmatrix} k_1^n & 0 \\ 0 & k_2^n \end{bmatrix}.$$

Therefore

$$R^n = A \begin{bmatrix} k_1^n & 0 \\ 0 & k_2^n \end{bmatrix} A^{-1}.$$

Hence

$$\begin{bmatrix} a_{n+1} \\ a_n \end{bmatrix} = A \cdot \begin{bmatrix} k_1^n & 0 \\ 0 & k_2^n \end{bmatrix} \cdot A^{-1} \cdot \begin{bmatrix} b \\ a \end{bmatrix}.$$

Since the elements of A are independent of n, we can conclude that $a_n = c_1 k_1^n + c_2 k_2^n$, where c_1, c_2 are certain complex numbers independent of n. We can determine the values of c_1, c_2 by setting $n = 0, 1$:

$$c_1 + c_2 = a; \qquad c_1 k_1 + c_2 k_2 = b.$$

These two equations, together with the values of k_1, k_2 obtained from the characteristic equation, give the desired result.

PROBLEM SET 8–6

1. Carry through the details of this method for the Fibonacci sequence:

$$a_0 = 1, \qquad a_1 = 1, \qquad a_{n+2} = a_{n+1} + a_n, \quad n \geq 0.$$

2. Carry through the method for Case 2, in which $p^2 + 4q = 0$, to obtain $a_n = k_0^{n-1}(c_1 n + c_2 k_0)$, where $k_0 = \frac{1}{2}p$, $c_1 = b - a k_0$, $c_2 = a$.

3. Let

$$D_n = \begin{vmatrix} a & -1 & 0 & & \cdots & & 0 \\ -1 & a & -1 & 0 & & \cdots & 0 \\ 0 & -1 & a & -1 & & \cdots & 0 \\ \vdots & & & & & & \\ 0 & \cdots & & & -1 & a & -1 \\ 0 & \cdots & & & 0 & -1 & a \end{vmatrix};$$

i.e., D_n is the determinant of an $n \times n$ matrix with a's along the principal diagonal and -1's just "above" and just "below" the principal diagonal.

(a) Show that $D_n = a \cdot D_{n-1} - D_{n-2}$.

(b) Find an explicit expression for D_n as a function of a and n. (This problem appears in the analysis of the small vibrations of n particles in a straight line.)

4. Let $[p_{ij}]$ be an $n \times n$ matrix where $p_{11} = a$, $p_{ii} = b$, $i = 2, \ldots, n$; $p_{i,i+1} \cdot p_{i+1,i} = c$, $i = 1, \ldots, n - 1$, with all other elements zero. Designate the determinant of this matrix by D_n.

(a) Obtain an explicit expression for D_n as a function of a, b, c, n.

(b) Show that if $a = \cos \theta$, $b = 2 \cos \theta$, $c = 1$, then $D_n = \cos n\theta$.

(c) Show that if $a = 2 \cos \theta$, $b = 2 \cos \theta$, $c = 1$, then $D_n = \sin (n+1)\theta/\sin \theta$
(P. L. Chessin, *Amer. Math. Monthly*, Jan., 1959, p. 62.)

5. The values of u_{2n+1}, v_{2n+1}, the numerators and denominators, respectively, of the odd-numbered terms in the continued fraction expansion of $\sqrt{3}$, are given by

$$u_1 = 2;$$

$$v_1 = 1;$$

$$u_{2n+1} = 2u_{2n-1} + 3v_{2n-1},$$

$$v_{2n+1} = u_{2n-1} + 2v_{2n-1}, \quad n = 1, 2, \ldots.$$

Express

$$\begin{bmatrix} u_{2n+1} \\ v_{2n+1} \end{bmatrix}$$

as a certain matrix times

$$\begin{bmatrix} u_{2n-1} \\ v_{2n-1} \end{bmatrix}$$

and thus use the method of this section to show that

$$u_{2n+1} = \frac{(2 + \sqrt{3})^{n+1} + (2 - \sqrt{3})^{n+1}}{2},$$

$$v_{2n+1} = \frac{(2 + \sqrt{3})^{n+1} - (2 - \sqrt{3})^{n+1}}{2}.$$

6. Consider the sequence $w_1 = 1$, $w_2 = 3$, $w_{n+2} = (w_{n+1} + w_n)/2$, $n \geq 1$, Find an explicit expression for w_n in terms of n, and determine $\lim_{n \to \infty} w_n$.

8–7 INVARIANT CROSS RATIO OF A COLLINEATION

If a collineation in S_1 has two fixed points U, V, and if it transforms two arbitrary points, X, Y, into X', Y', respectively, then, because cross ratio is preserved in a projectivity, $(UV, XY) = (UV, X'Y')$. By algebraic manipulation we can conclude that $(UV, XX') = (UV, YY')$ (Problem 1 below). This result we state as a theorem.

Theorem 8–11. In a nonparabolic collineation of S_1 the cross ratio in which a point and its transform separate the fixed points is constant.

This cross ratio is known as the invariant cross ratio, or the characteristic cross ratio, or simply, the *invariant* of the collineation. Actually, it has not been unambiguously defined above, for the value of the invariant depends upon which fixed point is called U and which V. But the ambiguity will not bother us in applications.

If the characteristic roots corresponding to U, V are k_1, k_2 respectively, then straightforward computation shows that, for all X,

$$(UV, XX') = \frac{k_1}{k_2}$$

(Problem 2 below). This result, exhibiting the cross ratio as being independent of the choice of X, furnishes another proof of Theorem 8–11.

The following theorem is an analogue, for parabolic collineations, of Theorem 8–11.

Theorem 8–12. In a parabolic collineation of S_1, the fixed point F and an arbitrary point X are separated harmonically by the point carried into X by the collineation and the point into which X is carried; i.e., if T is a parabolic collineation with $T(F) = F$, if X is an arbitrary point, with $T(X) = X'$ and $T^{-1}(X) = \widetilde{X}$, then $(FX, \widetilde{X}X') = -1$.

Proof. Let ϕ be a coordinate vector of F, so that $T \cdot \phi = k_0\phi$; let π be a coordinate vector of $T^{-1}(X)$, so that $T \cdot \pi = \pi'$ and $T \cdot \pi' = \pi''$, where π', π'' are coordinate vectors of X, $T(X)$, respectively. Then, as we saw in the proof of Theorem 8–10, we can write $\pi' = c_1\phi + k_0\pi$. Hence, $\pi'' = T \cdot \pi' = T \cdot (c_1\phi + k_0\pi) = c_1k_0\phi + k_0\pi'$. Thus, we have $k_0\pi = \pi' - c_1\phi$, and $(1/k_0)\pi'' = \pi' + c_1\phi$. $\square$

For another proof, we can use the canonical form for a collineation with a single fixed point (Problem 3 below).

PROBLEM SET 8–7

1. Show that if U, V are the fixed points of a one-dimensional collineation, T; if X, Y are arbitrary points and if $X' = T(X)$, $Y' = T(Y)$, then $(UV, XX') = (UV, YY')$. [*Hint:* Use the idea of linear combination in expressing the cross ratios.]

2. (a) If the collineation of Problem 1 has characteristic roots k_1, k_2, show that $(UV, XX') = k_1/k_2$. [*Hint:* Choose the coordinate frame corresponding to the canonical form of the collineation.]

(b) Show that the result of (a) is true for a collineation in S_n if F_1, F_2 are fixed points with associated characteristic roots k_1, k_2, respectively; and if the transform of X on line F_1F_2 is X', then $(F_1F_2, XX') = k_1/k_2$. [*Hint:* Let the matrix of the collineation be A, and coordinate vectors of F_1, F_2, X be ϕ_1, ϕ_2, ξ, respectively. Then, for some p, q, $\xi = p\phi_1 + q\phi_2$. Moreover, $A \cdot \phi_1 = k_1\phi_1$, etc.]

3. Use the canonical form of the collineation to prove Theorem 8–12.

4. Show that if the invariant of a collineation T is k, then the invariant of T^m is k^m.

5. Show that if the collineations with matrices S, T (relative to some coordinate frame) have the same fixed points, then the invariant of the collineation with matrix ST equals the product of the invariants of the collineations with matrices S, T.

8-8 INVOLUTORY TRANSFORMATIONS; INVOLUTIONS OF S_1; CYCLIC COLLINEATIONS; METRIC INVOLUTIONS

A transformation of a domain onto itself is called *involutory* if the transformation, applied twice in succession, is equivalent to the identity. Thus, an involutory transformation is its own inverse. Involutory transformations need not be linear; those which *are* linear and are not trivial (i.e., not themselves the identity) are called *involutions*. An $n \times n$ matrix T represents an involution of $V_n(C)$ provided that $T^2 = I_n$; and an $(n + 1) \times (n + 1)$ matrix W represents an involution of $S_n(C)$ provided that $W^2 = c \cdot I_{n+1}$ for some complex number c, which enters because ξ and $c\xi$ are coordinate vectors of the same point.

Here are some examples of involutory transformations.

Domain	p	$p' = T(P)$	Description of the transformation
1) S_n	$(p_0, p_1, \ldots, p_n)$	$(p_0, -p_1, \ldots, -p_n)$	Reflection in origin
2) S_n	$(p_0, p_1, \ldots, p_n)$	$(p_0, p_1, \ldots, p_{j-1}, -p_j, p_{j+1}, \ldots, p_n)$	Reflection in hyperplane $x_j = 0$
3) S_n	$(p_0, p_1, \ldots, p_n)$	$(\overline{p}_0, \overline{p}_1, \ldots, \overline{p}_n)$	Conjugation
4) $S_2 - (1, 0, 0)$	(p_0, p_1, p_2)	$(p_1^2 + p_2^2, p_1 p_0, p_2 p_0)$	Inversion in the unit circle
5) $n \times n$ matrices	$[a_{ij}]$	$[a_{ji}]$	Transposition
6) nonsingular matrices	$[a_{ij}]$	$[a_{ij}]^{-1}$	Inversion

It is left to you to decide which of the first four of these examples are involutions (Problem 1 below).

Theorem 8–13. A parabolic collineation of S_1 cannot be involutory.

Proof. The canonical form for a parabolic collineation is

$$T = \begin{bmatrix} k_0 & 0 \\ 1 & k_0 \end{bmatrix}.$$

We see that

$$T^2 = \begin{bmatrix} k_0^2 & 0 \\ 2k_0 & k_0^2 \end{bmatrix},$$

which cannot be a multiple of I for $k_0 \neq 0$. □

Since every involution of S_1 is nonparabolic, it is meaningful to refer to the invariant of an involution. The following theorem is basic.

Theorem 8–14.   The invariant of a one-dimensional involution is -1; i.e., in a one-dimensional involution every pair of corresponding points separates the fixed points harmonically.

Proof.   By the invariance of cross ratio under projectivity,

$$(UV, XX') = (UV, X'X).$$

But in general, $(UV, XX') = 1/(UV, X'X)$. Since all the points involved are distinct, $(UV, XX') \neq 1$. Therefore, $(UV, XX') = -1$. □

We know that a one-dimensional projectivity is determined by three pairs of corresponding points. How many pairs of the sort

$$T(X) = X', \qquad T(X') = X; \qquad T(Y) = Y', \qquad T(Y') = Y;$$

etc., are necessary to determine a collineation as being an involution? The answer is that *one* pair is sufficient.

Theorem 8–15.   If a collineation of S_1 interchanges one pair of points, it is an involution, i.e., it interchanges every pair of points.

Proof.   Suppose that $T(X) = X', T(X') = X, T(Y) = Y', T(Y') = Z$. We wish to prove that $Z = Y$. By virtue of the fact that T is a collineation, $(XX', YY') = (X'X, Y'Z)$. But we have the general result about cross ratios that $(XX', YY') = (X'X, Y'Y)$. Hence $Y = Z$. □

An alternative proof is left as a problem (Problem 2 below).

Corollary.   If a collineation has invariant -1, it is an involution.

This corollary is the converse of Theorem 8–14.

Theorem 8-16. The nonsingular matrix

$$T = \begin{bmatrix} a & b \\ c & d \end{bmatrix}$$

represents an involution of S_1 if and only if $a + d = 0$.

The proof is left as a problem (Problem 3 below).

In nonhomogeneous coordinates, the general one-dimensional collineation $x' = (ax + b)/(cx + d)$, can be written as the *bilinear equation*.

$$pxx' + qx + rx' + s = 0, \tag{1}$$

where p, q, r, s have obvious simple expressions in terms of a, b, c, d, and $ps - qr \neq 0$. In homogeneous coordinates this equation becomes

$$sx_0x_0' + rx_0x_1' + qx_1x_2' + px_1x_1' = 0. \tag{2}$$

If the collineation is an involution, we know from Theorem 8-16 that Eqs. 1 and 2 assume the *symmetric* forms:

$$pxx' + q(x + x') + s = 0 \tag{3}$$

and

$$sx_0x_0' + q(x_0x_1' + x_1x_0') + px_1x_1' = 0, \tag{4}$$

where $ps - q^2 \neq 0$.

The nontrivial, or proper, involution T on S_1 has the property that $T^2 = kI$ without T itself being a multiple of I. We may generalize the notion of an involution by considering transformations such that $T^p = kI$.

Definition 3. A transformation is *cyclic of period p* if $T^p = cI$ for some positive integer p and $T^q \neq dI$ for $0 < q < p$.

The analogue of Theorem 8-13 is immediate: A parabolic collineation of S_1 cannot be cyclic. Thus any cyclic collineation of S_1 must be nonparabolic, with characteristic roots k_1, k_2, say. We can characterize a cyclic collineation with matrix T through the following argument.

There exists a matrix A, such that

$$T = A \begin{bmatrix} k_1 & 0 \\ 0 & k_2 \end{bmatrix} A^{-1}.$$

Hence

$$T^p = A \begin{bmatrix} k_1^p & 0 \\ 0 & k_2^p \end{bmatrix} A^{-1} = cI,$$

by hypothesis. Therefore

$$\begin{bmatrix} k_1^p & 0 \\ 0 & k_2^p \end{bmatrix} = A^{-1}cIA = cI.$$

Thus $k_1^p = c = k_2^p$. You can verify that the only solution which satisfies our conditions is $k_1 = k_2 \cdot e$, where e is a primitive pth root of unity, i.e., $e^p = 1$ and $e^q \neq 1$ for $0 < q < p$ (Problem 5 below). We have thus established the following theorem.

Theorem 8–17. A collineation in S_1 is cyclic of period p if and only if the ratio of its characteristic roots is a primitive pth root of 1.

We shall introduce some metric aspects of involutions by considering a coordinate system that leads to a simple equation for the involution. Suppose that in a certain involution on S_1, points A and B are paired, and a coordinate system assigns to these points the coordinates $(1, 0)$ and $(0, 1)$. Then the equation of the involution [Eq. (4)] becomes

$$sx_0x_0' + px_1x_1' = 0, \tag{5}$$

or, in nonhomogeneous coordinates, $xx' = c$, where $c = -(s/p)$.

If we interpret this result in terms of the extended Euclidean space of Chapter 2, we conclude that an involution which pairs the ideal point on a line with the origin has the property of pairing points the product of whose distances from the origin is constant.

Conversely it is clear that the collineation defined by $xx' = c$, $x \neq 0$, $x' \neq 0$, is an involution of the extended line if we pair the origin with the ideal point. We thus obtain a method for constructing pairs of points of an involution on a line. On a line l, choose a point O. Choose two points A, B, on another line through O (Fig. 8–8). Draw a circle through A and B, cutting l in P, P'. Then $OP \cdot OP' = OA \cdot OB$. For each circle through A and B, the pair of points X, X' in which the circle meets l is such that $OX \cdot OX' = OA \cdot OB = c$, say. Hence, by the remarks above,

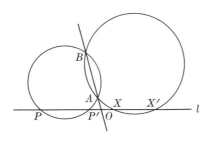

FIGURE 8–8

we conclude that the circles through A and B cut l in pairs of points of an involution. If M is the point of tangency of a tangent drawn from O to any one of these circles, then $OM^2 = c$. Hence the two points on l at distance OM from O are the fixed points of this involution. (Alternatively worded, the two circles through A and B which are tangent to l determine the fixed points.)

The involutions on a line bear an interesting relation to a problem in harmonic separation. If we have two points P, P' on a line, there are indefinitely many pairs of points X, Y such that P, P', X, Y form a harmonic set. (Indeed, we can choose X arbitrarily, and then Y will be uniquely determined.) Likewise, for a given pair Q, Q' there are indefinitely many pairs Z, W which separate Q, Q' harmonically. Are any of the X, Y pairs also Z, W pairs? That is, are there any pairs which separate both P, P' and Q, Q' harmonically? Yes, just one pair—the fixed points of the involution determined by the pairs P, P'; Q, Q'.

Theorem 8–18. In S_1 there is exactly one pair of points which separates harmonically each of two given pairs of points.

The proof of this theorem is left as a problem (Problem 6 below). The method of constructing the unique pair of Theorem 8–18 is suggested by Fig. 8–8 (Problem 7 below). On the real Euclidean line there are cases in which the points may be imaginary (Problem 8 below).

From the construction of Fig. 8–8, we arrive at the following theorem. In a plane, the circles of a family through two fixed points cut out pairs of points of an involution on any line not passing through either of the two fixed points. This result is a special case of *Desargues' involution theorem*, which we shall discuss in Chapter 11. We now turn to another

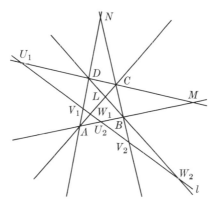

FIGURE 8–9

special case of the same theorem, a result which may also be considered to be a generalization of the harmonic properties of the complete quadrangle.

Theorem 8–19.   Let l be a line not passing through any of the vertices of a given complete quadrangle.   Then the three pairs of points in which l meets the pairs of opposite sides of the quadrangle belong to an involution.

Proof.   Suppose that l meets the pairs of opposite sides in U_1, U_2; V_1, V_2; W_1, W_2, as in Fig. 8–9.   Then

$$(U_1, V_1, W_1, W_2) \overset{D}{\wedge} (C, A, W_1, L) \overset{B}{\wedge} (V_2, U_2, W_1, W_2).$$

Hence, $(U_1V_1, W_1W_2) = (U_2V_2, W_2W_1)$.   Therefore the projectivity determined by $U_1 \to U_2$, $V_1 \to V_2$, $W_1 \to W_2$ is an involution, for in this projectivity $W_2 \to W_1$. $\square$

PROBLEM SET 8–8

1. (a) Which of the first four of the examples of involutory transformations of Section 8–8 are involutions?

(b) Let T be a projectivity of line l onto line l'.   Consider the transformation F of the set consisting of the union of the points of l and l' onto itself defined as follows:

$$F(X) = \begin{cases} T(X), & \text{if } X \in l; \\ T^{-1}(X), & \text{if } X \in l'. \end{cases}$$

Show that F is involutory.   Is F an involution?

2. Prove Theorem 8–15 in the following way.   Let T represent a collineation which interchanges one pair of points, and analyze T^2.   (Remember that a collineation has at least one fixed point.)

3. Prove Theorem 8–16.

4. (a) What are the characteristic roots and fixed points of the collineation of S_1 with matrix

$$T = \begin{bmatrix} 3 & 8 \\ 2 & -3 \end{bmatrix}?$$

Carry through the reduction of T to canonical form.   Verify that this collineation is an involution by showing that $T^2 = kI$, and by showing that the invariant cross ratio is -1.

(b) Same as (a) for

$$S = \begin{bmatrix} 3 & 4 \\ -2 & -3 \end{bmatrix}.$$

5. Complete the proof of Theorem 8–17 by establishing that e is a primitive pth root of unity.

6. Prove Theorem 8–18.

*7. (a) Given two pairs of points P, P'; Q, Q' on a real Euclidean line, describe how to construct the unique pair F, F' which separates each of the given pairs harmonically.

(b) Your method in part (a), based on the material of this section, will establish the following result.

If P, P'; Q, Q' are two pairs of points on l, if an arbitrary circle through P and P' meets an arbitrary circle through Q and Q' in M and N, then the line MN meets l in a *fixed* point O.

Prove this statement directly. [*Hint:* Use the result of Problem 26 of Section 1–1.]

8. Under what circumstances will F, F' of Problem 7(a) be imaginary?

9. (a) If T, R are both matrices of involutions in S_1, prove that TR is the matrix of an involution if and only if $TR = -RT$;

(b) Let R, T, RT be matrices of involutions in S_1, and let U, V be the fixed points of RT. Show, both algebraically and geometrically, that $R(U) = T(U) = V$ and that $R(V) = T(V) = U$. Describe the location of U, V relative to the fixed points of R and T.

(c) What is the generalization of part (a) for involutions in S_n? in V_n?

10. Suppose that T is a collineation of S_1, with a fixed point U and a certain point X such that $(UX, \tilde{X}X') = -1$, where $T(X) = \tilde{X}$, $T(X') = X$. Show that T is parabolic.

11. Verify that

$$x'_0 = x_0,$$
$$x'_1 = x_0 - x_1,$$
$$x'_2 = x_0 - 2x_1 + x_2$$

is an involution in S_2. Generalize (Euler).

12. Let X, Y be 2×2 matrices representing collineations on S_1. Show that the transformation with matrix $XY - YX$, if nonsingular, is involutory.

13. State the plane dual of Theorem 8–19.

*14. Let a, b, c be the sides of a triangle, and a', b', c' be lines through the respective opposite vertices. Let a line l meet these lines at A, B, C, A', B', C', assumed all distinct. Prove that a', b', c' are concurrent $\Leftrightarrow$ A, A'; B, B'; C, C' are pairs in an involution on l. [*Hint:* For "$\Leftarrow$," assume a', b', c' not concurrent; let b', c' meet at P, and draw a'' through P and the appropriate vertex of the triangle to meet l at A'', etc.]

15. State the dual of the result of Problem 14.

*16. Show that the correlation defined by $k\omega = B\xi$ is involutory if and only if the matrix B is symmetric.

8–9 QUADRATIC FORMS; INVARIANTS

This section will constitute a brief introduction to some topics of prime importance in geometry and algebra. The material will be encountered again in Chapters 10 and 11, but a thorough analysis of these topics is a matter for lengthy study (see the relevant references in the Bibliography).

Definition 4.   A homogeneous polynomial of degree n in two variables is called a *binary form* of order n.

For example,

$$F(x, y) \equiv ax^2 + bxy + cy^2$$

is a binary form of order 2, or a binary *quadratic* form. The binary quadratic form

$$f(w_0, w_1) \equiv a_{00}w_0^2 + 2a_{01}w_0w_1 + a_{11}w_1^2 \tag{1}$$

may be said to *represent* two points on a line l in the sense that the roots of $f(w_0, w_1) = 0$, (r_0, r_1) and (s_0, s_1), say, may be thought of as coordinate vectors of two points on l. The points will be distinct if and only if $a_{00}a_{11} - a_{01}^2 \neq 0$.

There is a neat matrix form for Eq. (1):

$$f(w_0, w_1) \equiv [w_0, \quad w_1]\begin{bmatrix} a_{00} & a_{01} \\ a_{01} & a_{11} \end{bmatrix}\begin{bmatrix} w_0 \\ w_1 \end{bmatrix}; \tag{2}$$

or, with obvious notation,

$$f(w_0, w_1) = \omega^t \cdot A \cdot \omega, \tag{3}$$

where A may be called the *matrix of the form*.

The points represented by the form will be distinct if and only if the matrix of the form is nonsingular; i.e., if and only if det $A \neq 0$.

Suppose now that we perform a nonsingular linear transformation T, which may be thought of either as the (active) projectivity of the points of l onto the points of another line l', or as the (passive) change of coordinate frame on l. We have

$$\omega = T\omega'.$$

Hence

$$\omega^t = (\omega')^t T^t,$$

and Eq. (3) becomes

$$f'(w_0', w_1') = (\omega')^t T^t A T \omega' \tag{4}$$

or

$$f'(w_0', w_1') = (\omega')^t A'\omega',$$

where $A' = T^t A T$.

Now

$$\det A' = (\det T^t) \cdot (\det A) \cdot (\det T) = (\det T)^2 \cdot (\det A). \qquad (5)$$

Since T is nonsingular, $\det T \neq 0$. Hence $\det A' = 0$ if and only if $\det A = 0$. This statement has a significant, though obvious, geometrical interpretation. The points represented by $f'(w_0', w_1')$ are distinct if and only if the points represented by $f(w_0, w_1)$ are distinct.

It is worth writing Eq. (5) in somewhat more explicit fashion:

$$\begin{vmatrix} a_{00}' & a_{01}' \\ a_{01}' & a_{11}' \end{vmatrix} = \begin{vmatrix} t_1 & t_2 \\ t_3 & t_4 \end{vmatrix}^2 \cdot \begin{vmatrix} a_{00} & a_{01} \\ a_{01} & a_{11} \end{vmatrix}, \text{ where } T = \begin{bmatrix} t_1 & t_2 \\ t_3 & t_4 \end{bmatrix}. \qquad (6)$$

We have here an example of an *invariant*, or more precisely, *of an invariant of the form $f(w_0, w_1)$ under the transformation T*. The formal definition reads as follows.

Definition 5. A function $\phi(a_{00}, a_{01}, a_{11})$ of the coefficients of the variables of a binary quadratic form is *invariant under* a linear transformation with matrix T if

$$\phi(a_{00}', a_{01}', a_{11}') = k \cdot \phi(a_{00}, a_{01}, a_{11}),$$

where a_{00}', a_{01}', a_{11}' are the coefficients of the variables of the form after the transformation, and k is a function of the elements of T alone (i.e., k is independent of the a's).

It can be shown that k will always equal $(\det T)^n$ where n is some integer, called the *weight* of the invariant. Thus, the *discriminant*, $a_{00}a_{11} - a_{01}^2$, is an invariant of weight two of the form (1) under linear transformations.

Geometrically, if an invariant ϕ of a binary form f equals zero, there is a relation between the points represented by f which is unchanged under coordinate change or projectivity. This fact accounts for the importance in geometry of the study of invariants.

There is nothing more to be said about a single binary quadratic form—either the points represented by the form are distinct or not—but some interesting results are obtainable if we consider a second form at the same time.

Let $g(w_0, w_1) \equiv b_{00}w_0^2 + 2b_{01}w_0w_1 + b_{11}^2 w_1^2 = \omega^t B \omega$ represent another pair of points on line l. For any value of the parameter x, the quadratic form

$$f(w_0, w_1) + x \cdot g(w_0, w_1) \equiv (a_{00} + xb_{00})w_0^2 + \cdots = \omega^t(A + x \cdot B)\omega$$

also represents a pair of points on l.

Now consider a nonsingular linear transformation

$$\omega = T\omega',$$

which takes f, g, $f + xg$ into f', g', $f' + xg'$, respectively. Let the matrices of these new forms be A', B', $A' + xB'$, respectively. From Eq. (5), we know that

$$\det (A' + xB') = (\det T)^2 \cdot \det (A + xB).$$

Straightforward calculation (Problem 1 below) shows that

$$\det (A + xB) = (a_{00} + xb_{00})(a_{11} + xb_{11}) - (a_{01} + xb_{01})^2$$

$$= \det A + x\psi + x^2(\det B),$$

where

$$\psi = a_{00}b_{11} - 2a_{01}b_{01} + a_{11}b_{00},$$

and similarly,

$$\det (A' + xB') = \det A' + x\psi' + x^2(\det B'),$$

where

$$\psi' = a'_{00}b'_{11} - 2a'_{01}b'_{01} + a'_{11}b'_{00}.$$

Thus

$$(\det T)^2 \cdot (\det A) + x\psi' + x^2 \cdot (\det T)^2(\det B)$$

$$= (\det T)^2[\det A + x\psi + x^2(\det B)].$$

Since $\det T$ is independent of x, we conclude that

$$\psi' = (\det T)^2 \cdot \psi. \tag{7}$$

We have here an example of a *simultaneous invariant* of the forms f and g under the transformation T.

Definition 6. A function $\Phi(a_{00}, a_{01}, a_{11}; b_{00}, b_{01}, b_{11})$ of the coefficients of the variables of two binary quadratic forms is a *simultaneous invariant* of the forms under a linear transformation with matrix T if

$$\Phi(a'_{00}, \ldots, b'_{11}) = k\Phi(a_{00}, \ldots, b_{11}),$$

where the primed letters are the coefficients of the variables of the forms after the transformation, and k is a function of the elements of T alone (i.e., k is independent of the a's and b's).

The geometric significance of a simultaneous invariant is analogous to that of a simple invariant: The vanishing of a simultaneous invariant of f and g expresses a projectively invariant relation among the sets of points represented by f and g.

The significance of the invariance of ψ, as given by Eq. (7), is contained in the following theorem.

Theorem 8–20. The pairs of points represented by

$$f \equiv a_{00}w_0^2 + 2a_{01}w_0w_1 + a_{11}w_1^2$$

and

$$g \equiv b_{00}w_0^2 + 2b_{01}w_0w_1 + b_{11}w_1^2$$

are harmonic conjugates if and only if

$$a_{00}b_{11} - 2a_{01}b_{01} + a_{11}b_{00} = 0.$$

Proof. Because we have established the invariance of ψ, we can choose a coordinate frame at will to simplify the problem. Let the points represented by f be the fundamental points $(1, 0)$ and $(0, 1)$ of the coordinate system. Then

$$a_{00} = 0 = a_{11}, \quad \text{and} \quad f \equiv 2a_{01}w_0w_1, \quad a_{01} \neq 0.$$

Hence $\psi = -2a_{01}b_{01}$. Thus ψ vanishes if and only if $b_{01} = 0$. If $b_{01} = 0$, $g \equiv b_{00}w_0^2 + b_{11}w_1^2$; and g represents the points $(\sqrt{b_{11}}, \pm i\sqrt{b_{00}})$, which are harmonic conjugates with respect to $(1, 0)$ and $(0, 1)$.

It is left to the reader to carry through the details in case the points represented by f are not distinct.

Theorem 8–21. The pair of points (r_0, r_1), (s_0, s_1) separate harmonically the pair represented by $f \equiv a_{00}w_0^2 + 2a_{01}w_1w_0 + a_{11}w_1^2$ if and only if

$$a_{00}r_0s_0 + a_{01}(r_0s_1 + r_1s_0) + a_{11}r_1s_1 = 0.$$

If (r_0, r_1) is written as the vector ρ and (s_0, s_1) as σ, this equation may be written as

$$\rho^t A\sigma = 0,$$

where A is the matrix

$$\begin{bmatrix} a_{00} & a_{01} \\ a_{01} & a_{11} \end{bmatrix},$$

and 0 is really [0], the matrix with single element 0.

Proof 1. A binary quadratic form whose zeros are (r_0, r_1) and (s_0, s_1) is

$$r_1s_1w_0^2 - (r_0s_1 + r_1s_0)w_0w_1 + r_0s_0w_1^2.$$

Letting this form play the role of g in Theorem 8–20 gives the desired result.

Proof 2. An independent proof is instructive in connection with work on ternary quadratic forms (conics) in Chapter 10. Consider a point X with coordinate vector ξ, where $\xi = k\rho + l\sigma$. The point X is represented by the quadratic form $f \equiv \omega^t A \omega$ provided that $\xi^t A \xi = 0$; i.e., if $(k\rho + l\sigma)^t A (k\rho + l\sigma) = 0$. Making use of the distributivity of matrix multiplication over matrix addition, we can expand the left side of this equation to give

$$k^2 \rho^t A \rho + kl(\rho^t A \sigma + \sigma^t A \rho) = l^2 \sigma^t A \sigma = 0.$$

Since $\sigma^t A \rho$ is a 1×1 matrix, and since A is symmetric,

$$\sigma^t A \rho = (\sigma^t A \rho)^t = \rho^t A \sigma.$$

Hence we have

$$k^2 \rho^t A \rho + 2kl\rho^t A \sigma + l^2 \sigma^t A \sigma = 0. \tag{8}$$

This quadratic has two roots, k_1/l_1 and k_2/l_2, say, such that $k_1\rho + l_1\sigma$ and $k_2\rho + l_2\sigma$ are coordinate vectors of the two points represented by f. These points are harmonic conjugates with respect to the points with coordinate vectors ρ and σ if and only if $(k_1/l_1) + (k_2/l_2) = 0$, i.e., if the sum of the roots of Eq. (8) is zero. But this is true if and only if $\rho^t A \sigma = 0$. $\square$

Definition 7. Two binary quadratic forms for which

$$\psi = a_{00}b_{11} + 2a_{01}b_{01} + a_{11}b_{00} = 0$$

are said to be *apolar.*

Thus, a pair of binary quadratic forms represents a harmonic set of points if and only if the forms are apolar.

The proofs of the next three theorems are left as problems.

Theorem 8–22. If the binary quadratic form $h(w_0, w_1)$ is apolar to each of the forms f and g then h is apolar to $xf + yg$ for all values of x, y.

Theorem 8–23. Let f and g be binary quadratic forms as before, and let

$$J = \begin{bmatrix} a_{00}w_0 + a_{01}w_1 & a_{01}w_0 + a_{11}w_1 \\ b_{00}w_0 + b_{01}w_1 & b_{01}w_0 + b_{11}w_1 \end{bmatrix}.$$

Then $\det J$ is a binary quadratic form apolar to each of f and g.

Note: The reader may recognize $4 \cdot \det J$ as the Jacobian,

$$\frac{\partial(f, g)}{\partial(w_0, w_1)} \, .$$

Theorem 8–24. The pairs of elements of the involution on l determined by the pairs represented by f and g are given by $xf + yg$, and the fixed elements of this involution are represented by $\det J$.

Theorem 8–24 will be needed in the proof of Desargues' Involution Theorem (Chapter 11).

PROBLEM SET 8–9

1. Carry out the algebraic details leading to Eq. (7).

2. Discuss Theorem 8–20 in the case that the discriminant of f is 0.

3. Prove Theorem 8–22.

4. Prove Theorem 8–23.

5. Prove Theorem 8–24.

6. (a) Show that the points represented by Eq. (1) are paired in the involution given by Eq. (4) of Section 8–8 if and only if

$$sa_{11} - 2qa_{01} + pa_{00} = 0.$$

(b) Use part (a) to prove Theorem 8–24.

7. Generalize the idea of invariance to more complicated forms.

8. Referring to the definition of an invariant of a quadratic form, prove that $k = (\det T)^n$ by considering $x'' = T_{\mathrm{adj}} \cdot x'$ and using the theorem that a determinant is an irreducible polynomial in its elements.

CHAPTER 9

Groups

9–1 INTRODUCTION

We shall continue the investigation of groups begun in Chapter 3, partly because of the applicability of some of the results to geometrical problems, and partly because of the intrinsic algebraic interest of the subject. We shall introduce work on subgroups through the following set of problems; also, the problems of Section 3–6 should be reviewed.

PROBLEM SET 9–1

*1. Verify that each of the following systems is a group, the operation being matrix multiplication: the set of all nonsingular matrices $A = [a_{ij}]$, $i, j = 0, 1, \ldots, n$, if

(a) $a_{ij} \in C$,
(b) $a_{ij} \in R$,
(c) $a_{ij} \in \mathfrak{R}$,
(d) $a_{ij} \in C$, det $A = \pm 1$,
(e) $a_{ij} \in R$, det $A = \pm 1$,
(f) $a_{ij} \in C$, det $A = 1$,
(g) $a_{ij} \in C$, the first row being 1, 0, 0, $\ldots$, 0,
(h) $a_{ij} \in C$, $a_{00} = 1$, $a_{ij} = \delta_{ij}$ for $j > 0$.

Indicate subgroup relationships among the groups described in parts (a) through (h).

2. Refer to Problem 9 of Section 6–6 for background on this problem.

(a) Consider the set of all nonsingular $n \times n$ matrices with complex elements such that, for any one matrix, the sum of the elements of each row is constant (but perhaps not the same constant for different matrices). Show that the set forms a group under multiplication.

(b) Show that the subset of the matrices in (a) for which the row sum is either $+1$ or -1 is a subgroup of the group in (a).

(c) Show that the subset of the matrices in (b) for which the row sum is $+1$ is a subgroup of the group in (b). (Huseyin Demir)

3. Which of the axioms of a group are satisfied by each of the following systems?

(a) The set of positive integers congruent to 1 (mod 4) [i.e., 1, 5, 9, 13, 17, ...] under multiplication.

(b) The subset of the $n \times n$ nonsingular matrices with elements from C, such that the determinant Δ of a matrix of the subset satisfies the relation $0 < \Delta \leq 1$, under matrix multiplication.

(c) The set of $n \times n$ matrices $[p_{ij}]$, $p_{ij} \in R$, $p_{ij} \geq 0$, $\sum_{j=1}^{n} p_{ij} = 1$ for each i (these are known as "stochastic matrices") under matrix multiplication.

(d) The set of all subsets of a set S, under $\cap$ (intersection of sets).

(e) The set of all subsets of a set S, under $\cup$ (union of sets).

*4. Show that under matrix multiplication, each of the following sets forms a group:

(a) $\mathcal{G} = \left\{ \begin{bmatrix} x & y \\ 0 & z \end{bmatrix} ; \quad x, y, z \in C; \quad x \neq 0, z \neq 0 \right\}$,

(b) $\mathcal{H} = \left\{ \begin{bmatrix} w & u \\ 0 & w \end{bmatrix} ; \quad w, u \in C; \quad w \neq 0 \right\}$,

(c) $\mathcal{J} = \left\{ \begin{bmatrix} t & v \\ 0 & t \end{bmatrix} ; \quad t, v \in R; \quad t \neq 0 \right\}$.

Show also that $\mathcal{G} \supset \mathcal{H} \supset \mathcal{J}$.

5. Among the $n \times n$ matrices whose elements belong to an arbitrary field $\mathfrak{F}$, consider matrices of the following types.

(a) P_r, $r > 0$, signifies a matrix all of whose elements are zero, except for elements on the rth "parallel" above the principal diagonal; at least one element on this rth parallel is not zero.

(b) P_r, $r < 0$, has the same significance as in (a) for the rth parallel below the principal diagonal.

(c) P_0 signifies a matrix all of whose elements are zero, except possibly for elements on the principal diagonal.

With the operation of multiplication of matrices, which axioms of a group are satisfied by the set of all matrices of type P_r, r an integer between $-(n-1)$ and $(n-1)$ (cf. Problem 16, Section 3–3)?

6. Let a, b be fixed complex numbers, and consider a system of ordered pairs (x, y) of complex numbers with multiplication defined as follows:

$$(x_1, y_1) \cdot (x_2, y_2) = [x_1(ax_2 + by_2), y_1(ax_2 + by_2)].$$

Decide on an appropriate definition for the *equality* of two pairs, and obtain the conditions for this system to be a group.

7. (a) Let S be the set of nonsingular $n \times n$ lower triangular matrices (Definition 4, Section 7–3) with elements from the complex numbers C. Show that with the operation of matrix multiplication, S is a group.

(b) Let $\mathcal{J}$ be the subset of S for which the elements on the principal diagonal are all equal, and likewise for the elements on each diagonal parallel to the principal diagonal (i.e., $x_{ii} = x_{jj}$, all i, j; $x_{21} = x_{32} = \cdots = x_{n,n-1}$; $x_{31} = x_{42} = \cdots = x_{n,n-2}; \ldots; x_{n-1,1} = x_{n,2}$). Show that $\mathfrak{J}$ is an Abelian group.

8. Let S be a system of elements with two binary operations, $\oplus$ and $\odot$, satisfying Axioms A1 through A4, M1, M3, and D of a field. Let $\mathfrak{F}$ be a field, with operations denoted in the usual way. If x is an element of $\mathfrak{F}$ and S an element of S, let xS be an element of S satisfying the following conditions.

(a) For all x, $y \in \mathfrak{F}$ and each $S \in \mathsf{S}$, $(x + y)S = xS \oplus yS$.
(b) For all x_1, $x_2 \in \mathfrak{F}$ and all S_1, $S_2 \in \mathsf{S}$, $(x_1 S_1) \odot (x_2 S_2) = (x_1 x_2)(S_1 \odot S_2)$.
(c) If o is the additive identity of $\mathfrak{F}$ and 0 is the $\oplus$ identity of S, then

$$\text{(i)} \quad oS = 0, \quad \text{for all} \quad S \in \mathsf{S},$$

and

$$\text{(ii)} \quad x0 = 0, \quad \text{for all} \quad x \in \mathfrak{F}.$$

Let S_0, S_1, $\ldots$, S_{n-1} be a set of n elements of S with

$$S_i \odot S_j = \begin{cases} S_{i+j}, & i+j \le n-1, \\ 0, & i+j > n-1. \end{cases}$$

Show that the set of all elements of the form

$$x_0 S_0 \oplus x_1 S_1 \oplus \cdots \oplus x_{n-1} S_{n-1}, \qquad x_i \in \mathfrak{F}, \quad x_0 \ne o,$$

forms an Abelian group under the operation $\odot$.

9. Use Problem 8 to solve Problem 7(b).

10. Under assumptions (a), (b), and (c) of Problem 8, let S_0, S_1, $\ldots$, S_{n-1} be a set of n elements of S with

$$S_i \odot S_j = \begin{cases} S_i, & \text{if} \quad i = j, \\ 0, & \text{if} \quad i \ne j. \end{cases}$$

Show that the set of all elements of the form

$$x_0 S_0 \oplus x_1 S_1 \oplus \cdots \oplus x_{n-1} S_{n-1}, \quad x_i \in \mathfrak{F},$$

each $x_i \ne o$, forms an Abelian group under the operation $\odot$.

11. Use Problem 10 to establish that the set of all matrices of the type

$$\begin{bmatrix} x & x - y \\ 0 & y \end{bmatrix},$$

x, y nonzero elements of a field, forms an Abelian group under multiplication.

12. Generalize Problem 11.

13. Establish a statement of the general sort exemplified by Problems 8 and 10 which will have the result of Problem 7(a) as a corollary.

14. Consider Pythagorean number-triples: $X(x_1, x_2, x_3)$ where the x_i are rational numbers such that

$$x_1^2 = x_2^2 + x_3^2, \qquad x_3 \neq 0.$$

Show that the set of such number-triples forms a group under the following operation. If Y is the triple (y_1, y_2, y_3), then

$$X \cdot Y = (x_1 y_1 + x_2 y_2, \; x_1 y_2 + x_2 y_1, \; x_3 y_3).$$

(G. Kushner, *Elem. Math.*, 1957.)

9–2 SUBGROUPS; COSET DECOMPOSITION

We shall expand somewhat on the material contained in the foregoing set of problems and in the problems of Section 3–6.

Straightforward construction of group tables shows that all groups of order less than 6 are Abelian. The group of symmetries of an equilateral triangle (Problem 6, Section 3–6) is a non-Abelian group of order 6.

There are just two abstract groups of order 4:

(1)				
$\cdot$	u	a	b	c
u	u	a	b	c
a	a	b	c	u
b	b	c	u	a
c	c	u	a	b

(2)				
$\cdot$	u	p	q	r
u	u	p	q	r
p	p	u	r	q
q	q	r	u	p
r	r	q	p	u

For the group (1), we observe that $a \cdot a = b$, $a \cdot a \cdot a = c$. It is natural to abbreviate the notation by writing $a^2 = b$, $a^3 = c$. Clearly, if a is an element of a group, so is a^k for all positive integers, k. If, as is the case with group (1), all elements are powers of a single element, the group is said to be *cyclic*, and that single element is said to *generate* the group.

In group (1), the cyclic group of order 4, we have $a^1 = a$, $a^2 = b$, $a^3 = c$, $a^4 = u$. For each element x of a finite group, there is a positive integer m, such that $x^m = u$ (Problem 1 below). The least positive integer q such that $x^q = u$ is called the *order* of the element x. Obviously, a cyclic group of order n can be generated only by an element of order n. The cyclic group of order 4 can be generated either by a or by c; the element b, being of order 2, generates not the whole group, but rather the sub-group $\{u, b\}$.

The group (2) has 3 elements of order 2: p, q, r. It is called the "fours-group."

The hierarchy of subgroups in the group of symmetries of a square can be sketched as follows.

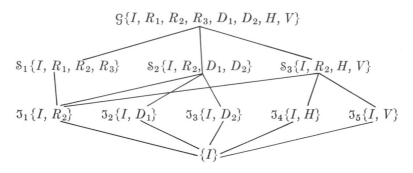

$$\mathcal{G}\{I, R_1, R_2, R_3, D_1, D_2, H, V\}$$

$$\mathcal{S}_1\{I, R_1, R_2, R_3\} \qquad \mathcal{S}_2\{I, R_2, D_1, D_2\} \qquad \mathcal{S}_3\{I, R_2, H, V\}$$

$$\mathcal{J}_1\{I, R_2\} \quad \mathcal{J}_2\{I, D_1\} \quad \mathcal{J}_3\{I, D_2\} \quad \mathcal{J}_4\{I, H\} \quad \mathcal{J}_5\{I, V\}$$

$$\{I\}$$

In this lattice each line segment joins a group to one of its subgroups. It is easy to see that $\mathcal{S}_1$ is isomorphic to the cyclic group of order 4, and that each of $\mathcal{S}_2$, $\mathcal{S}_3$ is isomorphic to the fours-group.

The hierarchy of subgroups of Problem 1 of the preceding section looks like this:

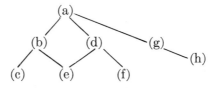

(a)

(b)   (d)   (g)

(c)   (e)   (f)   (h)

The elements of group (a) are the matrices of the nonsingular projective transformations, in accordance with our definition in Chapter 6. It is often called the *full linear group* over the complex field, and designated by $L_{n+1}(C)$.

A typical element of group (g) is a matrix which defines the transformation

$$rx_0' = x_0,$$

$$rx_1' = a_{10}x_0 + a_{11}x_1 + \cdots + a_{1n}x_n,$$

$$\vdots$$

$$rx_n' = a_{n0}x_0 + a_{n1}x_1 + \cdots + a_{nn}x_n.$$

By this transformation, any ideal point (a point with its first coordinate zero) is carried into an ideal point, and any ordinary point (a point with its first coordinate not equal to zero) is carried into an ordinary point. Those projective transformations which distinguish in this way between ordinary and ideal points are called *affine transformations*.

Similarly, a typical element of group (h) is a matrix which defines the transformation

$$rx'_0 = x_0,$$

$$rx'_1 = a_{10}x_0 + x_1,$$

$$rx'_2 = a_{20}x_0 + x_2,$$

$$\vdots$$

$$rx'_n = a_{n0}x_0 + x_n.$$

In the ordinary language of geometry, this is called a *translation*. The group of translations, then, is a subgroup of the group of affine transformations, which, in turn, is a subgroup of the full linear group.

Some important properties of groups and subgroups stem from a consideration of what is called a *coset decomposition* of a group. As an introduction to this topic, we extend a notion which we have encountered before.

It will be remembered that if S_1, S_2 are subsets of a set S in which "$+$" is defined as a binary operation, then $S_1 + S_2$ is the set of all elements $s_1 + s_2$, $s_1 \in S_1$, $s_2 \in S_2$. Likewise, if the binary operation is "$\cdot$", then $S_1 \cdot S_2$ is the set of all elements $(s_1 \cdot s_2)$, $s_1 \in S_1$, $s_2 \in S_2$. In particular, if S_1 consists of the single element $\tilde{s}$, we write $\tilde{s} \cdot S_2$ to represent the set of all elements $(\tilde{s} \cdot s_2)$, $s_2 \in S_2$. If the operation "$\cdot$" is associative, then $S_1 \cdot (S_2 \cdot S_3) = (S_1 \cdot S_2) \cdot S_3$; in particular,

$$(s \cdot t) \cdot S_3 = s \cdot (t \cdot S_3).$$

We are now ready for the definition of "coset."

Definition 1. If H is a subgroup of the group G, then a *left coset* of H is the set $g \cdot H$, where g is some element of G.

Theorem 9–1. No two elements of a left coset are identical.

Proof. If $g \cdot h_i = g \cdot h_j$, then $g^{-1}gh_i = g^{-1}gh_j$, i.e., $h_i = h_j$. ⊔

Theorem 9–2. If $g \in H$, then $gH = H$.

Proof. Since H is a group, it is clear that $gh \subseteq H$. Let h_k be an arbitrary element of H. Does there exist an $x \in H$ such that $g \cdot x = h_k$? Yes: $x = g^{-1}h_k$. Hence $gh \subseteq H$. Therefore, $gH = H$. □

Theorem 9–3. Two left cosets of a subgroup are either disjoint or identical.

Proof. Suppose that there is an element common to $a \cdot H$ and $b \cdot H$; i.e., suppose that for some h_i, h_j, $a \cdot h_i = b \cdot h_j$. Then $(a \cdot h_i) \cdot H =$

$(b \cdot h_j) \cdot H$. Hence, by associativity, $a \cdot (h_i \cdot H) = b(h_j \cdot H)$. But, by Theorem 9–2, $h_i \cdot H = H = h_j \cdot H$. Therefore $a \cdot H = b \cdot H$, or the cosets are identical. $\square$

Theorem 9–4. The elements of a group G can be divided among mutually exclusive left cosets of a subgroup H of G.

Proof. Any element x of G belongs to a left coset of H, viz., to $x \cdot H$. By Theorem 9–3, x cannot belong to two cosets of H. $\square$

Thus, any element $\tilde{a}$ of a left coset, $a \cdot H$, generates that coset. If $\tilde{a} \in aH$, then $\tilde{a} \cdot H = a \cdot H$. Any element of the coset may be thought of as a *representative* of the coset. The decomposition of a group into mutually exclusive left cosets of a subgroup is a decomposition of the group into equivalence classes (Section 3–2).

Definition 2. The element x of group G is *left congruent* to y *modulo the subgroup H* if there exists $h_{xy} \in H$ such that $x = y \cdot h_{xy}$. Notation: $x \equiv y(\mathrm{mod}\, H_l)$.

It is easy to verify that "left congruence mod H" is an equivalence relation (Problem 7 below); thus we may speak of x and y as being left congruent mod H. Moreover, it is straightforward to demonstrate that x and y are left congruent mod H if and only if x and y belong to the same left coset of H (Problem 8 below).

We have a development comparable to the foregoing for "right cosets" and "right congruence, mod H". In the rest of this section we shall omit the designation "left" or "right," leaving it to the reader to supply either adjective.

EXAMPLE 1. If G is the group of integers, the operation being addition, and if H is the subgroup of integral multiples of some fixed integer n, then the decomposition of G into cosets of H is the same as that of the set of integers into residue classes mod n:

$$H = \{\dots, -2n, -n, 0, n, 2n, \dots\},$$

$$1 + H = \{\dots, 1 - 2n, 1 - n, 1, 1 + n, 1 + 2n, \dots\},$$

$$2 + H = \{\dots, 2 - 2n, 2 - n, 2, 2 + n, 2 + 2n, \dots\},$$

and so forth.

In this case, each of G, H has infinitely many elements, and there are n cosets of H.

EXAMPLE 2. If G is the group of rational numbers except 0, the operation being multiplication, and if H is the subgroup consisting of 1 and -1, then the decomposition of G involves infinitely many cosets, each containing two elements, $\pm p/q$. On the other hand, if we decompose G into cosets of K, the subgroup consisting of the positive rationals, we obtain just two cosets: K itself, and the set of negative rationals.

EXAMPLE 3. If G is the group of all nonsingular $n \times n$ matrices over C, the operation being matrix multiplication, and if H is the subgroup consisting of those matrices of G whose determinants are 1, then any two matrices in a coset have the same determinant. Conversely, any two matrices with the same determinant will appear in the same coset (Problem 9 below). Thus, there will be a coset corresponding to each complex number other than zero.

Clearly, if H is a finite subgroup of an infinite group G the decomposition of G must involve infinitely many cosets. We have above an example of an infinite group with an infinite subgroup in which the decomposition involves a finite number of cosets (Example 2), and another example involving infinitely many cosets (Example 3).

Definition 3. If there is a finite number k of cosets of H in G, then k is called the *index* of H in G.

Theorem 9–5 (*Lagrange*). In a finite group, the order of a subgroup is a divisor of the order of the group.

Proof. Let the order of the group be n, the order of the subgroup m, and the index of the subgroup in the group k. By Theorem 9–1, there are m elements in each coset; by Theorem 9–3, the cosets are pairwise disjoint. Hence $n = m \cdot k$. □

Corollary 1. In a finite group, the order of any element is a divisor of the order of the group.

Proof. An element of order r generates a cyclic group of order r, which is a subgroup of the given group. □

Corollary 2. A group of prime order is cyclic.

Proof. Let a be an element other than the identity. Then r, the order of a, must equal the order of the group. In other words, the cyclic group generated by a is the entire group. □

A basic theorem of number theory also appears as a corollary of Theorem 9–5.

Corollary 3 (*Fermat*). If a is an integer and p is a prime, then

$$a^p \equiv a(\mathrm{mod}\ p).$$

Proof. The group of Problem 3(c), Section 3–6, is of order $p - 1$, with 1 as its identity. Hence, for any $a \not\equiv 0 \pmod{p}$, we have $a^{p-1} \equiv 1 \pmod{p}$. Therefore, $a^p \equiv a \pmod{p}$. If $a \equiv 0 \pmod{p}$, the theorem is trivially true.   □

PROBLEM SET 9–2

1. (a) Prove that for each element x of a finite group, there is a positive integer m such that $x^m = u$. [*Hint:* Since the group is finite, $x^r = x^s$ for some r, s.]

(b) Show that if a finite subset S of a group G is closed under the group operation, then S is a subgroup of G.

2. Consider the group $\mathcal{G}$ of symmetries of a square, and the subgroups as designated in the diagram of Section 9–2. Write out the indicated coset decompositions of $\mathcal{G}$:

(a) left cosets of $\mathcal{S}_1$,

(b) left cosets of $\mathcal{S}_2$,

(c) right cosets of $\mathcal{S}_2$,

(d) left cosets of $\mathcal{J}_2$,

(e) right cosets of $\mathcal{J}_2$.

3. Under what circumstance is the coset aH a group?

*4. If H is a subgroup of G of index 2, show that $aH = Ha$ for all $a \in G$.

5. Show that a necessary and sufficient condition that xH, yH be identical is that $y^{-1} \cdot x \in H$.

*6. (a) Show that in a group G the set of all x such that $xa = ax$ for each $a \in G$ forms a subgroup of G. This subgroup is called the *center* of G (cf. Problem 7, Section 3–6).

(b) Find the center of the group of symmetries of a square.

7. Verify that "left congruence mod H" is an equivalence relation.

8. Show that x, y are left congruent, mod H, if and only if x and y belong to the same left coset of H.

9. Prove that for G, H as in Example 3, each coset consists of all matrices with a given determinant.

10. Give several examples of infinite groups with subgroups of finite index; with subgroups having infinitely many cosets.

11. Set up an isomorphism in as many ways as possible between the multiplicative group of the sixth roots of unity and the additive group of residues, mod 6.

12. Show that the fours-group can be characterized as a group of order 4 containing at least two elements of order 2.

13. Show that in a group G, the set of all elements which have finite order is a subgroup of G.

14. Let G be a group of order $p \cdot q$ for primes p and q. Show that G is cyclic or else has an element of order p.

15. Let a be an element of order $n > 0$ in the multiplicative group G. Show that an rth root of a exists (i.e., there exists an x in G such that $x^r = a$) if and only if n and r are relatively prime. (You will need some algebraic results on greatest common divisor.)

16. Show that $\{1, 10\}$ is a subgroup of J_{11}, the group of nonzero residues, mod 11, under multiplication. Write out all the cosets of $\{1, 10\}$ in J_{11}.

17. Let $A_1, A_2, \ldots, A_n$ be groups in which the operation is represented by $\circ$ in each A_i. Let the direct product, $A_1 \times A_2 \times \cdots \times A_n$, be the set of all ordered n-tuples $(a_1, \ldots, a_n)$, $a_i \in A_i$, with a binary operation defined for the n-tuples as follows:

$$(a_1, \ldots, a_n) \circ (a'_1, \ldots, a'_n) = (a_1 \circ a'_1, \ldots, a_n \circ a'_n).$$

(a) Show that the direct product $A_1 \times \cdots \times A_n$ is a group.
(b) If B_i is a subgroup of A_i, $i = 1, \ldots, n$, show that $B_1 \times \cdots \times B_n$ is a subgroup of $A_1 \times \cdots \times A_n$.

18. (a) Let A be a proper subgroup of $\mathfrak{R}$, the additive group of rationals, let b be a rational number not in A, and let kb signify $b + b + \cdots + b$ (k times). Show that there exists some integer n such that $nb \in A$.

(b) Show that $\mathfrak{R}$ has no "maximal" subgroup, i.e., show that for each proper subgroup A of $\mathfrak{R}$ there exists another proper subgroup of $\mathfrak{R}$ containing A properly. (*Amer. Math. Monthly*, Jan. 1959, p. 67.)

9–3 CONJUGATE ELEMENTS; AUTOMORPHISMS

In Section 8–6 we found that $A^{-1}TA$ plays an important role in the problem of simplifying the matrix of a collineation by coordinate transformation. The same sort of expression appears in other connections as well. Suppose that we designate certain positions of a square as indicated in Fig. 9–1 (see Problem 5, Section 3–6).

Then the transformation H (rotation about a horizontal axis) carries a into a'; or, symbolically, $a' = H(a)$. Similarly, $a = R_1(b)$ and $a' = R_1(b')$. Hence,

$$R_1(b') = H\big(R_1(b)\big) = (HR_1)(b), \quad \text{or} \quad b' = (R_1^{-1}HR_1)(b).$$

We verify that $R_1^{-1}HR_1 = V$, a not surprising result; for if we first rotate the configuration through 90° clockwise (a shift of coordinate frame), then the transformation "rotation about a horizontal axis" becomes "rotation about a vertical axis."

Considerations of this sort motivate us to state the following definition.

Definition 4. In a group G, the element x is *conjugate* to the element y if there is an element a such that $x = a^{-1}ya$.

It is easy to verify that in a group, conjugation is an equivalence relation (Problem 1 below), so that it is meaningful to say "x and y are conjugate." The same concept can be applied to subsets, S_1, S_2 of group $\mathcal{G}$; S_1 and S_2 are conjugate if there is an element $a \in G$ such that $S_1 = a^{-1}S_2a$.

Definition 5. An *automorphism* of a system is an isomorphism of the system with itself.

It can be shown that the correspondence $x \to a^{-1}xa$ is an automorphism of a group.

Theorem 9–6. If a is some element of a group G, then the correspondence $x \to a^{-1}xa$ for all $x \in G$ is an automorphism of G.

Proof. The correspondence is one to one, for each x has the unique correspondent, $x' = a^{-1}xa$; and each $x' \in G$ is the correspondent of the unique $x = ax'a^{-1}$. The correspondence preserves the group operation, for if $x \to a^{-1}xa$ and $y \to a^{-1}ya$, then $xy \to a^{-1}xya = a^{-1}xa \cdot a^{-1}ya$. □

Definition 6. An automorphism of the type $g \to a^{-1}ga$ for each $g \in G$ is called an *inner automorphism* of the group G, and is said to be *induced* by a. Automorphisms not of this type are called "outer."

EXAMPLE. Consider the automorphisms of the group of symmetries of a square: $\mathcal{G} = \{I, R_1, R_2, R_3, D_1, D_2, H, V\}$. From Theorem 3–10(b) we conclude that in any automorphism I must correspond to itself. Moreover, it is readily established (Problem 2 below) that if two elements correspond in an automorphism, they have the same order. Hence, either $R_1 \to R_1$ and $R_3 \to R_3$, or $R_1 \to R_3$ and $R_3 \to R_1$. In either case, $R_2 \to R_2$. We then find the following eight automorphisms:

A_1		A_2		A_3		A_4		A_5		A_6		A_7		A_8	
I	I	I	I	I	I	I	I	I	I	I	I	I	I	I	I
R_1	R_1	R_1	R_1	R_1	R_1	R_1	R_1	R_1	R_3	R_1	R_3	R_1	R_3	R_1	R_3
R_2	R_2	R_2	R_2	R_2	R_2	R_2	R_2	R_2	R_2	R_2	R_2	R_2	R_2	R_2	R_2
R_3	R_3	R_3	R_3	R_3	R_3	R_3	R_3	R_3	R_1	R_3	R_1	R_3	R_1	R_3	R_1
D_1	D_1	D_1	D_2	D_1	H	D_1	V	D_1	D_1	D_1	D_2	D_1	H	D_1	V
D_2	D_2	D_2	D_1	D_2	V	D_2	H	D_2	D_2	D_2	D_1	D_2	V	D_2	H
H	H	H	V	H	D_2	H	D_1	H	V	H	H	H	D_1	H	D_2
V	V	V	H	V	D_1	V	D_2	V	H	V	V	V	D_2	V	D_1

Now I and R_2 can be shown each to induce the (inner) automorphism A_1; R_1 and R_3, A_2; D_1 and D_2, A_5; H and V, A_6. Hence the automorphisms A_3, A_4, A_7, A_8 are outer. For an obvious reason, A_1 is called the *identity automorphism*.

The example above illustrates the following theorem.

Theorem 9–7. The elements a and b of group G induce the same inner automorphism if and only if ba^{-1} belongs to the center of G.

The proof is left as a problem (Problem 4 below).

Corollary 1. An element p of group G induces the identity automorphism if and only if p belongs to the center of G.

Definition 7. If S is a subgroup of G with the property that $x^{-1}Sx = S$ for all $x \in G$, then S is called a *normal* (or, *invariant*, or *self-conjugate*) subgroup of G.

Normality may be thought of as a kind of weak commutativity. If s_i is an element of a normal subgroup S, then, although we can't conclude that $s_i \cdot x = x \cdot s_i$, we know that there is an $s_j \in S$ such that $s_i \cdot x = x \cdot s_j$. Clearly, the center of a group, consisting of those elements which *do* commute with all elements of the group, is a normal subgroup.

We can verify that

$$S_1 = \{I, R_1, R_2, R_3\}$$

is a normal subgroup of $\mathcal{G}$, the group of symmetries of a square. Note that if S is a normal subgroup of G, a subgroup of S is not necessarily normal in G. For example,

$$S_2 = \{I, R_2, D_1, D_2\}$$

is a normal subgroup of $\mathcal{G}$, but

$$\mathcal{I}_2 = \{I, D_1\} \subset S_2$$

is *not* a normal subgroup of $\mathcal{G}$.

Theorem 9–8. If S_1, S_2 are normal subgroups of G, then so is $S_1 \cap S_2$.

The proof is left as a problem (Problem 6 below).

We come now to an important result characterizing normal subgroups.

Theorem 9–9. S is a normal subgroup of G if and only if left cosets of S are also right cosets.

Proof. If S is normal, then $x^{-1}Sx = S$, for all $x \in G$. Hence $Sx = xS$ for all $x \in G$.

Conversely, if for each $y \in G$ there is an $x \in G$ such that $xS = Sy$, then $y^{-1}xS = y^{-1}Sy$. Thus $(y^{-1}x)S$ is a left coset of S which contains the group identity, viz., $y^{-1}uy = u$. Hence, since $(y^{-1}x)S$ contains an element of S, $y^{-1}xS = S$, by Theorem 9–3. In other words, $y^{-1}Sy = S$, for each $y \in G$. □

Corollary. A subgroup of index 2 is normal.

Proof. Use Problem 4, Section 9–2 and Theorem 9–9.

This corollary insures, without further verification, the normality of S_1, S_2, S_3 (each of order 4) in the group G (of order 8) of symmetries of a square.

We turn now to a consideration of the automorphisms of a group as themselves constituting a system. The automorphisms being transformations, we define the product of two automorphisms, A_iA_j, in a familiar manner: the transformation A_i *followed by* the transformation A_j. For example, for the automorphisms of the group of symmetries of a square, as given in the example in this section, we have $A_2 \cdot A_5 = A_6$.

Theorem 9–10. With the interpretation of multiplication just defined, the automorphisms of a group form a group.

Proof. First, we must show that the product of two automorphisms is an automorphism.

If
$$x \xrightarrow{A_i} x' \xrightarrow{A_j} x'', \qquad y \xrightarrow{A_i} y' \xrightarrow{A_j} y'',$$
then
$$xy \xrightarrow{A_i} x'y' \xrightarrow{A_j} x''y''.$$

Thus, A_iA_j is a one-to-one correspondence preserving the group operation; i.e., A_iA_j is an automorphism.

Next, in a set of transformations, the operation "followed by" is always associative.

Clearly, there is an identity element, viz., the identity automorphism.

Finally, if
$$x \xrightarrow{A} x'$$
is an automorphism, the inverse transformation, $x' \to x$, is an automorphism which is the inverse of A. □

Theorem 9–11. The inner automorphisms of a group G constitute a normal subgroup of the group of all automorphisms of G.

The proof is left as a problem (Problem 8 below).

PROBLEM SET 9–3

1. Show that conjugation is an equivalence relation.

2. Show that if two elements of a group correspond in an automorphism, they have the same order.

3. Work out the omitted details of the Example of this section.

4. Prove Theorem 9–7.

5. (a) List all the normal subgroups of G, the group of symmetries of a square.
(b) Similarly, for the group of symmetries of an equilateral triangle.

6. Prove Theorem 9–8.

7. Show that in an Abelian group, all subgroups are normal and the only inner automorphism is the identity.

8. Prove Theorem 9–11.

9. List the automorphisms of the fours-group. Which are inner? How can you describe the group of automorphisms in this case?

10. There are $3! = 6$ permutations of 1, 2, 3 (cf. Problem 2(c), Section 3–6). They form a group, called the *symmetric group on 3 elements*, designated as Σ_3.

(a) Write out the operation table for Σ_3. To what group which you have already encountered is Σ_3 isomorphic?
(b) What is the center of Σ_3?
(c) List the elements of the group of automorphisms of Σ_3. Which are the inner automorphisms?
(d) Write out the operation table for the group of automorphisms of Σ_3. To which group is Σ_3 isomorphic?

11. For the groups of Problem 1, Section 9–1, indicate normal subgroup relationships; e.g., is (e) a normal subgroup of (a)? of (b)? of (d)?

12. Show that with multiplication of sets as defined in Section 9–2, the set of all left cosets of a normal subgroup, N, of a given group, G, forms a group.

13. List the automorphisms of the cyclic group of order eight.

14. List the automorphisms of the group of symmetries of the equilateral triangle. Which are inner?

15. If G, H, J are groups with $G \supset H \supset J$, there are several possible normality relationships which may exist. For instance, H may be normal in G, J may be normal in H, and J may be normal in G; or H may be normal in G, J may not be normal in either H or G; etc.
State the normality relations for each of the following triads of groups:

(a) Problem 1, Section 9–1; groups (a), (d), (f),
(b) Problem 1, Section 9–1; groups (a), (b), (c),
(c) Problem 1, Section 9–1; groups (a), (g), (h),
(d) Problem 2, Section 9–1; groups (a), (b), (c),
(e) Problem 4, Section 9–1; groups (a), (b), (c).

16. (a) Show that if H is a subgroup of G, and N is a normal subgroup of G, then $H \cap N$ is a normal subgroup of H.

(b) Suppose that U, V are subgroups of a group G, and that W is a normal subgroup of V. Show that $U \cap W$ is a normal subgroup of $U \cap V$.

17. If S is an ordered set, an "order automorphism" of S is a one-to-one mapping, α, of S upon itself such that for a, b in S and $a < b$, then $\alpha(a) < \alpha(b)$. With the usual definition of product of automorphisms, show that the set of all order automorphisms of S forms a group (P. M. Cohn, *Mathematika*, 1957, p. 41).

9–4 ORTHOGONAL TRANSFORMATIONS

Among the subgroups of $L_n(C)$, the group of nonsingular $n \times n$ matrices over the complex numbers, are several with particular geometric interest. We shall concern ourselves principally with matrices determining transformations related to Euclidean geometry. In so doing we shall have occasion to refer to the material of Sections 4–6 and 4–7. Unless otherwise indicated, our universe will be $V_n(R)$.

Definition 8. A linear transformation T is *orthogonal* if

$$\|T(\xi)\| = \|\xi\|,$$

for all

$$\xi \in V_n(R).$$

Thus, an orthogonal transformation preserves the lengths of vectors. The name comes from the fact that it also preserves the angle between vectors, as is seen from the third part of the following theorem.

Theorem 9–12. An orthogonal transformation preserves (i) distance; (ii) inner product; (iii) angle. That is, if T is an orthogonal transformation, and if ξ, η are any vectors of $V_n(R)$, then
(i) $\|T(\xi) - T(\eta)\| = \|\xi - \eta\|$;
(ii) $T(\xi) \cdot T(\eta) = \xi \cdot \eta$;
(iii) $\cos \theta' = \cos \theta$, where θ is the angle between ξ and η; and θ' is the angle between $T(\xi)$ and $T(\eta)$.

Proof. Since T is orthogonal,

$$\|T(\xi - \eta)\| = \|\xi - \eta\|.$$

But

$$T(\xi - \eta) = T(\xi) - T(\eta).$$

This proves (i). Now

$$(\xi + \eta) \cdot (\xi + \eta) = \xi \cdot \xi + 2\xi \cdot \eta + \eta \cdot \eta.$$

Hence

$$2\xi \cdot \eta = \|\xi + \eta\|^2 - \|\xi\|^2 - \|\eta\|^2.$$

Since the right-hand side of this equation involves only the lengths of vectors, which are preserved under orthogonal transformation, we have established (ii).

Since the cosine of the angle between vectors is defined in terms of length and inner product, we have (iii).   □

We shall now characterize an orthogonal transformation in terms of the matrix which represents the transformation.

Theorem 9-13.   An $n \times n$ matrix P with real elements represents an orthogonal transformation relative to a normal orthogonal basis ⇔ the column vectors of P form a normal orthogonal set.

Proof. "⇒."   Let the equation of the transformation be $\xi' = P \cdot \xi$. Choose ξ successively as the unit vectors $\epsilon_1, \epsilon_2, \ldots, \epsilon_n$. Then ξ' will be, successively, $\bar{\pi}_1, \bar{\pi}_2, \ldots, \bar{\pi}_n$, which are the column vectors of P. Since the ϵ's form a normal orthogonal set, so do the $\bar{\pi}$'s (by Theorem 9-12).
   "⇐."   We have

$$\|\xi'\| = \left[(\Sigma p_{i1}^2)x_1^2 + \cdots + (\Sigma p_{in}^2)x_n^2 + 2 \sum_{j \neq k} p_{ij}p_{ik}x_jx_k \right]^{1/2}$$

$$= [x_1^2 + x_2^2 + \cdots + x_n^2]^{1/2},$$

if the column vectors of P form a normal orthogonal set. In other words, $\|\xi'\| = \|\xi\|$. Thus P is orthogonal.   □

Corollary.   An $n \times n$ matrix P with real elements represents an orthogonal transformation relative to a normal orthogonal basis ⇔ $P^t \cdot P = I$.

The equation $P^t \cdot P = I$ is meaningful when the elements of P come from any field, so that we can use this equation to extend the concept of orthogonality.

Definition 9.   A square matrix P over any field is called *orthogonal* if $P^t P = I$.

Thus the transpose of an orthogonal matrix P is a left inverse of P. Hence, by Theorem 7-20, P is nonsingular: $P^{-1} = P^t$. From this we conclude that $P \cdot P^t = I$, or $(P^t)^t \cdot P^t = I$. In other words, P^t is orthogonal. It is clear from the definition of an orthogonal matrix that its column vectors form a normal orthogonal set; thus, the column vectors of P^t form such a set. We have the following theorem.

Theorem 9–14. A square matrix over any field is orthogonal if and only if its row vectors form a normal orthogonal set.

Theorem 9–15. The set of all $n \times n$ orthogonal matrices over a field forms a group.

Proof. Let A and B be orthogonal matrices. Then $A^{-1} = A^t, B^{-1} = B^t$. Hence $(AB)^{-1} = B^{-1} \cdot A^{-1} = B^t A^t = (AB)^t$. Thus AB is orthogonal, i.e., the set is closed. Associativity, and the existence of the identity are immediate. Finally, the inverse of an orthogonal matrix is orthogonal. $\square$

In this section we have made reference to transformations of V_n. Comparable statements could be made for S_n by considering $(n+1) \times (n+1)$ matrices. The group of $(n+1) \times (n+1)$ orthogonal matrices, $\mathfrak{O}_{n+1}(\mathfrak{F})$, is a subgroup of the full linear group, $L_{n+1}(\mathfrak{F})$.

A *rigid* motion is a transformation which preserves distance. It can be shown that a rigid motion is necessarily linear; hence the rigid motions are the transformations of the orthogonal group (Problem 1 below). Felix Klein suggested that it is profitable to characterize geometries in terms of the *invariants* of certain groups. For example, Euclidean geometry deals with those aspects of a configuration which are not altered by the transformations of the orthogonal group. As we have seen, length and angle are invariant under these transformations, and it is a study of these (metric) notions which constitutes Euclidean geometry. Under an orthogonal transformation, a circle is carried into a circle—indeed, into a circle with the same radius as the original. Thus, in Euclidean geometry, we distinguish among the ellipse, the parabola, and the hyperbola; moreover, we distinguish among ellipses of different eccentricities; finally, we distinguish between two ellipses of the same eccentricity but different sizes, putting two ellipses into the same category only if they are *congruent*.

In projective geometry, on the other hand, we study those properties invariant under the transformations of the full linear group. Incidence of point and line (P lies on l, or l passes through P) is of prime importance here. Also, cross ratio is preserved under the projective transformations. We shall see in the next chapter that projective geometry makes no distinction among nondegenerate conics; any nondegenerate conic can be carried by a projective transformation into any other one.

Between the extremes of Euclidean geometry and projective geometry lie many others, each corresponding to a group of transformations lying between $\mathfrak{O}_{n+1}(R)$ and $L_{n+1}(C)$. We have mentioned, for example, the affine group (p. 240), whose geometry distinguishes between ordinary and ideal points. In affine geometry of the complex domain, we differentiate parabolas, which are "tangent" to the ideal line, from ellipses and hyberbolas, which meet the ideal line in two distinct points. But we do not distinguish between an ellipse and an hyperbola, or between one ellipse and another. Of course, in affine geometry of the *real* domain, we distinguish between an ellipse, which does not meet the ideal line, and an hyperbola, which meets it in two points.

Thus to each subgroup H of $L_{n+1}(\mathfrak{F})$ corresponds a geometry, the study of those properties left invariant by the transformations of H. Klein's point of view provides a structure within which to organize geometrical results so as to exhibit relationships in an elegant manner.

Current geometrical research has proceeded along somewhat different lines from what Klein envisaged, but the *group* concept continues to play an important role in geometry.

PROBLEM SET 9-4

1. (a) Show that any linear transformation which preserves distance must be orthogonal.

   (b) Let T be a one-to-one mapping of $V_n(R)$ onto $V_n'(R)$ such that

   $$\| T'(\xi) \| = \| \xi \| \qquad \text{for all} \quad \xi \in V_n(R).$$

Does T preserve distance? (Note that we are *not* assuming that T is linear.)

2. If

$$
A = \begin{bmatrix} \cos \phi & \sin \phi & 0 \\ -\sin \phi & \cos \phi & 0 \\ 0 & 0 & 1 \end{bmatrix} \quad \text{and} \quad B - \begin{bmatrix} 1 & 0 & 0 \\ 0 & \cos \theta & \sin \theta \\ 0 & -\sin \theta & \cos \theta \end{bmatrix},
$$

find AB and test it for orthogonality.

3. Find an orthogonal matrix with

   (a) first row 0, 0, 1 and second row $\frac{12}{13}$, $-\frac{5}{13}$, 0;

   (b) first row $1/\sqrt{2}$, $1/\sqrt{2}$, 0 and second row $\frac{2}{3}$, $\frac{2}{3}$, $-\frac{1}{3}$.

CHAPTER 10

Conics

The conic sections, or *conics*, furnish one of the most satisfying topics in projective geometry because of the beautiful simplicity and coherence of the completed results. The tools of matrix theory will help greatly to simplify and unify the study of these curves. As in the preceding chapters, we shall generally employ algebraic definitions and concepts, our "universe of discourse" being $S_2(C)$, a two-dimensional projective space in the complex domain; but we shall occasionally draw figures to guide our thoughts and to illustrate our results.

10–1 DEFINITION OF CONICS

We shall begin, not with the plane sections of a cone nor with the geometric loci which in elementary (metric) analytic geometry yield various kinds of conics, either separately or collectively, but with the loci of equations of the second degree.

Definition 1. In the plane $S_2(C)$, the set of points $P(x_0, x_1, x_2)$ satisfying the equation

$$a_{00}x_0^2 + 2a_{01}x_0x_1 + 2a_{02}x_0x_2 + a_{11}x_1^2 + 2a_{12}x_1x_2 + a_{22}x_2^2 = 0 \quad (1)$$

is called a *conic.*

For this to be a reasonable definition, the property of being a conic must not depend on the choice of coordinate system. This is easy to check: a shift of coordinate frame corresponds to a nonsingular linear transformation (Eqs. (1), Section 5–2 and Example 4, Section 6–5). Hence, if $\mathcal{C}$ has a second degree equation in one coordinate frame, then $\mathcal{C}$ will have a second degree equation relative to any coordinate frame.

It may be that the locus of Eq. (1) is not what we usually think of as a conic in elementary geometry. If the left-hand side of Eq. (1) factors into two linear forms, $(b_0x_0 + b_1x_1 + b_2x_2)(c_0x_0 + c_1x_1 + c_2x_2)$, say, the locus consists of the two straight lines corresponding to the equations obtained by setting each of these linear forms equal to zero. A particular case of interest is that in which $a_{11} = 0 = a_{12} = a_{22}$ so that Eq. (1) becomes $x_0(a_{00}x_0 + 2a_{01}x_1 + 2a_{02}x_2) = 0$; thus the locus consists of the ideal line together with the line whose equation is

$$a_{00}x_0 + 2a_{01}x_1 + 2a_{02}x_2 = 0.$$

In case of such factorization, we choose to call the locus a "degenerate conic," and we say that Eq. (1) is "reducible." Once again, if these terms are to be meaningful, the degeneracy or nondegeneracy of a conic should be independent of the coordinate frame. The verification of this fact is left as a problem (Problem 1 below).

In discussing reducibility, it is necessary to specify the domain in which we work. It is possible, for example, that a quadratic expression with real coefficients is not factorable as the product of linear forms with real coefficients (i.e., it is "irreducible over the real field") but that it *is* factorable if imaginary coefficients are permitted (i.e., it is "reducible over the complex field"). Hereafter, unless otherwise stated, the domain will be the complex field.

It is not immediately evident why some of the coefficients in Eq. (1) are written with the factor "2," although it should be clear that it is always possible so to write a second-degree equation. One reason for the special form of the coefficients is that Eq. (1) can be written in a neat simple way:

$$[x_0 x_1 x_2] \begin{bmatrix} a_{00} & a_{01} & a_{02} \\ a_{01} & a_{11} & a_{12} \\ a_{02} & a_{12} & a_{22} \end{bmatrix} \begin{bmatrix} x_0 \\ x_1 \\ x_2 \end{bmatrix} = [0], \qquad (2)$$

or

$$\xi^t A \xi = 0, \qquad (3)$$

where ξ is the column matrix of x's, A is the 3×3 *symmetric* matrix of coefficients, and the zero on the right-hand sides of Eqs. (2) and (3) is the 1×1 zero-matrix (with the brackets omitted for simplicity).

The conic, then, is specified relative to a given coordinate frame once the matrix A is given; in a fixed coordinate frame, there is a one-to-one correspondence between conics and 3×3 symmetric matrices.

In elementary analytic geometry, it is customary to simplify the equation of a conic by a change of coordinate frame. By rigid motions of the axes (translations and rotations), we can make an ellipse, for example, assume the standard form $(x^2/a^2) + (y^2/b^2) = 1$, or, in terms of homogeneous coordinates of the extended Euclidean plane,

$$x_0^2 - \frac{x_1^2}{a^2} - \frac{x_2^2}{b^2} = 0.$$

If we should be willing to consider a linear transformation in the complex domain,

$$rx'_0 = x_0,$$

$$rx'_1 = \frac{i}{a} x_1,$$

$$rx'_2 = \frac{i}{b} x_2,$$

(not a rigid motion), we obtain the neat form $x_0^2 + x_1^2 + x_2^2 = 0$.

We consider the analogous process for conics in $S_2(C)$ under linear transformation of coordinate frames. Suppose that we make the change defined by $\xi = M \cdot \eta$, where M is a nonsingular 3×3 matrix. Then $\xi^t = \eta^t M^t$, and Eq. (3) becomes

$$\eta^t M^t A M \eta = 0. \tag{4}$$

The question is: What choice of M will make the matrix $M^t A M$ as simple as possible? Note the similarity of this question to the problem of "diagonalizing" a matrix, studied in Section 7–7. There we saw that by row transformations and column transformations on I, we could find nonsingular matrices P and Q such that

$$PBQ = \begin{bmatrix} I_r & 0 \\ 0 & 0 \end{bmatrix}.$$

Now we wish to right-multiply and left-multiply by a matrix and its transpose. However, we have one new property of the matrix which we are reducing, i.e., A is symmetric. It turns out that we can reduce to diagonal form, as before. We state and prove the theorem for $n \times n$ matrices, thereby obtaining a result applicable to quadrics in S_n, as well as to conics in S_2.

Theorem 10–1. If A is an $n \times n$ symmetric matrix of rank r, there exists a nonsingular matrix M such that

$$M^t A M = \begin{bmatrix} I_r & 0 \\ 0 & 0 \end{bmatrix}.$$

Proof. Let

$$A = [a_{ij}] = [\tilde{\alpha}_1 \quad \tilde{\alpha}_2 \quad \ldots \quad \tilde{\alpha}_n] = \begin{bmatrix} \alpha_1 \\ \vdots \\ \alpha_n \end{bmatrix}.$$

(1) Suppose that $a_{nn} \neq 0$. Then $a_{nj}, j = 1, \ldots, n-1$, can be replaced by zeros by replacing $\tilde{\alpha}_j$ by $\tilde{\alpha}_j - (a_{nj}/a_{nn})\tilde{\alpha}_n$. Likewise, a_{in}, $i = 1, \ldots, n-1$, can be replaced by zeros by analogous operations on

rows. We are replacing A by $E^t A E$ (Problem 6, Section 7–1). From Problem 8(b), Section 6–5, we know that $E^t A E$ is symmetric.

(2) Suppose that $a_{nn} = 0$. If a_{nj} also equals zero for $j = 1, \ldots, n-1$, we can proceed directly to step (3) below. If there is an $a_{nj} \neq 0$ for some j, $1 \leq j \leq n-1$, choose $k \neq 0$ such that $ka_{jj} + 2a_{nj} \neq 0$. Then, by replacing $\tilde{\alpha}_n$ by $\tilde{\alpha}_n + k\tilde{\alpha}_j$, and next replacing the new α_n by the new $\alpha_n + k \cdot (\text{new } \alpha_j)$, we obtain a new $a_{nn} \neq 0$. As in step (1), the new matrix is still symmetric. We now proceed as in step (1).

(3) Having a symmetric matrix with all elements in the nth row and the nth column equal to zero, except possibly for a_{nn}, we ignore the last row and column and operate on the matrix consisting of the first $n-1$ rows and columns as in step (1) [or step (2) and step (1)]. We eventually obtain a matrix whose only nonzero elements occur on the main diagonal.

By further column operations, and the analogous row operations, the matrix can be transformed into

$$\begin{bmatrix} I_r & 0 \\ 0 & 0 \end{bmatrix}$$

(Problem 2 below).

Since we used nothing but elementary column operations and the corresponding row operations, we know that we have replaced A by $M^t A M$, which has the same rank as A. □

Corollary. A change of coordinate frame can be found to reduce the equation of the conic $\xi^t A \xi = 0$, where $A \neq O$, to one of the three forms:

$$y_0^2 = 0;$$

$$y_0^2 + y_1^2 = 0; \tag{5}$$

$$y_0^2 + y_1^2 + y_2^2 = 0,$$

according as the rank of A is 1, 2, 3.

A geometric description (i.e., the location of the triangle of reference to achieve this form of equation) will appear later (Problem 7, Section 10–4).

In the first case, in Eqs. (5), the locus is described as the line $y_0 = 0$, repeated; in the second case, the locus consists of the pair of lines $y_0 = iy_1$ and $y_0 = -iy_1$; in the third case, the equation is irreducible over the complex field and represents a *nondegenerate conic*.

Since the equation of every conic can be reduced to precisely one of these three equations by appropriate coordinate change, Eqs. (5) constitute "canonical forms" for conics.

Definition 2.   The polynomial

$$a_{00}x_0^2 + 2a_{01}x_0x_1 + 2a_{02}x_0x_2 + a_{11}x_1^2 + 2a_{12}x_1x_2 + a_{22}x_2^2$$

is called a *ternary quadratic form*.   The *rank* of the form is the rank
of the matrix

$$A = \begin{bmatrix} a_{00} & a_{01} & a_{02} \\ a_{01} & a_{11} & a_{12} \\ a_{02} & a_{12} & a_{22} \end{bmatrix}.$$

The *discriminant* of the form is det A.

Thus a ternary quadratic form represents a nondegenerate conic if its
rank is 3; otherwise it represents a degenerate conic.

The preceding discussion emphasizes the "equivalence" of two quadratic forms of the same rank.   If A, B are two symmetric 3×3 matrices
of the same rank, there is a coordinate transformation which will change
the equation of a conic from $\xi^t A \xi = 0$ into $\eta^t B \eta = 0$, as we can see
by transforming both equations to canonical form (Problem 7 below).

We have been using the language of the "passive" transformation; we
can cast the foregoing statement in terms of an active transformation as
follows.

Theorem 10–2.   If two conics $\mathcal{C}_1$ and $\mathcal{C}_2$ have, relative to a given
coordinate frame, matrices of the same rank, then there exists a nonsingular projective transformation which carries $\mathcal{C}_1$ into $\mathcal{C}_2$.

The proof is left as a problem (Problem 8, below).

Many of our subsequent results will apply to degenerate, as well as to
nondegenerate, conics, except that we shall have to treat separately the
point of intersection of two lines, L_1 and L_2, when they constitute a
conic, and of all points on L_1, when the conic consists of the line L_1,
counted twice.   We are led to make the following definition.

Definition 3.   A point is called a *singular point* of a conic if every line
determined by it and a point of the conic is contained in the conic.

An algebraic condition that a point be singular appears in Theorem 10–9.

PROBLEM SET 10–1

1. (a) Show that if a conic is degenerate relative to one coordinate frame in
$S_2(C)$, then it is also degenerate relative to any other coordinate frame.
   (b) Show that the conic with equation

$$x_0^2 + 4x_0x_1 - 2x_0x_2 + 4x_1x_2 - 3x_2^2 = 0$$

is degenerate, both by factoring the quadratic and by finding the rank of its
matrix.

2. Complete the proof of Theorem 10–1.

3. Find a matrix C corresponding to a change of coordinate frame which transforms

$$x_0^2 + 2x_0x_1 + 4x_0x_2 + 3x_1^2 - 6x_1x_2 + 2x_2^2 = 0$$

into canonical form. [*Hint:* Use Theorem 7–2.]

*4. An $n \times n$ matrix P is said to be *congruent* to an $n \times n$ matrix Q if there exists a nonsingular matrix M such that $P = M^tQM$.

(a) Prove that congruence is an equivalence relation.

(b) Why does the following statement *not* constitute a proof of (a)? Congruence is a special case of rational equivalence (Section 7–7).

*5. Strictly speaking, the word *conic* throughout the foregoing section should be replaced by *point conic*. Dualize Definition 1 to formulate a definition of *line conic*, and dualize the description of the three canonical forms.

*6. Verify that $x_0x_2 - x_1^2 = 0$ is the equation of a nondegenerate conic.

7. If

$$P^tAP = \begin{bmatrix} I_r & 0 \\ 0 & 0 \end{bmatrix} = Q^tBQ,$$

express the matrix M such that $\xi = M\eta$ carries the conic $\xi^tA\xi = 0$ into $\eta^tB\eta = 0$.

8. Prove Theorem 10–2.

*9. Draw a considerable number of lines of two projective, nonperspective, pencils (using the method either of Problem 9, Section 6–3, or of Problem 3(b), Section 8–2). Determine the points of intersection of pairs of corresponding lines, and guess a result about the location of these points.

10–2 PROJECTIVE GENERATION OF CONICS

Problem 9 of the last section is concerned with the points of intersection of corresponding lines of two projective, nonperspective, pencils. In a careful drawing these points will appear to lie on a conic, as is, in fact, the case. In classical synthetic projective geometry, this property is taken as the defining one, and all the other properties of nondegenerate conics developed from it. If the pencils are perspective,

$$V(a, b, c, \ldots) \overset{u}{\wedge} V'(a', b', c', \ldots),$$

then we know [Section 8–1 (iv)] that corresponding lines meet on u, the axis of perspective; moreover all the points of the common (self-corresponding) line VV' lie on corresponding lines of the two pencils. In this case the locus is "degenerate," consisting of the two lines u and VV'. We prove at once the basic theorem.

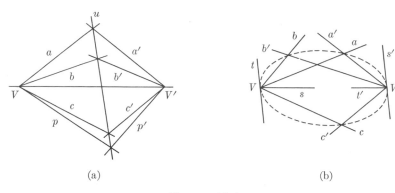

(a)   (b)

FIGURE 10–1

Theorem 10–3. The points of intersection of corresponding lines of two projective pencils constitute a conic. If the pencils are perspective, the conic is degenerate; otherwise it is nondegenerate. In any case, the conic passes through the vertices of the pencils.

Proof. Suppose that the projectivity is defined by $a \leftrightarrow a'$, $b \leftrightarrow b'$, $c \leftrightarrow c'$. Let coordinate vectors of the lines be α, α'; β, β'; γ, γ', so chosen that $\gamma = \alpha + \beta$, $\gamma' = \alpha' + \beta'$. Let p, p' be an arbitrary pair of corresponding lines of the pencils. If π, π' are coordinate vectors of p, p', and if $\pi = \alpha + k\beta$, then $\pi' = \alpha' + k\beta'$, because cross ratio is preserved in a projectivity. Now P, the point of intersection of p and p', is a point of the required locus. If ξ is a coordinate vector of P, then $\pi \cdot \xi = 0$ and $\pi' \cdot \xi = 0$. Hence $\alpha \cdot \xi + k\beta \cdot \xi = 0$ and $\alpha' \cdot \xi + k\beta' \cdot \xi = 0$. Eliminating k between these two equations leads to

$$(\alpha \cdot \xi)(\beta' \cdot \xi) - (\alpha' \cdot \xi)(\beta \cdot \xi) = 0. \tag{1}$$

Since each of the inner products appearing in Eq. (1) is a linear form in x_0, x_1, x_2, this equation is a quadratic and hence represents a conic.

If the projectivity is a perspectivity, choose the common line VV' as b (and also, therefore, as b'). Then the equation of the conic becomes

$$(\beta \cdot \xi)[(\alpha \cdot \xi) - (\alpha' \cdot \xi)] = 0,$$

which is clearly degenerate.

Since the coordinates of V satisfy $\alpha \cdot \xi = 0$ and $\beta \cdot \xi = 0$, V lies on the conic with Eq. (1) whether or not it is degenerate; likewise with V'.

If the projectivity is not a perspectivity, the line VV' is not part of the locus. If the conic were degenerate, it would have to consist of some line through V and some line through V'. Suppose that the hypothetical line through V is chosen as a. Then we have, again, Eq. (1) as the equation of the supposedly degenerate conic. Although $\alpha \cdot \xi$ is a factor of $(\alpha \cdot \xi)(\beta' \cdot \xi)$, it is not a factor of $(\alpha' \cdot \xi)(\beta \cdot \xi)$ since a is distinct from a' and from b. Thus $\alpha \cdot \xi$ is not a factor of the left-hand side of Eq. (1), contradicting the assumption of degeneracy. $\square$

Conversely, any conic can be "projectively generated," i.e., its points may be thought of as the points of intersection of corresponding lines of two projective pencils. To see this, choose a coordinate frame so that the equation of the (nondegenerate) conic is $y_0^2 + y_1^2 + y_2^2 = 0$. Rewriting this equation as $(y_0 + iy_1)(y_0 - iy_1) - (y_2)(-y_2) = 0$, and comparing the result with Eq. (1), we see that the given conic is the locus of points of intersection of corresponding lines of the projectivity determined by $a \leftrightarrow a'$, $b \leftrightarrow b'$, $c \leftrightarrow c'$, where the lines have equations as indicated below.

$$a: \qquad\qquad y_0 + iy_1 = 0,$$

$$a': \qquad\qquad\qquad\quad y_2 = 0,$$

$$b: \qquad\qquad\qquad\; -y_2 = 0,$$

$$b': \qquad\qquad y_0 - iy_1 = 0,$$

$$c: \qquad y_0 + iy_1 - y_2 = 0 \qquad (\gamma = \alpha \mid \beta),$$

$$c': \qquad y_0 - iy_1 \mid y_2 - 0 \qquad (\gamma' = \alpha' + \beta').$$

A shift in coordinate frame will not vitiate the conclusion. A similar argument can be used if the conic is degenerate.

It will be observed that there are numerous ways in which the terms of $y_0^2 + y_1^2 + y_2^2$ can be arranged to make the equation of the conic correspond with Eq. (1). There are, then, many projective pencils which generate the same conic. We shall show that the conic generated by projective pencils with vertices V, V' may also be generated by projective pencils with vertices A, B *any* two points of the conic.

Suppose that the lines VA, VB, $V'A$, $V'B$ are called a, b, a', b'. Set up a projectivity between pencils with vertices A and B in the familiar fashion: to any line s with coordinate vector $\sigma = m\alpha + n\alpha'$ make correspond the line t with coordinate vector $\tau = m\beta + n\beta'$. Then Q, the point of intersection of s and t, has coordinates which satisfy

$$m(\alpha \cdot \xi) + n(\alpha' \cdot \xi) = 0$$

and also

$$m(\beta \cdot \xi) + n(\beta' \cdot \xi) = 0.$$

The locus of Q is found by eliminating m, n between these two equations, but this leads to Eq. (1) again. Thus the projective pencils with vertices A, B generate the same conic as those with vertices V, V'.

The foregoing discussion virtually establishes the following theorem and its corollaries. The filling in of the formal proofs is left for the problems.

Theorem 10-4 (*Chasles*). The pencils of lines joining the points of a conic to two fixed points of the conic are projective.

Corollary 1 (*Steiner*). The cross ratio of the lines joining four fixed points of a conic to a fifth point of the conic is independent of the position of the fifth point.

Corollary 2. There is one and only one conic which passes through five given coplanar points, no three collinear. (For short, five points determine a conic.)

EXAMPLE. The method of the proof of Theorem 10-3 can be used to find the equation of a conic determined by five points. Suppose that we wish to find the equation of the conic determined by the following points (coordinates are nonhomogeneous): $P(2, 0)$; $Q(0, -2)$; $R(1, 1)$; $S(-1, 1)$; $T(2, -1)$. We choose P and Q as vertices of two pencils and set up the correspondence:

$$PR = a \quad \leftrightarrow \quad QR = a',$$

$$PS = b \quad \leftrightarrow \quad QS = b',$$

$$PT = c \quad \leftrightarrow \quad QT = c'.$$

We find equations of these lines to be as follows:

$$a: \quad \alpha \cdot \xi \equiv 3(2x_0 - x_1 - x_2) = 0,$$

$$b: \quad \beta \cdot \xi \equiv -(2x_0 - x_1 - 3x_2) = 0,$$

$$c: \quad \gamma \cdot \xi \equiv 4x_0 - 2x_1 = 0,$$

$$a': \quad \alpha' \cdot \xi \equiv 7(2x_0 - 3x_1 + x_2) = 0,$$

$$b': \quad \beta' \cdot \xi \equiv 5(2x_0 + 3x_1 + x_2) = 0,$$

$$c': \quad \gamma' \cdot \xi \equiv 6(4x_0 - x_1 + 2x_2) = 0.$$

(Coefficients have been chosen to make $\gamma = \alpha + \beta$, $\gamma' = \alpha' + \beta'$.) Hence, Eq. (1) becomes

$$3(2x_0 - x_1 - x_2)(5)(2x_0 + 3x_1 + x_2)$$

$$- 7(2x_0 - 3x_1 + x_2)(-1)(2x_0 - x_1 - 3x_2) = 0,$$

which reduces to

$$22x_0^2 + x_0x_1 - 7x_0x_2 - 6x_1^2 - x_1x_2 - 9x_2^2 = 0,$$

or, in nonhomogeneous coordinates,

$$6x^2 + xy + 9y^2 - x + 7y - 22 = 0.$$

The principal argument of this section may be generalized to apply to other projectively generated loci. The interested reader is referred to Todd, *op. cit.*, pp. 100–103 and 117–123.

PROBLEM SET 10–2

1. Prove Theorem 10–4.

2. Prove Corollary 1 of Theorem 10–4.

3. (a) Prove Corollary 2 of Theorem 10–4.

(b) What can be said about conics through coplanar sets of five points if no restriction is placed on their collinearity?

(c) Give five points with simple coordinates on the conic $x_0^2 + x_1^2 + x_2^2 = 0$.

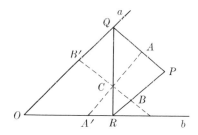

FIGURE 10–2

*4. (*Maclaurin's generation of a conic.*) As in Fig. 10–2, the lines a, b and the points A, B, C are fixed. A variable triangle PQR moves so that Q traces the line a, R the line b, QR passes through C, QP through A, RP through B. Show that the locus of P is a conic which passes through A, B, A', B', O. Discuss special cases (e.g., A, B, O collinear). Dualize (cf. Problem 16, Section 1–2).

5. Carry through the argument that any degenerate conic can also be projectively generated.

6. A projectivity is defined by the correspondence of three lines of one pencil with homogeneous coordinates $(1, -1, 0)$, $(1, 1, -2)$, $(3, -1, -2)$ to three lines of another pencil with coordinates $(1, 0, -2)$, $(0, 1, 0)$, $(1, -2, -2)$, respectively. What is the equation of the locus of points of intersection of corresponding lines of the two pencils? Is the locus degenerate?

7. (a) Check the algebraic details of the Example of this section.

(b) Carry through the derivation of the equation of the conic of the Example by using two points other than P and Q as vertices of the pencils.

*8. State the dual of Theorem 10–3, and draw the figure dual to that of Problem 9 of Section 10–1.

9. Use the results of this section to solve (a) Problem 4, Section 1–1; (b) Problem 22, Section 1–1.

10. Find an equation of the conic through the following points.
(a) $(-2, 0, 1)$, $(2, 0, 1)$, $(-1, 2, 1)$, $(1, 2, 1)$, $(0, 3, 1)$
(b) $(1, 1)$, $(1, -1)$, $(-1, 1)$, $(-1, -1)$, $(\sqrt{2}, 0)$

10–3 PARAMETRIC REPRESENTATION OF A CONIC; TANGENTS

We saw in the corollary of Theorem 10–1 that relative to an appropriate coordinate frame, the equation of a nondegenerate conic is

$$x_0^2 + x_1^2 + x_2^2 = 0.$$

It turns out that a different equation,

$$x_0 x_2 - x_1^2 = 0, \tag{1}$$

met in Problem 6 of Section 10–1, is particularly useful in certain connections. Following the development of Section 10–1, we know that a coordinate frame can be found so that any given nondegenerate conic will have Eq. (1) as its equation. It is instructive to derive Eq. (1) directly.

Choose two points A, B of the given conic as $(0, 0, 1)$ and $(1, 0, 0)$, (Fig. 10–3). In accordance with Theorem 10–4, the pencils of lines joining the points of the conic to A and B are projective. Since the conic is not degenerate, the line AB is *not* self-corresponding. Suppose that AB of pencil A corresponds to line BC, and that BA of pencil B corresponds to line AC. Take C as $(0, 1, 0)$, the third vertex of the triangle of reference, and let $D(1, 1, 1)$ be any point on the conic other than A or B. (Query: Why is C surely not on the conic?) Then the equation of AB is $x_1 = 0$, that of AC is $x_0 = 0$, and that of BC is $x_2 = 0$. It is

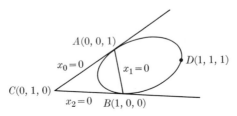

FIGURE 10–3

easy to verify that the equation of AD is $x_0 - x_1 = 0$, and that the equation of BD is $x_1 - x_2 = 0$. Let $P(x_0, x_1, x_2)$ be an arbitrary point of the conic. We can write the equation of AP as a linear combination of the equations of AC and AB: $kx_0 + lx_1 = 0$, say. Similarly, the equation of BP is $mx_1 + nx_2 = 0$, for some m, n.

We thus have the following situation. In the projectivity,

AC, with equation $x_0 = 0$, corresponds to BA, with equation $x_1 = 0$;

AB, with equation $x_1 = 0$, corresponds to BC, with equation $x_2 = 0$;

AD, with equation $x_0 - x_1 = 0$, corresponds
$\qquad$ to BD, with equation $x_1 - x_2 = 0$;

AP, with equation $kx_0 + lx_1 = 0$, corresponds
$\qquad$ to BP, with equation $mx_1 + nx_2 = 0$.

Since cross ratio is preserved in a projectivity, the foregoing correspondences imply that $k:l = m:n$. We now obtain Eq. (1) as the equation of the locus of P by eliminating k, l between the equations for AP and BP: $kx_0 + lx_1 = 0$, $kx_1 + lx_2 = 0$.

We can go further and solve the equations of AP and BP for x_0, x_1, x_2 as follows:

$$x_0:x_1:x_2 = l^2:-lk:k^2 \quad \text{or} \quad x_0:x_1:x_2 = 1:r:r^2,$$

where $r = -(k/l)$, if $l \neq 0$.

Thus homogeneous coordinates of points on the conic are $(l^2, -lk, k^2)$, and nonhomogeneous coordinates are (r, r^2). Any pair of complex numbers (l, k) determines a point on the conic, viz., the point with coordinates $(l^2, -lk, k^2)$. The pair (cl, ck), for $c \neq 0$, determines the same point as (l, k). Conversely, for any point on the conic there is determined a pair (l, k) or, rather, a ratio of such pairs. The points with coordinates $(l_1^2, -l_1k_1, k_1^2)$ and $(l_2^2, -l_2k_2, k_2^2)$ are distinct if and only if $l_1k_2 \neq l_2k_1$. Thus, the points of the conic are determined by a pair of homogeneous coordinates: *The points of a conic form an S_1.*

Hence we can immediately apply to conics those theorems about S_1's which are true "in general." The significance of the last phrase is this: some of our earlier results depend on the S_1's being a hyperplane in an S_2 (e.g., a line in a plane). A conic, of course, is not a line in the plane. Only those theorems about S_1's which do not depend on the S_1's being "embedded" in an S_2 will be automatically true for conics. We immediately have the following results.

From Theorem 6–3, there is exactly one linear transformation of one-dimensional homogeneous coordinates which carries three arbitrary points of one conic into three arbitrary points of another. In particular, a collineation of a conic is determined by three pairs of corresponding points.

From Problem 4(a), Section 8–1, if a collineation of a conic has more than two fixed points, then it is the identity transformation.

Other theorems on conics or S_1's will appear later in this chapter; we now turn to a consideration of *tangency*.

In Fig. 10–3, any line a of the pencil with vertex A has a unique correspondent b of the pencil with vertex B. If a is different from AC, then b is different from BA, and a and b meet in a point P different from A, on the conic. The line AP, then, meets the conic in two distinct points, A and P, and only in these points. If a is AC, then b is BA, and P coincides with A. The line AC meets the conic only at A. We call the line AC a tangent to the conic, and A is its *point of tangency* or *contact point*.

Since the conic may be thought of as being generated by two projective pencils whose vertices are *any* two points of the conic, we have the result that each point of the conic is a point of tangency of a unique tangent to the conic.

We may think of the tangent as having two *coincident* intersections with the conic at the point of tangency. We do not wish to introduce notions of *limit* or *continuity** into the discussion, so we proceed algebraically as follows.

The point with coordinates $(1, r, r^2)$ lies on the line u with equation $u_0x_0 + u_1x_1 + u_2x_2 = 0$ if and only if

$$u_0 + u_1r + u_2r^2 = 0.$$

This quadratic equation in r has two roots r_1, r_2, say. If $r_1 \neq r_2$, we have the result that the line with coordinates (u_0, u_1, u_2) meets the conic $x_0x_2 - x_1^2 = 0$ in two distinct points: $(1, r_1, r_1^2)$ and $(1, r_2, r_2^2)$. If $r_1 = r_2$, the line meets the conic in only one point, i.e., is tangent to the conic. Thus, incidentally, we have established the fact that a line meets a nondegenerate conic in two points or is tangent to the conic.

Since a necessary and sufficient condition that the roots of the quadratic $ax^2 + bx + c = 0$ be equal is that $b^2 - 4ac = 0$, we conclude that the line with coordinates (u_0, u_1, u_2) is tangent to the conic $x_0x_2 - x_1^2 = 0$ if and only if

$$u_1^2 - 4u_0u_2 = 0. \tag{2}$$

Being quadratic, this equation also represents a conic, called a *line conic* (Problem 5, Section 10–1) because the "elements" of the conic are lines with coordinates (u_0, u_1, u_2). These lines are clearly the tangents to the *point conic*, $x_0x_2 - x_1^2 = 0$. Dually, if we interpreted $x_0x_2 - x_1^2 = 0$ as a line conic to start with, the equation $u_1^2 - 4u_0u_2 = 0$ would repre-

---

* But such notions are inherent in Axiom LUB, Section 3–5.

sent the contact points on these lines. Thus, if A is nonsingular, the configuration consisting of the points satisfying $\xi^t A \xi = 0$ and the lines tangent to this locus is self-dual.

PROBLEM SET 10–3

1. In a certain two-dimensional homogeneous projective coordinate system, a conic $\mathcal{C}$ has equation $x_0 x_2 - x_1^2 = 0$; and coordinates of a typical point P of $\mathcal{C}$ are given by $(l^2, -lk, k^2)$ for some l, k. Thus, one-dimensional homogeneous projective coordinates of P are (l, k).

(a) If points R, S of $\mathcal{C}$ have two-dimensional coordinate vectors $\rho(1, 2, 4)$ and $\sigma(1, 0, 0)$, respectively, what are one-dimensional coordinate vectors, ρ' and σ', of R and S?

(b) Does the point corresponding to the coordinate vector $2\rho + 3\sigma$ lie on $\mathcal{C}$? If so, find a one-dimensional coordinate vector of this point.

(c) Does the point corresponding to the coordinate vector $2\rho' + 3\sigma'$ lie on $\mathcal{C}$? If so, find a two-dimensional coordinate vector of this point.

2. (a) Derive Eq. (2) of this section by solving $x_0 x_2 - x_1^2 = 0$ and $u_0 x_0 + u_1 x_1 + u_2 x_2 = 0$ simultaneously.

(b) Similarly, find the equation of the line conic formed by the tangents to $x_0^2 + x_1^2 + x_2^2 = 0$.

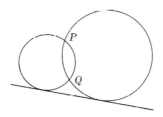

FIGURE 10–4

*3. That a conic is *not* uniquely determined by four points and a line to which it is to be tangent (at some point) may be inferred from the fact that, as in Fig. 10–4 there are *two* circles passing through the four points P, Q, I, J and tangent to the given line. Show that a conic is uniquely determined by (a) four points and the tangent at one of them; (b) three points and the tangents at two of them.

*4. State the duals of the results in 3 above.

5. Find the equation of the conic passing through points P, Q, R, S of the Example of Section 10–2 and tangent to the line:

(a) $23x + 9y - 46 = 0$ at P. [*Answer:* Same as that of the Example of Section 10–2.]

(b) $2x_0 - x_1 - 2x_2 = 0$ at P.
    [*Answer:* $4x_0^2 - 20x_0 x_1 - 8x_0 x_2 + 9x_1^2 + 20x_1 x_2 - 5x_2^2 = 0$.]

6. Find the equation of the conic passing through the points P, Q, R of the Example of Section 10-2, tangent to the line $2x_0 - x_1 - 2x_2 = 0$ at P and also tangent to the line:

(a) $2x_0 - 5x_1 + x_2 = 0$ at Q. [*Answer*: Same as 5b.]
(b) $2x_0 - 2x_1 + x_2 = 0$ at Q.
  [*Answer*: $20x_0^2 - 28x_0x_1 - 4x_0x_2 + 9x_1x_2 - 7x_2^2 = 0$.]

7. Discuss "tangency" in the case of a degenerate point-conic. Use an algebraic argument and interpret your results in terms of figures drawn in the ordinary plane.

10-4 POLARS

Consider the conic $\xi^t A \xi = 0$ in which A is nonsingular. Let R, S, with coordinate vectors ρ, σ, be two points of the plane, and let P with coordinate vector $\pi = k\rho + l\sigma$ be some point on the line RS. If P is to lie on the conic, we must have $[k\rho + l\sigma]^t A [k\rho + l\sigma] = 0$.

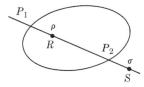

FIGURE 10-5

Making use of the distributivity of multiplication over addition for matrices, of the commutativity of multiplication of matrices and scalars, and of the symmetry of A, we can write the above equation as

$$\rho^t A \rho \cdot k^2 + 2\rho^t A \sigma \cdot kl + \sigma^t A \sigma \cdot l^2 = 0. \tag{1}$$

This quadratic equation in the ratio k/l generally has two roots k_1/l_1, k_2/l_2, say, corresponding to the two points P_1, P_2 in which the line RS meets the conic.

Now we ask the following question: Is it possible to choose R, S so that they will be separated harmonically by the points P_1, P_2 in which the line RS meets the conic?

We have the following situation: R, with coordinate vector ρ; S, with σ; P_1, with $k_1\rho + l_1\sigma$; P_2, with $k_2\rho + l_2\sigma$. By Problem 8(c), Section 8-3, we know that $(R, S; P_1, P_2) = -1$ if and only if

$$\frac{k_1}{l_1} = -\frac{k_2}{l_2} \quad \text{or} \quad \frac{k_1}{l_1} + \frac{k_2}{l_2} = 0.$$

Thus, the criterion for harmonic separation is that the sum of the roots of Eq. (1) be zero, i.e., that $\rho^t A \sigma = 0$.

Definition 4.   Two points R, S are said to be *conjugate with respect to a conic* $\mathcal{C}$ if they are separated harmonically by the points in which the line RS meets $\mathcal{C}$.

We have just established the following results.

Theorem 10–5.   A necessary and sufficient condition that R, S with coordinate vectors ρ, σ be conjugate with respect to the conic $\xi^t A \xi = 0$ is that $\rho^t A \sigma = 0$.

Note that R and S enter symmetrically in Definition 4; it is to be expected, then, that ρ and σ appear symmetrically in Theorem 10–5. That this is, indeed, the case follows from the fact that $\rho^t A \sigma = 0 \Leftrightarrow \sigma^t A \rho = 0$. (Why?)

It is worthwhile to compare the foregoing material with Proof 2 of Theorem 8–21.

Suppose now that R is held fixed and that S is allowed to move. For each line through R, there is one point S on the line which is conjugate to R with respect to the conic. What is the locus of S? The equation of the locus is $\rho^t A \sigma = 0$ for fixed ρ—a linear equation in s_0, s_1, s_2. Thus we have the following theorem.

Theorem 10–6.   The locus of points conjugate to a fixed point with respect to a given nondegenerate conic is a straight line.

Definition 5.   The straight line of Theorem 10–6 is called the *polar of the point with respect to the conic*.

In Fig. 10–5, neither R nor S lies on the conic, but the same algebraic argument can be followed through if R, say, lies on the conic. In this case $\rho^t A \rho = 0$, which implies that R lies on the polar of R. Moreover, if a point P lies on the polar in this case, Eq. (1) becomes $\sigma^t A \sigma \cdot l^2 = 0$. Now $\sigma^t A \sigma \neq 0$; otherwise the whole line RS would lie on the conic, in contradiction to the assumed nondegeneracy of the conic. Hence $l = 0$; i.e., $\pi = k\rho$, or R is the *only* point in which the polar meets the conic. We have proved the following theorem.

Theorem 10–7.   The polar with respect to a conic of a point on that conic is the tangent to the conic at that point.

The following theorem is a basic result.

Theorem 10–8.   If the polar of M (with respect to a given conic) passes through N, then the polar of N passes through M.

Proof.   The equation of the polar of M is $\mu^t A \xi = 0$. If N lies on this line, then $\mu^t A \eta = 0$. Hence $\eta^t A \mu = 0$. But this last equation is precisely the condition that M lies on the polar of N. $\square$

The proofs of the following corollaries are left as problems.

Corollary 1.   Let the polars of R and S meet at P. Then the polar of P is the line RS.

Corollary 2.   Let the tangents to $\mathbb{C}$ from the point P meet $\mathbb{C}$ at T_1 and T_2. Then the polar of P is the line $T_1 T_2$.

Corollary 1 leads to the concept of a pair of triangles which are polar with respect to a conic. Let the polars of A, B, and C with respect to conic $\mathbb{C}$ be a, b, c, respectively. Let a and b meet at C'; b and c at A'; c and a at B'. Then BC is the polar of A', CA of B', and AB of C'. Thus we have two triangles in which the polar of a vertex of either triangle is a side of the other triangle. They are called *polar triangles* with respect to $\mathbb{C}$. It is possible that the polar triangles in a pair be coincident; i.e., that each side of the triangle be the polar of the opposite vertex.

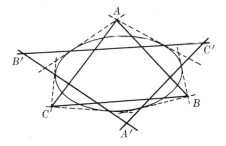

FIGURE 10–6

Suppose that we choose an arbitrary point X not on a given conic $\mathbb{C}$. On x, the polar of X, choose any point Y not on $\mathbb{C}$. Let y, the polar of Y, meet x at Z. Then the polar of Z is the line XY (Corollary 1). Indeed, the polar of each vertex of the triangle XYZ is the opposite side of the triangle; the triangle XYZ is said to be *self-polar with respect to* $\mathbb{C}$. Note that there are infinitely many triangles self-polar with respect to a given conic.

The foregoing material on polars also applies to degenerate conics *except* when we come to consider the polar of a singular point (defined in Section 10–1). The following algebraic condition characterizing singular points shows the difference.

Theorem 10–9. The point R, with coordinate vector ρ, is a singular point of the conic $\xi^t A \xi = 0 \leftrightarrow \rho^t A \xi$ is identically zero.

The proof is left as Problem 15 below.

Thus, if R is not a singular point of the conic, degenerate or not, then the line $\rho^t A \xi = 0$ is the locus of points conjugate to R; but, if R is a singular point of the (degenerate) conic, conjugate points are not defined, and $\rho^t A \xi \equiv 0$.

PROBLEM SET 10–4

1. (a) Find the equation of the tangent to the conic

$$x_1^2 - x_0 x_1 - x_0 x_2 - x_1 x_2 = 0$$

at the point $(1, 1, 0)$.

(b) Find the equations of the tangents to the conic of (a) which pass through $(1, -1, -3)$.

2. Verify that the equation of the tangent at (p_0, p_1, p_2) to the conic with Eq. (1) of Section 10–1 can be written as

$$a_{00} p_0 x_0 + a_{01}(p_0 x_1 + p_1 x_0) + a_{02}(p_0 x_2 + p_2 x_0) + a_{11} p_1 x_1 \\ + a_{12}(p_1 x_2 + p_2 x_1) + a_{22} p_2 x_2 = 0.$$

3. Prove that the property of two points being conjugate with respect to a conic is independent of the choice of coordinate frame.

4. (a) Prove Corollary 1 of Theorem 10–8.

(b) Prove Corollary 2 of Theorem 10–8.

*5. Prove that if the vertices of a complete quadrangle Q lie on $\mathcal{C}$, then the diagonal triangle of Q is self-polar with respect to $\mathcal{C}$.

6. Given a conic $\mathcal{C}$, drawn on paper. Show how to construct with ruler alone, (a) the polar of a point P with respect to $\mathcal{C}$; (b) the tangents from a point P to $\mathcal{C}$.

*7. Prove that the matrix of a conic is diagonal (i.e., $a_{ij} = 0$, $i \neq j$) if and only if the triangle of reference (of the coordinate frame) is self-polar with respect to the conic.

8. (a) Prove the following theorem. If ABC, $A'B'C'$ are polar triangles with respect to a conic, then they are in the relationship of Desargues. [Sketch of an algebraic proof: Choose a coordinate system so that A has coordinates $(1, 0, 0)$, B has coordinates (b_0, b_1, b_2), C has coordinates $(c_0, c_1, 0)$. Let A be one vertex of a triangle, self-polar with respect to the conic, with one of its sides lying along AC, so that the equation of the conic is

$$x_0^2 + x_1^2 + x_2^2 = 0$$

(see Problem 7 above). Find the equations of the polars of A, B, C and thence find the coordinates of A', B', C'. Finally, obtain the equations of AA', BB', CC', and show them to be linearly dependent.]

(b) Alternatively, show that the points of intersection of corresponding sides of triangles ABC, $A'B'C'$ are collinear.

(c) What is a relation between the point of intersection of AA', BB', CC' and the line of part (b)?

(d) Establish the converse theorem: Two Desarguesian triangles are polar triangles with respect to some conic, and the line on which corresponding sides meet is the polar of the point of intersection of the lines joining corresponding vertices.

9. Establish the following corollary of the theorem of Problem 8(a): Suppose that a nondegenerate conic is inscribed in triangle ABC, touching BC, CA, AB at D, E, F, respectively. Then AD, BE, CF are concurrent.

10. Prove the following theorem. A triangle which is self-polar with respect to a conic is the diagonal triangle of a complete quadrangle whose vertices lie on the conic. Indeed, there are indefinitely many quadrangles with the given triangle as diagonal triangle. (See Problem 5 above.)

(a) Sketch of an algebraic proof: Draw an arbitrary line through one of the vertices of the given triangle, and label one of the intersections of this line with the conic $(1, 1, 1)$. Let the given triangle be the triangle of reference. Complete the quadrangle in the obvious manner and discover that the other vertices are $(1, 1, -1)$, $(1, -1, 1)$, and $(1, -1, -1)$. Check that this quadrangle has the given triangle as its diagonal triangle.

(b) Sketch of a geometric proof: Let the given triangle be PQR. Through P draw an arbitrary line meeting the conic at A and B. Draw QA and QB to meet the conic at C and D, respectively. Let PR meet QA at X and QB at Y. Then PC is the harmonic conjugate of PA with respect to PX and PQ, and PD is the harmonic conjugate of PB with respect to PY and PQ. Hence P, D, C are collinear. Let BC and AD meet at Z. Why does Z coincide with R?

*11. In the extended Euclidean plane let $\mathcal{C}$ be a *central conic*, that is, an ellipse or a hyperbola which has a center of symmetry, O, say. What is the polar of O with respect to $\mathcal{C}$?

12. Show that the triangle with vertices $(1, 0, 1)$, $(1, 1, 0)$, $(0, 1, 1)$ is self-polar with respect to the conic

$$x_0^2 + x_1^2 + x_2^2 + 2x_0x_1 + 2x_0x_2 - 6x_1x_2 = 0.$$

*13. Show that if the vertices of the triangle of reference of the coordinate frame lie on a conic, an equation of the conic is

$$Ax_0x_1 + Bx_0x_2 + Cx_1x_2 = 0.$$

14. Prove that if the vertices of two triangles lie on a nondegenerate conic, then the sides of the triangles are tangent to a nondegenerate conic. [*Hint:* If the triangles have vertices A, B, C, and A', B', C', apply Corollary 1 of Theorem 10-4 to the lines joining each of A and A' to B, B', C, C'; obtain a projectivity between points of BC and $B'C'$, and apply the dual of Theorem 10-3.]

*15. Suppose that the symmetric 3×3 matrix A is singular, with the conic $\xi^t A \xi = 0$ consisting of the lines L_1, L_2 with equations $a_0x_0 + a_1x_1 + a_2x_2 = 0$ and $b_0x_0 + b_1x_1 + b_2x_2 = 0$. Show that

$$2\rho^t A \xi = (a_0r_0 + a_1r_1 + a_2r_2)(b_0x_0 + b_1x_1 + b_2x_2)$$
$$+ (a_0x_0 + a_1x_1 + a_2x_2)(b_0r_0 + b_1r_1 + b_2r_2).$$

Hence conclude that if the point R with coordinate vector ρ lies on

(a) L_1, but not on L_2, then the locus of $\rho^t A \xi = 0$ is L_2;

(b) L_2, but not on L_1, then the locus of $\rho^t A \xi = 0$ is L_1;

(c) both L_1 and L_2, then $\rho^t A \xi$ is identically zero.

Show, conversely, that if $\rho^t A \xi$ is identically zero, then R lies on both L_1 and L_2.

Complete the proof of Theorem 10–9 by considering the case in which the conic consists of the line L_1 counted twice.

*16. Let the degenerate conic, $\mathcal{C}$, consist of the lines L_1, L_2 meeting at P. Show that points R, S have the same polar with respect to $\mathcal{C}$ if and only if R, S, P are collinear.

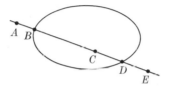

FIGURE 10–7

*17. In a figure similar to Fig. 10–7, sketch the polars of each of A, B, C, D, E with respect to the conic, make a conjecture, and prove it if you can.

10–5 POLARS; TANGENTIAL EQUATIONS; POLES

Even a rough sketch of the configuration of Problem 17 above suggests the following theorem.

Theorem 10–10. The polars of a range of points, with respect to a nondegenerate point conic, form a pencil of lines. There is a natural projectivity between the range and the pencil.

Proof. Let the conic have the equation $\xi^t A \xi = 0$. Let the range of points form the line l. Suppose that R, S, with coordinate vectors ρ, σ, are two points of l. Then the polars of R, S are lines r, s with equations $\rho^t A \xi = 0$, $\sigma^t A \xi = 0$, respectively. If T, with coordinate vector τ, is any point of l, then τ can be written as a linear combination of ρ and σ: $\tau = a\rho + b\sigma$, say. The line t, the polar of T, has equation $\tau^t A \xi = 0$. This may be written as

$$a\rho^t A \xi + b\sigma^t A \xi = 0.$$

In other words, the equation of T is the *same* linear combination of the equations of r and s that the coordinates of T are of the coordinates of R and S. Hence, not only are all the polars concurrent, but the correspondence between point and polar is a projectivity. □

Discussion of the modification of the statement of Theorem 10–10 which must be made if the conic is degenerate appears in the problems, as well as the formulation of the equally important dual of Theorem 10–10.

Since the figure consisting of the points of a conic and the tangents to the conic is a self-dual construct, it sometimes suits our purpose to deal with the equation satisfied by the coordinates of the tangents (the equation of a line conic) rather than with the equation satisfied by the points. The equation of the *line conic* is often called the *tangential equation of the conic*. In Problem 2, Section 10-3, we found two such tangential equations. We now proceed to obtain a general expression for the tangential equation of a conic.

Let e be a nondegenerate point conic with matrix A, so that its (point) equation is $\xi^t A \xi = 0$. If μ is a coordinate vector of a point M on e, the equation of the tangent line t at M is $\mu^t A \xi = 0$. Hence, if τ is a coordinate vector of the line t, $\tau^t = \mu^t A$, or

$$\tau = A\mu. \tag{1}$$

We obtain the tangential equation of e by eliminating μ between Eq. (1) and $\mu^t A \mu = 0$. Thus, $\mu^t = \tau^t A^{-1}$, $\mu = A^{-1}\tau$, so $\tau^t A^{-1} A A^{-1}\tau = 0$, or $\tau^t A^{-1}\tau = 0$. Since $A^{-1} = A_{\text{adj}}/\det A$, we can write the tangential equation of e as

$$\tau^t A_{\text{adj}}\tau = 0. \tag{2}$$

Considering the lines of the plane as elements of an S_2, we obtain the following dualization of our foregoing work on polars.

Definition 6. Two lines l, m are called conjugate with respect to a line conic if they are separated harmonically by the lines of the conic through their point of intersection.

Theorem 10-11 (*Dual of Theorem* 10-5). A necessary and sufficient condition that l, m with coordinate vectors λ, μ be conjugate with respect to the line conic with Eq. (2) is that $\lambda^t A_{\text{adj}}\mu = 0$.

Theorem 10-12 (*Dual of Theorem* 10-6). The set of lines conjugate to l with respect to the line conic with Eq. (2) forms a pencil whose vertex is the point with equation $\lambda^t A_{\text{adj}}\tau = 0$.

Definition 7. The point of Theorem 10-12 is called the pole of the line l with respect to the conic.

Theorem 10-13 (*Dual of Theorem* 10-7). The pole with respect to a line conic of a line of that conic is the contact point of the line.

(Indeed, the locus of the poles of the lines of the line conic $\tau^t A_{\text{adj}}\tau = 0$ is the point conic $\xi^t (A_{\text{adj}})_{\text{adj}} \xi = 0$, i.e., the "original" point conic, e).

We conclude this section with a simple but basic result, the proof of which is left as a problem.

Theorem 10–14.   The line l is the polar of the point L with respect to the point conic $\xi^t A \xi = 0$ if and only if L is the pole of l with respect to the line conic $\tau^t A_{\text{adj}} \tau = 0$.

It is this reciprocal relation which permits us to use the elliptical expression "the pole of l with respect to the (point) conic, $\mathcal{C}$." What we mean is "the pole of l with respect to the line conic consisting of the tangents to $\mathcal{C}$" *or* "the point whose polar with respect to $\mathcal{C}$ is l."

PROBLEM SET 10–5

1. (a) Solve Problem 2, Section 10–3, by using Eq. (2) of this section.

(b) Find the tangential equation of the conic $\mathcal{C}$ with point equation

$$2x_0^2 + 2x_0 x_1 - x_1^2 + 6x_1 x_2 + x_2^2 = 0.$$

(c) Hence, what is the equation of the locus of the contact points of the line conic $2t_0^2 + 2t_0 t_1 - t_1^2 + 6t_1 t_2 + t_2^2 = 0$?

(d) Verify that the locus of the contact points of the line conic obtained in (b) is $\mathcal{C}$.

2. Prove Theorem 10–14.

*3. Prove that two lines are conjugate with respect to a conic if and only if each contains the pole of the other.

4. State the duals of (a) Theorem 10–8 and its two corollaries; (b) Theorem 10–10.

5. Review the proof of Theorem 10–10 to see if it remains valid in case the conic is degenerate. [*Hint:* See Theorem 10–9.]

6. Given the point conic $x_0^2 + 2x_0 x_1 + x_1^2 - 2x_0 x_2 + 2x_1 x_2 + x_2^2 = 0$.

(a) Find the equation of the corresponding line conic.

(b) Find the pole of $x_0 = 0$.

(c) Find the polar of $(1, 0, 0)$.

(d) Is the line $(-2, 2, 1)$ tangent to the conic?

10–6 GEOMETRY ON A CONIC

We gather together into this section some of the best-known projective theorems about conics. Basically, the material depends upon the fact that a conic is an S_1.

Theorem 10–15.   The points of a conic are projectively related to the lines joining these points to any fixed point, O, of the conic. In this projectivity O corresponds to the tangent to the conic at O.

Proof. Choose a coordinate system on the conic so that O has the (one-dimensional homogeneous) coordinates $(0, 1)$. Let an arbitrary point P of the conic have coordinates (l, k). Two-dimensional coordinates of O and P are respectively $(0, 0, 1)$ and $(l^2, -lk, k^2)$. Therefore, the equation of the line OP is $kx_0 + lx_1 = 0$, if $l \neq 0$. Hence, if $P_1(l_1, k_1)$, $P_2(l_2, k_2)$ and $R(cl_1 + dl_2, ck_1 + dk_2)$ are three points on the conic, the equations of OP_1, OP_2, OR are respectively

$$k_1x_0 + l_1x_1 = 0, \qquad k_2x_0 + l_2x_1 = 0,$$

$$c(k_1x_0 + l_1x_1) + d(k_2x_0 + l_2x_1) = 0;$$

that is, the equation of OR is the *same* linear combination of the equations of OP_1 and OP_2 that the coordinates of R are of the coordinates of P_1 and P_2. Thus, the cross ratio of four points on the conic equals the cross ratio of the lines joining the points to O.

The proof of the second sentence of the theorem is left as a problem.

REMARK. Note that Theorem 10–4 follows immediately from this theorem.

Theorem 10–16.   If A, B, C, D are four points on conic $\mathfrak{C}$, $(AB, CD) = -1 \Leftrightarrow AB$ and CD are conjugate lines with respect to $\mathfrak{C}$.

Proof. "$\Rightarrow$." Suppose that AB meets CD at V, and that the tangent at A meets CD at T. Then, by Theorem 10–15, $(CD, VT) = -1$. Similarly, thinking of B rather than A as the vertex of a pencil, we obtain the result that the tangent to $\mathfrak{C}$ at B meets CD in the harmonic conjugate of V with respect to C and D. In other words, the tangents at A and B meet at T on CD. Thus, the pole of AB lies on CD; and therefore, by Problem 3, Section 10–5, AB and CD are conjugate lines.

"$\Leftarrow$." If AB and CD are conjugate lines, the pole T of AB lies on CD. Hence $(CD, VT) = -1$; if AC, AD, AV, AT are called c, d, v, t, respectively, then $(cd, vt) = -1$; $(CD, BA) = -1$. $\square$

Theorem 10–17.   On a conic $\mathfrak{C}$ let $P_i \leftrightarrow Q_i$ define a projectivity other than the identity. Suppose that the lines P_jQ_k and P_kQ_j, $j \neq k$, meet at R_{jk}. Then the locus of R_{jk} is a straight line (called the *cross axis of the projectivity*).

Proof. We can almost duplicate a proof of Pappus' theorem (Section 8–2). Take any fixed pair of points P_a, Q_a, say, and form two pencils of lines by joining P_a to all the Q's and Q_a to all the P's. By Theorem 10–15, the pencil with vertex P_a is projective to the range $\{Q_i\}$; likewise the pencil with vertex Q_a is projective to the range $\{P_i\}$. Since the ranges $\{P_i\}$ and $\{Q_i\}$ are projective by hypothesis, we conclude that the two pencils in question are projective. Indeed, they are perspective, for the common line P_aQ_a is self-corresponding. Hence, the points R_{ai}, as i varies, are collinear. Thus, for each choice of a, we obtain in this way a certain line. To complete the proof of the theorem we must show that all the lines so obtained are identical.

In case the given projectivity on the conic has two distinct fixed points, the problem is immediately solved, for each of the lines in question clearly passes through both the fixed points.

In case the given projectivity on the conic has only one fixed point, U, say, we consider the two lines resulting from the perspective pencils with vertices P_b, Q_b and with vertices P_c, Q_c. These lines both pass through U and R_{bc}, hence the lines are identical. Therefore, *all* the lines coincide. Moreover, in this case, the cross axis must be tangent to the conic, for any point common to the cross axis and the conic must be self-corresponding in the given projectivity. (Verify this.) Thus we have established the following characterization of the cross axis of a projectivity on a conic.

If the projectivity is nonparabolic, with two fixed points M, N, the cross axis is the line MN; if the projectivity is parabolic with a single fixed point, U, the cross axis is the tangent to the conic at U.

REMARK. Pappus' theorem (Theorem 8–1) is the special case of Theorem 10–17 when the conic is degenerate and each of the ranges $\{P_i\}$, $\{Q_i\}$ is on a separate line of the degenerate conic.

A corollary of Theorem 10–17 is the famous Pascal hexagon theorem.

Theorem 10–18.   If a hexagon is inscribed in a conic, the three points of intersection of pairs of opposite sides are collinear.*

Proof.   Consider Fig. 10–8. There is a projectivity on the conic in which A_1, A_2, A_3 correspond respectively to B_1, B_2, B_3. Hence, . . .

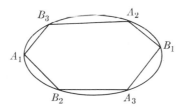

FIGURE 10–8

* This beautiful theorem, discovered by Pascal when he was sixteen years old, has been the subject of a large number of proofs. Likewise, the Pascal hexagon theorem has been shown to have a vast number of consequences.

If the six vertices of the hexagon are not all distinct, Pascal's theorem remains valid if suitably interpreted.

Theorem 10–19. If A_1, A_2, A_3, B_1, B_3 are five distinct points on a conic, and if l is the tangent line at A, then the points of intersection of A_2B_3 and A_3A_1, of A_3B_1 and A_1B_3, and of l and A_2B_1 are collinear.

Other special cases are left for you to state.

Theorem 10–20 (*Converse of Pascal's theorem*). Let A_1, A_2, A_3, B_1, B_2, B_3 be six distinct points in a plane, with A_2B_3 and A_3B_2 intersecting at L, A_3B_1 and A_1B_3 at M, and A_1B_2 and A_2B_1 at N. If L, M, N are collinear, then there is a conic (which may be degenerate) through the six points.

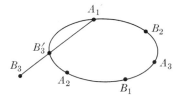

FIGURE 10–9

Proof. If no three of the given six points are collinear, we show that there is a nondegenerate conic through them all. By Corollary 2 of Theorem 10–4, there is a unique conic $\mathcal{C}$ through A_1, A_2, A_3, B_1, and B_2. Since no three of the five points are collinear, $\mathcal{C}$ is nondegenerate. Let the line A_1B_3 meet $\mathcal{C}$ in A_1 and B_3'. (For all we know, B_3' might coincide with A_1.) We shall show that B_3' is the same as B_3. By Pascal's theorem applied to the hexagon $A_1A_2A_3B_1B_2B_3'$ inscribed in $\mathcal{C}$, we know of the existence of three collinear points: L', the intersection of A_2B_3' and A_3B_2, M', the intersection of A_3B_1 and A_1B_3', and N. Since A_1B_3' is the same line as A_1B_3, M' is the same point as M. Since A_1, B_2, B_3 are not collinear, M is distinct from N. Hence L' lies on the line LMN. This line is distinct from A_3B_2, for if M lies on A_3B_2, either M coincides with A_3, in which case A_1, A_3, B_3 are collinear, or B_1 lies on A_3B_2, and either conclusion is contrary to the hypothesis that no three of the given six points are collinear. Hence L' coincides with L. Moreover, L is distinct from A_2, since A_3, A_2, B_2 are not collinear. Therefore the lines A_2B_3' and A_2B_3 both coincide with A_2L; and, since A_1 does not lie on this line, B_2' coincides with B_3. Thus B_3 lies on $\mathcal{C}$. $\square$

In case the assumption of noncollinearity is not satisfied, the conic is degenerate (see Todd, *op. cit.*, for a careful analysis of all the special cases).

The converse of Pascal's theorem permits us to state comparable converses of the theorems which correspond to the cases where not all vertices of the hexagon are distinct. For example, we have the following converse of Theorem 10-19.

Theorem 10-21. If a line through a vertex of a pentagon, no three of whose vertices are collinear, meets the opposite side in a point collinear with the intersections of the pairs of remaining opposite sides, the line is tangent to the conic which circumscribes the pentagon.

Another special case of Pascal's theorem and its converse can be stated neatly as follows.

Theorem 10-22. If two triangles are so situated that each vertex of the first lies on a side of the second, there exists a conic circumscribing the first and inscribed in the second if and only if the triangles are in the relationship of Desargues.

PROBLEM SET 10-6

1. Fill in omitted details of the proof of Theorem 10-15.

2. State two theorems in addition to Theorems 10-19 and 10-22 which can be obtained from Pascal's theorem by coincidences of some of the six vertices.

*3. (a) State the plane dual of Theorem 10-18. (This dual is known as Brianchon's theorem.)

(b) State the special cases of Brianchon's theorem, corresponding to Theorem 10-19, Theorem 10-22, and your answer to Problem 2 (cf. Problem 9, Section 10-4).

4. Show that six points on a conic determine 60 Pascal lines. (These pass by threes through 20 points; the 20 points lie by fours on 15 lines, three of the lines going through each point.)

5. Suppose that five real points A_i, $i = 1, \ldots, 5$, are given, no three collinear, thus determining a nondegenerate conic $\mathcal{C}$. Let P be a point not on $\mathcal{C}$. Show how to construct, with ruler alone,

(a) arbitrarily many more points on $\mathcal{C}$;

(b) the tangent to $\mathcal{C}$ at any one of the points A_i;

(c) the other intersection with $\mathcal{C}$ of any of the lines PA_i;

(d) the polar of P with respect to $\mathcal{C}$.

6. Let l be a given line in the plane of the conic $\mathcal{C}$ of Problem 5. Show how to construct, with ruler and compass, the points in which l meets $\mathcal{C}$. [*Hint:* Use Problem 7, Section 8-8.] Can you solve this problem with ruler alone?

7. Justify Maclaurin's method for generating a conic by using Pascal's theorem to prove that the points O, A', B', A, B, P of Problem 4, Section 10-2, lie on a conic.

8. Prove that if a conic which is inscribed in a triangle is tangent to two of the sides at their midpoints, then it is also tangent to the third side at its midpoint.

9. Let A, B be the points of tangency of tangents to conic $\mathcal{C}$ from point K on line l. Let P be a point of $\mathcal{C}$, with PA, PB meeting l in R, S. Let P' be another point of $\mathcal{C}$, with $P'R$, $P'S$ meeting $\mathcal{C}$ in A', B'. Show that $A'B'$ passes through the pole of l with respect to $\mathcal{C}$. (A. Zirakzadeh, *Amer. Math. Monthly*, Nov., 1961.)

10-7 CORRELATIONS AND POLAR RECIPROCATION

In Section 8-1, a correlation was defined as a proper projectivity between the points of an S_n and the primes of the same S_n. The relation of point and polar furnishes an important example of correlations in S_2. Suppose that we choose a point X and a conic $\mathcal{C}$ which, relative to a given coordinate frame, have, respectively, coordinate vector ξ and (symmetric) matrix A. Then p, the polar of X with respect to $\mathcal{C}$, has coordinate vector π given by $\pi^t = \xi^t A$ or $\pi = A\xi$.

A correlation need not have a symmetric matrix, of course. In case the correlation *does* have a symmetric matrix (which, by Problem 16, Section 8-8, means that the transformation is involutory), the correlation may be pictured as the relationship between point and its polar with respect to the conic with that matrix: Point and line are called *polar reciprocals* with respect to the conic, and the process of obtaining the polar reciprocal of a configuration is known as *polar reciprocation*.

The phraseology of the preceding sentence implies a symmetrical relationship which does, indeed, exist: In accordance with Theorem 10-14 and the remark which follows that theorem, the polar reciprocal with respect to $\mathcal{C}$ of the line with coordinate vector μ is the point with coordinate vector η given by $\eta^t = \mu^t A^{-1}$, or $\eta = A^{-1}\mu$.

Hence, reciprocating the point X with respect to $\mathcal{C}$ leads to the line p, and reciprocating p with respect to $\mathcal{C}$ leads back to X:

$$\xi \to A\xi \to A^{-1}(A\xi) = \xi.$$

Suppose now that we consider the effect of reciprocating all the points of one conic, $\mathcal{P}$, with respect to another, $\mathcal{M}$, with matrices P and M, respectively. Each point of $\mathcal{P}$, $\xi^t P \xi = 0$, is carried into the line with coordinate vector $\tau = M\xi$. Hence the point conic $\mathcal{P}$ is transformed into the line conic $\tau^t M^{-1} P M^{-1} \tau = 0$. Following the discussion of Section 10-5, we can write the point equation of this line conic as

$$\xi^t M P^{-1} M \xi = 0.$$

We thus have the following theorem.

Theorem 10–23. The point conic with matrix P reciprocates, with respect to the point conic with matrix M, into the line conic whose point-equation matrix is $MP^{-1}M$.

An important result is that "the relation of pole and polar is preserved under polar reciprocation." More precisely, we have the following theorem.

Theorem 10–24. Let the point M, the line p, and the conic $\mathfrak{C}$ be reciprocated with respect to a conic, $\mathfrak{S}$, into the line m, the point P and the conic $\mathfrak{D}$, respectively. Then p is the polar of M with respect to $\mathfrak{C}$ if and only if m is the polar of P with respect to $\mathfrak{D}$.

Proof. Let the point equation of $\mathfrak{C}$ be $\xi^t A \xi = 0$, and that of $\mathfrak{S}$ be $\xi^t B \xi = 0$. Then by Theorem 10–23, the point equation of $\mathfrak{D}$ is

$$\xi^t B A^{-1} B \xi = 0.$$

Let a coordinate vector of M be μ and a coordinate vector of m be μ'. Then

(i) $\mu' = B\mu.$

Let a coordinate vector of p be π, and a coordinate vector of P be π'. Then

(ii) $\pi' = B^{-1}\pi.$

(iii) Now p is the polar of M with respect to $\mathfrak{C} \Leftrightarrow \pi = A\mu$, and,

(iv) m is the polar of P with respect to $\mathfrak{D} \Leftrightarrow \mu' = BA^{-1}B\pi.$

It is easy to verify that (i), (ii), and (iii) imply (iv), and that (i), (ii), and (iv) imply (iii).

PROBLEM SET 10–7

1. Show that the polar reciprocal of the parabola $y^2 = 2mx + m^2$, with respect to the circle $x^2 + y^2 = 1$, is the line circle whose point equation is $m(x^2 + y^2) + 2x = 0$.

2. Fill the gaps in the following geometric proof of the theorem of Problem 8(a), Section 10–4. Let CC' meet AB, $A'B'$ in D, D', respectively. Let AB, $A'B'$ meet at S. If we can exhibit a perspectivity between the ranges AB, $A'B'$ in which A, B, D correspond respectively to A', B', D', we will be able to conclude that AA', BB', DD' are concurrent. Designate $B'C'$ by u, $A'C'$ by v, SC' by w, and CC' by x. Then $(AB, DS) = (uv, wx) = (B'A', SD') = (A'B', D'S)$. Thus we have the desired perspectivity.

3. Complete the algebraic details of Theorem 10–24.

10–8 APPLICATIONS OF POLAR RECIPROCATION

One of the uses of polar reciprocation is the proof of general results from special cases, in a way which will shortly be made clear. The reader will observe that the language employed is, in part, that of metric geometry. Such usage represents a convenient shorthand—wherever metric concepts appear, comparable algebraic terminology appropriate to our general development could be introduced instead. Indeed, the algebraic terminology must be used to establish the results rigorously.

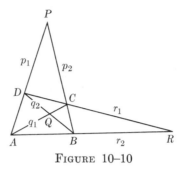

FIGURE 10–10

Our first illustration concerns the harmonic properties of the complete quadrangle (Section 8–3). These properties can be established in the real domain in the following manner: Start with an arbitrary complete quadrangle $ABCD$, with diagonal points P, Q, R. Reciprocate this figure with respect to a central conic whose center is at P. The polar of P is the ideal line (why?); thus p_1 and p_2 will reciprocate into two ideal points, P_1 and P_2. Hence A and D will reciprocate into two lines, a and d, with the ideal point P_1 in common, and B and C go into b and c, with the ideal point P_2 in common (Fig. 10–11).

But now, the harmonic properties of a parallelogram, as a *quadrilateral*, are self-evident. Hence, since polar reciprocation is a linear transformation (preserving cross ratio), we obtain the harmonic properties of the complete quadrangle by reciprocating back.

We next consider a sequence of definitions and theorems which can be used to obtain theorems about conics, in a way which will be described at the end of the sequence.

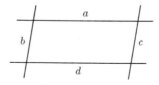

FIGURE 10–11

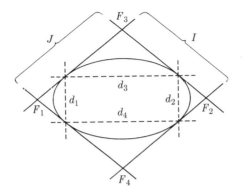

FIGURE 10–12

Definition 8. (i) Lines of slope i or $-i$ are called *isotropic lines*.
(ii) A tangent to a curve of slope i or $-i$ is called an *isotropic tangent*.
(iii) A point of intersection (other than I or J) of two isotropic tangents to a conic is called a *focus* of the conic.
(iv) The polar with respect to a conic $\mathfrak{C}$ of a focus, F, of $\mathfrak{C}$ is called the *directrix corresponding to F*.

From the fact that the line equation of a conic is of the second degree, we conclude that a conic "generally" has two tangents with any given slope. Thus a conic "generally" has four foci and four directrices. This situation is symbolized in Fig. 10–12. But it is possible that a conic have only one tangent of a certain slope. For example, consider the isotropic tangents to a circle. We know that every circle passes through I and J (Problem 3(a), Section 2–3). Thus the tangents through I and J are, in the case of a circle, tangents at points *on* the curve; there is, then, one tangent of slope i, and one tangent of slope $-i$, giving rise to one focus.

We find it convenient to make the following definition.

Definition 9. A tangent to a curve at an ideal point on the curve is called an *asymptote*.

Thus, the asymptotes of a circle are isotropic lines. The proof of the following theorem is left as a problem.

Theorem 10–25. The asymptotes of a circle intersect at its center, or the center of a circle is its (sole) focus.

Traditionally, the terms "focus" and "directrix" are associated with the metric definition of a conic: "a conic is the locus of a point the ratio of whose distances from a fixed point (focus) and a fixed line (directrix) is constant." In a cartesian coordinate frame, parts (iii) and (iv) of Definition 8 are equivalent to the metric definitions, but this equivalence will not be proved here.

For our purpose the following theorem is basic.

Theorem 10–26. The reciprocal of a circle S_1 with center C with respect to a circle S_2 with center O is a nondegenerate conic with O as focus and the polar of C as corresponding directrix.

Proof. That the reciprocal is a nondegenerate conic follows from the fact that the circle is nondegenerate (since it has a center) and that the rank of a matrix is unchanged by a linear transformation.

The polar of C with respect to S_1 is the ideal line, which reciprocates into O. Hence, by Theorem 10–24, O and the polar of C with respect to S_2 are pole and polar with respect to the conic.

It remains only to prove that O is a focus of the conic. Now I and J, which lie on S_1, reciprocate into two lines of the conic. But since I and J lie also on S_2, they reciprocate into the tangents to S_2 at I and J (the polar of a point on a conic is the tangent at that point). In other words, I and J reciprocate into isotropic tangents to the conic, meeting at O. □

The following converse of Theorem 10–26 is proved by an argument similar to the foregoing; the details are left as a problem.

Theorem 10–27. Let $\mathcal{C}$ be a nondegenerate conic with focus O and corresponding directrix, d. The reciprocal of $\mathcal{C}$ with respect to a circle S_2 centered at O is a circle S_1 whose center is the pole of d with respect to S_2.

We shall need a metric result.

Theorem 10–28. Let the polar of P with respect to a circle centered at O be p. Then p is perpendicular to OP and meets OP at Q, where $OP \cdot OQ = r^2$, r being the radius of the circle.

The proof is left as a problem.

Corollary. Let A and B have polars a and b with respect to a circle centered at O. Then one of the angles between a and b equals the angle AOB.

We are now in a position to obtain theorems about conics in the following way: We reciprocate a general conic $\mathcal{C}$ with respect to a circle centered at a focus of $\mathcal{C}$, thus obtaining a circle as the reciprocated curve (Theorem 10–27). We then consider some property of the circle (presumably well known, or easy to prove) and reciprocate back. If we know what happens to the property under consideration, we obtain a theorem about $\mathcal{C}$.

PROBLEM SET 10-8

1. Prove Theorem 10–25.

2. Prove Theorem 10–27.

3. Prove Theorem 10–28.

By the method suggested above, obtain a theorem about a conic in the real domain from each of the following simple theorems about a circle. (Problems 4 through 8.)

4. A tangent to a circle is perpendicular to the radius drawn to the point of contact.

5. The locus of the point of intersection of two tangents to a circle which cut at a constant angle is a concentric circle.

6. An angle inscribed in a semicircle is a right angle.

7. The polar of a point P with respect to a circle is perpendicular to the line joining P to the center of the circle.

8. The envelope of a chord of constant length in a circle is a concentric circle. (Note the relationship of 7 to 4, of 8 to 5.)

9. Given a central conic drawn on paper. Describe a method of locating, with ruler and compasses, (a) the center; (b) the real foci.

*10. The following chain of results leads to a definition of angle and perpendicularity due to Laguerre, a 19th century French geometer.

(a) Show that $I(0, 1, i)$ and $J(0, 1, -i)$ are left fixed by every rigid motion of the plane:

$$k\xi' = \begin{bmatrix} 1 & 0 & 0 \\ a & \cos\theta & -\sin\theta \\ b & \sin\theta & \cos\theta \end{bmatrix} \cdot \xi.$$

(b) Show that any rigid motion of the plane carries an isotropic line through I into an isotropic line through I, and likewise for J.

(c) Show that the cross ratio $r = (l_1 l_2, l_I l_J)$ of two finite nonisotropic lines l_1, l_2 and the two isotropic lines l_I, l_J through their point of intersection is invariant under rigid motion.

(d) If l_1 has slope m_1 and l_2 has slope m_2, show that the cross ratio r of part (c) is given by

$$r = \frac{(1 + m_1 m_2) + i(m_2 - m_1)}{(1 + m_1 m_2) - i(m_2 - m_1)},$$

and that an angle θ between l_1 and l_2 is given by

$$\tan\theta = \frac{m_2 - m_1}{1 + m_1 m_2}.$$

(e) Show that

$$\tan \theta = \frac{1}{i} \frac{r-1}{r+1},$$

and thus prove that two finite nonisotropic lines are perpendicular if and only if they are separated harmonically by the isotropic lines through their point of intersection.

Show that this result is valid even if the slope of l_1 or l_2 does not exist.

10–9 INVOLUTIONS ON A CONIC

The material of Section 8–8 on involutions on a line can immediately be duplicated for a conic, since a conic is an S_1. The definition and the results will be quickly summarized, and the reader can picture them for himself.

A projectivity on the conic with matrix T, such that $T^2 = kI$, is called an *involution*. Every involution is nonparabolic, i.e., it has two distinct fixed (or "double") elements. An involution is determined by two pairs of corresponding elements, or by its fixed elements. A projectivity which interchanges the elements of a pair is an involution. The characteristic cross-ratio of an involution is -1; i.e., the fixed elements are separated harmonically by each pair of elements of the involution. There exists a unique pair of elements which separates harmonically each of two pairs, viz., the fixed elements of the involution determined by the two pairs.

In addition to the foregoing results about involutions in S_1's, there is an elegant characterization of involutions on conics. Consider a non-degenerate conic $\mathcal{C}$ and a point O not on $\mathcal{C}$. Let the pencil of lines with vertex O cut the conic in the pairs P_1, P_2; Q_1, Q_2; etc. Without carrying out any of the algebraic details, we can see that the coordinate vector of any point X_2 is linearly related to the coordinate vector of its mate, X_1. Moreover, the correspondence is one-to-one and symmetrical: If X_2 corresponds to X_1, then X_1 corresponds to X_2. Hence this construction defines an involution on $\mathcal{C}$. Moreover, every involution on the conic can be thought of as being generated in this way, for if an involution U pairs P_1 and P_2, Q_1 and Q_2, we simply draw P_1P_2 and Q_1Q_2 to meet at O. Then the involution determined by the pencil of lines through O must be identical with U since an involution is determined by two pairs of corresponding points. This is our basic theorem. (See Fig. 10–13.)

Theorem 10–29. The pencil of lines through O, a point not on the conic $\mathcal{C}$, cuts out pairs of points of an involution on $\mathcal{C}$. Conversely, every involution on $\mathcal{C}$ can be thought of as being generated in this way.

Restatement. A necessary and sufficient condition that a projectivity on a conic be an involution is that the lines joining corresponding points be concurrent.

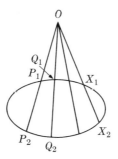

FIGURE 10–13

Clearly, the fixed points of the involution on $\mathcal{C}$ determined by the pencil with vertex O are the points of contact of the tangents from O. The point O is called the *center* of the involution, and the line joining the fixed points H, K is called its *axis*. The axis is also the cross axis of the projectivity on the conic (Theorem 10–17). An involution on a conic is determined once its center or its axis is specified.

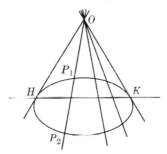

FIGURE 10–14

If $(HK, P_1P_2) = -1$, P_1 and P_2 are paired in the involution of which H and K are fixed points. Hence P_1P_2 passes through O, the pole of HK, which implies that P_1P_2 and HK are conjugate lines with respect to $\mathcal{C}$. This argument constitutes a proof of one half of Theorem 10–16. The argument can be reversed to prove the other half of the theorem.

PROBLEM SET 10–9

1. Dualize the statement of Theorem 10–29.

2. Let A, B be conjugate points with respect to $\mathcal{C}$; let P_1, P_2 be two points of $\mathcal{C}$ collinear with B; suppose that P_1A, P_2A meet $\mathcal{C}$ in Q_1, Q_2, respectively. Show that Q_1, Q_2, B are collinear.

3. Prove that the lines joining two points A and B on a nondegenerate conic $\mathcal{C}$ to a third point P on $\mathcal{C}$ are separated harmonically by the tangent at P and the line joining P to the pole of AB.

10–10 INVOLUTIONS IN THE PLANE

There is a close relation between involutions in the plane and involutions on certain conics in the plane. To discuss the situation we must distinguish between collineations and correlations.

The facts about involutory correlations have essentially already been presented. Each such involution may be looked upon as the transformation between pole and polar with respect to some conic, $\mathfrak{C}$, say. This transformation effects an involution *on* $\mathfrak{C}$, considered as a locus of points *and* tangent lines—indeed each point of $\mathfrak{C}$ corresponds to the tangent line at that point.

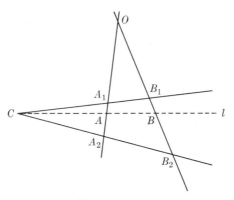

FIGURE 10–15

The involutory collineations are best studied by a geometrical analysis of their fixed points and fixed lines. Suppose that a nontrivial involution T interchanges A_1 and A_2, B_1 and B_2, where no three of these four points are collinear. Then the lines, A_1A_2, B_1B_2 are self-corresponding under T. (This does *not* mean that every point on A_1A_2, for example, remains fixed under T, but merely that the transform of every point of the line is on the line.) Hence, O, the point of intersection of A_1A_2 and B_1B_2 (Fig. 10–15), is fixed under T. A slightly different argument shows that C, the point of intersection of A_1B_1 and A_2B_2, is also fixed under T. Let A be the harmonic conjugate of O with respect to A_1, A_2; and let B be the harmonic conjugate of O with respect to B_1, B_2. Then A and B are also fixed under T. Therefore, l, the line AB, is self-corresponding under T. From the harmonic properties of the complete quadrangle, we conclude that l passes through C. The involution T establishes a collineation of l, which has three fixed points: A, B, C. Hence, by Problem 4(a), Section 8–1, we know that *every* point of l is fixed under T. Therefore, every line through O is self-corresponding, for every such line has two fixed points, viz., O, and the point in which the line meets l. We have now shown that O and the points of l are fixed points under T, and l and the lines through O are self-corresponding lines under T.

There are no other fixed points or self-corresponding lines; for, if there were, for example, another fixed point, it would be possible to find four fixed points, no three collinear. But this is impossible. (Why?)

On any line through O, T sets up a one-dimensional involution whose fixed points are O and the point of intersection of the line with l; O is called the *center* of the involution; l is called its *axis*.

The foregoing remarks are sufficient to establish the following theorem.

Theorem 10–30. If an involution T of a plane has center O and axis l, it establishes an involution U of any conic $\mathfrak{C}$ with respect to which O and l are pole and polar, interchanging the two points of $\mathfrak{C}$ on any line through O. Conversely, an involution U of the points of a conic determines a unique involution T of the plane which leaves the conic fixed, and which is equivalent to U on the conic.

PROBLEM SET 10–10

1. Fill in omitted details of the argument of Section 10–10.

2. Prove Theorem 10–30 by an algebraic argument.

3. Find the center and axis of the involution of S_2 determined by the equations of Problem 11, Section 8–8, and find all conics left fixed by this involution.

10–11 NONINVOLUTORY PROJECTIVITIES ON A CONIC; SUMMARY

The joins of corresponding points in a perspectivity between lines l and l' are concurrent, while the joins of corresponding points of a nonperspective projectivity between lines l and l' form a nondegenerate line conic (Problem 8, Section 10–2). In a sense, Theorem 10–29, which states that the joins of corresponding points in an involution on a conic are concurrent, is an analogue of the perspectivity mentioned above, and so we may ask about the joins of corresponding points of a noninvolutory projectivity on a conic. The following theorem gives a satisfying answer.

Theorem 10–31. The joins of corresponding points of a noninvolutory projectivity on a nondegenerate point conic form a nondegenerate line conic. If the given projectivity has two fixed points, the two conics are tangent at those points.

Proof. Suppose that a coordinate frame is chosen so that the given point conic has equation $x_0 x_2 - x_1^2 = 0$.

A typical point P on the conic will have one-dimensional homogeneous coordinates (l, k), and its transform P' under the given projectivity will have coordinates (l', k'), where

$$r \cdot \begin{bmatrix} l' \\ k' \end{bmatrix} = \begin{bmatrix} a & b \\ c & d \end{bmatrix} \begin{bmatrix} l \\ k \end{bmatrix}, \qquad ad - bc \neq 0.$$

This matrix equation will be more useful with r eliminated to give

$$cll' + dkl' - alk' - bkk' = 0. \tag{1}$$

Two-dimensional homogeneous coordinates of P are $(l^2, -lk, k^2)$, and of P', $(l'^2, -l'k', k'^2)$ (Section 10–3). Hence an equation of line PP' is

$$kk'x_0 + (kl' + lk')x_1 + ll'x_2 = 0, \tag{2}$$

so long as P' is distinct from P. Thus, coordinates u_0, u_1, u_2 of line PP' are

$$u_0 = kk',$$
$$u_1 = kl' + lk',$$
$$u_2 = ll'.$$

We shall find an equation of the required line locus by eliminating l, k, l', k' between these equations and Eq. (1). The algebra is a bit involved:

$$(kl' + lk')^2 = u_1^2;$$

therefore

$$(kl' - lk')^2 = u_1^2 - 4kk'll' = u_1^2 - 4u_0u_2.$$

Hence

$$kl' = \tfrac{1}{2}(u_1 + \sqrt{u_1^2 - 4u_0u_2}),$$

and

$$lk' = \tfrac{1}{2}(u_1 - \sqrt{u_1^2 - 4u_0u_2}).$$

Thus, Eq. (1) becomes

$$cu_2 + \tfrac{1}{2}d\,(u_1 + \sqrt{u_1^2 - 4u_0u_2}) - \tfrac{1}{2}a\,(u_1 - \sqrt{u_1^2 - 4u_0u_2}) - bu_0 = 0.$$

By squaring, we arrive at

$$[cu_2 + \tfrac{1}{2}(d - a)\,u_1 - bu_0]^2 = \tfrac{1}{4}(d + a)^2\,(u_1^2 - 4u_0u_2). \tag{3}$$

Equation (3) represents a line conic; its discriminant is

$$\Delta = \tfrac{1}{4}(a + d)^4\,(ad - bc). \tag{4}$$

Since the given projectivity was assumed to be noninvolutory, $a + d \neq 0$; hence, the conic (3) is nondegenerate. [Note that if the projectivity is an involution, Eq. (3) reduces to

$$[cu_2 + \tfrac{1}{2}(d - a)u_1 - bu_0]^2 = 0,$$

which is the equation of the center of the involution, counted twice.]

If the projectivity is nonparabolic, we may choose one fixed point as $l = 1$, $k = 0$, and the other as $l = 0$, $k = 1$. Then, in the equation of the projectivity, $b = 0 = c$, and Eq. (3) becomes

$$(d - a)^2 u_1^2 = (d + a)^2(u_1^2 - 4u_0u_2),$$

or

$$adu_1^2 = (a + d)^2 u_0u_2.$$

It can readily be verified that this conic, as well as the original $x_0x_2 - x_1^2 = 0$, is tangent to the line $x_2 = 0$ at the point with two-dimensional coordinates $(1, 0, 0)$ and to $x_0 = 0$ at $(0, 0, 1)$.   □

We can summarize some of our results to emphasize the analogies with which this section began.

(a) In a plane, the lines joining corresponding points of two projectively related ranges on two lines form a line conic, which is degenerate if and only if the projectivity is a perspectivity. If the line conic is not degenerate, it is tangent to the two given lines.

(b) In a plane, the lines joining corresponding points of two projectively related ranges on a nondegenerate conic form a line conic which is degenerate if and only if the projectivity is involutory. If the given projectivity is nonparabolic and noninvolutory then the line conic is tangent to the given conic at the fixed points of the projectivity.

Other analogies between a projectivity from line l to line l' and a projectivity on a conic, such as the existence of a cross axis, have already been stressed.

PROBLEM SET 10–11

1. Obtain Eq. (2) for the line PP'.

2. Obtain Eq. (4) for the discriminant of the conic (3).

3. Verify that the conics are tangent, as stated in the last sentence of the proof of Theorem 10–31.

4. What can be said of the relation of the line conic to the original conic in Theorem 10–31 in case the projectivity is parabolic?

10–12 REDUCTION OF REAL SYMMETRIC MATRICES BY ORTHOGONAL MATRICES

Near the beginning of this chapter we referred to the rigid motions by means of which we can simplify the equations of conics. Then, in Theorem 10–1, we showed that the matrix of a conic (or quadric) could be put in diagonal form by means of a linear transformation of the coordinate frame. We shall close the chapter with a stronger result, if we are in the real domain, namely, that the matrix of a *real* conic or quadric can be put in diagonal form by means of an *orthogonal* transformation of the coordinate frame. This is the analogue of the rigid motions of the first sentence above.

Everything hinges on a basic theorem.

Theorem 10–32. A real symmetric matrix has real characteristic values, and the characteristic vectors corresponding to different characteristic values are orthogonal.

Proof. Let ξ be a characteristic vector of the real symmetric matrix A, corresponding to the characteristic value k. Then

$$A\xi = k\xi.$$

By taking the conjugate transpose of both sides, we have

$$\bar{\xi}^t A = \bar{\xi}^t \bar{k}.$$

Left-multiplying the first of these equations by $\bar{\xi}^t$ gives

$$\bar{\xi}^t A\xi = \bar{\xi}^t k\xi.$$

Right-multiplying the second equation by ξ gives

$$\bar{\xi}^t A\xi = \bar{\xi}^t \bar{k}\xi.$$

Hence

$$\bar{\xi}^t k\xi = \bar{\xi}^t \bar{k}\xi, \quad \text{or} \quad \bar{\xi}^t \xi(k - \bar{k}) = 0.$$

Therefore, $k = \bar{k}$. (Why?) Thus, k is real.

Now suppose that η is a characteristic vector corresponding to the characteristic value $l(\neq k)$. Then $A\eta = l\eta$. Hence, $\xi^t A\eta = \xi^t l\eta$. But, from the first equation $\eta^t A\xi = \eta^t k\xi$. Therefore $\xi^t A\eta = \xi^t k\eta$. Thus,

$$(k - l)\xi^t \eta = 0.$$

Hence, $\xi^t \eta = 0$, that is, ξ, η are orthogonal. $\square$

Theorem 10–33. If A is a real $(n + 1) \times (n + 1)$ symmetric matrix, there exists a real orthogonal matrix N such that

$$N^t A N = D,$$

where D is a real diagonal matrix.

Proof. Let the characteristic values of A be $k_0, k_1, \ldots, k_n$, with associated characteristic vectors $\xi_0, \xi_1, \ldots, \xi_n$. (There may be repetitions and zeros among the k's.)

Consider the "normalized" vectors

$$\eta_i = \frac{\xi_i}{\|\xi_i\|}, \qquad i = 0, \ldots, n.$$

Let $N = [\eta_0 \quad \eta_1 \quad \cdots \quad \eta_n]$. By Theorem 10–32, we know N to be orthogonal. Then

$$N^t A N = \begin{vmatrix} \eta_0 \\ \eta_1 \\ \vdots \\ \eta_n \end{vmatrix} A[\eta_0 \quad \eta_1 \quad \cdots \quad \eta_n] = \begin{vmatrix} \eta_0 \\ \eta_1 \\ \vdots \\ \eta_n \end{vmatrix} [k_0\eta_0 \quad k_1\eta_1 \quad \cdots \quad k_n\eta_n]$$

$$= \begin{vmatrix} k_0 & 0 & \cdots & 0 \\ 0 & k_1 & \cdots & 0 \\ \vdots & & & \\ 0 & \cdots & 0 & k_n \end{vmatrix}, \quad \square$$

If the rank of A is r, there will be r nonzero characteristic values, not necessarily all distinct. We have shown that by means of an orthogonal transformation of coordinate frame, we can make any real quadric assume the equation

$$k_0 x_0^2 + k_1 x_1^2 + \cdots + k_{r-1} x_{r-1}^2 = 0.$$

In the real domain we cannot, of course, go further to make the coefficients of all the x's be 1. But we can divide the terms into those with positive coefficients and those with negative coefficients, and perform another coordinate transformation to obtain

$$x_0^2 + x_1^2 + \cdots + x_{p-1}^2 - x_p^2 - x_{p+1}^2 - \cdots - x_r^2 = 0.$$

CHAPTER 11

Pairs and Pencils of Conics

A host of significant results attend a study of certain types of "families" of conics. One of the most interesting types of family to consider is the "pencil,"—so called in analogy with the definition of a pencil of lines, the system of conics whose equations are linear combinations of the equations of two "base" conics.

But some preliminary analysis is required. Whereas it is clear that two distinct lines always intersect in one point, it requires some work to be certain of the number of points common to two conics. We turn our attention first to this problem.

11–1 THE INTERSECTION OF TWO CONICS

Our experience with graphs of conics in elementary analytic geometry leads us to suppose that two conics "usually" intersect in four points, with fewer than four visually apparent intersections arising when some intersections are imaginary or ideal or "multiple", or perhaps a combination of these special cases. At least we know that two nondegenerate conics do not have *more* than four points in common, since five points, no three collinear, determine a conic (Fig. 11–1).

To be certain of our results, we attack the problem systematically, using algebraic methods. We begin with two (distinct) conics, $\mathcal{C}$ and $\mathcal{C}'$, with $\mathcal{C}$, at least, being nondegenerate. From Section 10–3 we know that a coordinate frame can be chosen so that the equation of $\mathcal{C}$ will be $x_0 x_2 - x_1^2 = 0$, with points on $\mathcal{C}$ having coordinates $(1, r, r^2)$ in terms of a parameter r. Moreover, since there is considerable freedom in the choice of this coordinate system, point A of Fig. 10–3 can be taken not to lie on $\mathcal{C}'$. The equation of $\mathcal{C}'$ relative to this coordinate frame will be

$$\xi^t M \xi = 0$$

or

$$m_{00} x_0^2 + m_{11} x_1^2 + m_{22} x_2^2 + 2m_{01} x_0 x_1 + 2m_{02} x_0 x_2 + 2m_{12} x_1 x_2 = 0.$$

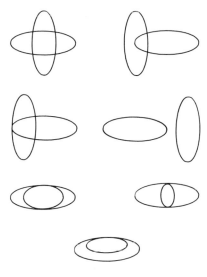

FIGURE 11–1

The point $R(1, r, r^2)$ of $\mathcal{C}$ lies on $\mathcal{C}'$ if and only if r satisfies the quartic equation

$$m_{22}r^4 + 2m_{12}r^3 + (m_{11} + 2m_{02})r^2 + 2m_{01}r + m_{00} = 0. \qquad (1)$$

Since $A(0, 0, 1)$ does not lie on $\mathcal{C}'$, $m_{22} \neq 0$. Hence Eq. (1) has four roots r_1, r_2, r_3, r_4, not necessarily all distinct. Indeed, there are five cases to consider:

   (i) four simple roots (all roots distinct);
   (ii) two simple roots and one double root;
   (iii) two double roots;
   (iv) one triple root and one simple root;
   (v) one quadruple root.

If we agree to count the point corresponding to a double, triple, or quadruple root as two, three, or four points of intersection, we immediately have the following theorem.

Theorem 11–1. Two conics, at least one of which is nondegenerate, intersect in four points.

In case $\mathcal{C}$ and $\mathcal{C}'$ are both degenerate, each consisting of a pair of distinct lines, or a line counted twice, it is easy to count the number of common points, with an obvious convention about multiplicity, to obtain the following theorem.

Theorem 11–2. Two distinct conics which do not have a line in common intersect in four points.

In order to analyze Cases (i) through (v) completely, it will be useful to have some results on linear combinations of equations of conics (Section 11–2). We complete this section with a theorem which seems intuitively valid.

Theorem 11–3. Two nondegenerate conics are tangent at P if and only if P is a multiple point of intersection of the conics.

Proof. Once again, choose the coordinate system of Section 10–3, taking $B(1, 0, 0)$ as the point P. Then the equation of $\mathcal{C}$ is $x_0 x_2 - x_1^2 = 0$, and the equation of the tangent to $\mathcal{C}$ at P is $x_2 = 0$; the equation of $\mathcal{C}'$ is $m_{11}x_1^2 + m_{22}x_2^2 + 2m_{01}x_0x_1 + 2m_{02}x_0x_2 + 2m_{12}x_1x_2 = 0$, and the equation of the tangent to $\mathcal{C}'$ at P is $m_{01}x_1 + m_{02}x_2 = 0$; and Eq.(1) takes the form

$$m_{22}r^4 + 2m_{12}r^3 + (m_{11} + 2m_{02})r^2 + 2m_{01}r = 0.$$

Now 0 is at least a double root of this last equation if and only if $m_{01} = 0$. But this is precisely the condition that the tangents to $\mathcal{C}$ and $\mathcal{C}'$ at P coincide. □

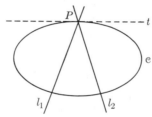

FIGURE 11–2

For the sake of uniformity of expression, we will say that two point conics, one or both of which are degenerate, are tangent at a common point P if P is a multiple point of intersection. Thus, in Fig. 11–2, the degenerate conic $l_1 l_2$ and the conic $\mathcal{C}$ are tangent at P. The line t is the tangent to $\mathcal{C}$ at P—it is the unique line which has no point other than P in common with $\mathcal{C}$. We shall say that *any* line through P is "tangent" to the degenerate conic, $l_1 l_2$.

PROBLEM SET 11–1

1. Prove Theorem 11–2.

2. Check the algebraic details of Theorem 11–3.

3. Draw sketches to exemplify those of Cases (i) through (v) which can occur when (a) one of the conics $\mathcal{C}$, $\mathcal{C}'$ is degenerate; (b) both the conics are degenerate.

11–2 PENCILS OF CONICS

Let $\mathfrak{A}$, $\mathfrak{B}$ with equations

$$f \equiv \xi^t A \xi = 0, \qquad g \equiv \xi^t B \xi = 0 \tag{1}$$

be two distinct conics. Then for all complex numbers h, k, not both zero,

$$hf + kg \equiv h \cdot \xi^t A \xi + k \cdot \xi^t B \xi \equiv \xi^t (hA + kB) \xi = 0 \tag{2}$$

is the equation of a conic passing through all the points common to $\mathfrak{A}$ and $\mathfrak{B}$ (cf. Problem 10(d), Section 2–2). Such conics, linearly dependent on two conics, constitute what is known as a *pencil*.

Definition. (a) The set of all point conics whose equations are linear combinations of the equations of two particular conics is called a *pencil of point conics*. (b) The two particular conics of part (a) are called *base conics* of the pencil.

The same pencil can be generated by more than one pair of base conics. Indeed, any pair in the pencil will serve.

Theorem 11–4. Any two distinct conics of a pencil can be used as base conics of the pencil.

Proof. Consider the pencil with Eq. (2) and let $\mathfrak{R}$, $\mathfrak{S}$, with equations

$$r \equiv h_1 f + k_1 g = 0, \qquad s \equiv h_2 f + k_2 g = 0$$

be two distinct conics of the pencil. Then

$$\begin{bmatrix} h_1 & k_1 \\ h_2 & k_2 \end{bmatrix}$$

is nonsingular. Now any conic $\mathfrak{J}$ belonging to the pencil with base conics $\mathfrak{R}$ and $\mathfrak{S}$, belongs to the original pencil, for if the equation of $\mathfrak{J}$ is

$$t \equiv mr + ns = 0,$$

then t can also be written as

$$t \equiv (mh_1 + nh_2)f + (mk_1 + nk_2)g = 0.$$

Conversely, since we can solve for f and g in terms of r and s, any linear combination of the former pair is expressible as a linear combination of the latter pair, so that any conic of the original pencil is a conic of the $\mathfrak{R}$, $\mathfrak{S}$ pencil as well. $\square$

If conics $\mathfrak{A}$, $\mathfrak{B}$ are fixed, any pair of complex numbers (h, k), not both zero, determines a conic of the pencil of Eq. (2). The pair (ch, ck), where c is any nonzero complex number, determines the same conic as (h, k). Moreover, to any conic of the pencil corresponds a pair (h, k), or rather, a set of pairs (ch, ck). The conics of a pencil, then, constitute an S_1, with homogeneous coordinates (h, k) relative to a frame in which $\mathfrak{A}$, $\mathfrak{B}$ are the fundamental elements. Shifting to $\mathfrak{R}$, $\mathfrak{S}$ as base conics of the pencil corresponds to a change of coordinate frame.

The remainder of this section is devoted to the development of certain properties of pencils which will permit a complete analysis of all types of pencils, to be carried out in the next section.

It is left to you to show that any pair of conics of a pencil intersect in the same set of points as any other pair of the pencil.

The point P with coordinate vector π lies on a conic of the pencil with Eq. (2) provided that

$$h(\pi^t A \pi) + k(\pi^t B \pi) = 0.$$

If $\pi^t A \pi$ and $\pi^t B \pi$ are not both zero, there is a unique ratio $h:k$ which will satisfy this equation. We have thus established the following theorem.

Theorem 11–5. If P is not one of the points common to all the conics of a pencil, there passes precisely one conic of the pencil through P.

If two conics $\mathfrak{A}$, $\mathfrak{B}$ have exactly four distinct points in common, P_1, P_2, P_3, P_4, say, then no three of these points are collinear (why?). Hence, there are at least three distinct degenerate conics in the pencil determined by $\mathfrak{A}$ and $\mathfrak{B}$, namely,

$\mathfrak{D}_1$, consisting of the pair of lines $P_1 P_2$ and $P_3 P_4$;

$\mathfrak{D}_2$, consisting of the pair of lines $P_1 P_3$ and $P_2 P_4$;

$\mathfrak{D}_3$, consisting of the pair of lines $P_1 P_4$ and $P_2 P_3$;

or, more briefly, the pairs of opposite sides of the complete quadrangle with vertices P_1, P_2, P_3, P_4.

We can show that there are never more than three degenerate conics in a pencil, unless all the conics are degenerate.

Theorem 11–6. If a pencil of point conics contains at least one non-degenerate conic, it contains at most three distinct degenerate conics.

Proof. Choose a nondegenerate conic as $\mathfrak{A}$, one of the base conics of the pencil. Then $\det A \neq 0$. A conic of the pencil given by Eq. (2) is degenerate if and only if its discriminant is zero:

$$\det [hA + kB] = 0.$$

It can be checked (Problem 3 below) that

$$\det [hA + kB] = h^3(\det A) + h^2k\Theta + hk^2\Theta' + k^3(\det B), \qquad (3)$$

where Θ and Θ' are polynomials in the elements of the matrices A and B. We are dealing, then, with a cubic equation in the ratio $h:k$, which has three (not necessarily distinct) roots, d_0, d_1, d_2, say. $\square$

For our present purpose we do not need to know the expressions for Θ, Θ' in terms of the elements of A and B, but we shall encounter Θ and Θ' again in Section 11–6.

Theorem 11–7. If P is an n-fold (single, double, triple, or quadruple) point of intersection of two conics of a pencil, P is also an n-fold point of intersection for any other pair of conics of the pencil.

Proof. We shall assume that the pencil contains at least one nondegenerate conic, in which case it contains many such (Theorem 11–6). Choose two of these nondegenerate conics, $\mathfrak{a}$, $\mathfrak{B}$, as base conics of the pencil, with equations as given by Eqs. (1). The tangents to $\mathfrak{a}$, $\mathfrak{B}$ at P have equations

$$\pi^t A \xi = 0; \qquad \pi^t B \xi = 0. \qquad (4)$$

If conics $\mathfrak{R}$, $\mathfrak{S}$ have equations

$$r = h_1 f + k_1 y; \qquad s = h_2 f + k_2 g,$$

then the equations of the tangents to $\mathfrak{R}$, $\mathfrak{S}$ at P have equations

$$h_1 \pi^t A \xi + k_1 \pi^t B \xi = 0; \qquad h_2 \pi^t A \xi + k_2 \pi^t B \xi = 0. \qquad (5)$$

The lines represented by Eqs. (4) are identical if and only if the lines represented by Eqs. (5) are identical. (Why?—be careful in considering the cases where either or both of $\mathfrak{R}$, $\mathfrak{S}$ are degenerate.) Hence, P is a simple or multiple point for one pair of conics of the pencil according as P is a simple or multiple point of any other conic of the pencil.

It must now be shown that the "order" of intersection is the same for each pair of conics of the pencil. This can be done by enumerating all the cases. Suppose, for example, that conics $\mathfrak{a}$, $\mathfrak{B}$ intersect in P_1, P_1, P_2, P_3; i.e., that P_1 is a double point, and that each of P_2, P_3 is a simple intersection. We know that any two conics $\mathfrak{R}$, $\mathfrak{S}$ will have P_1, P_2, P_3 as the total set of points of intersection; and, from the foregoing argument, P_2 and P_3 must be simple points. This leaves no choice for P_1 but that it be a double point of intersection of $\mathfrak{R}$ and $\mathfrak{S}$. $\square$

PROBLEM SET 11–2

1. Prove that any pair of conics of a pencil intersect in the same set of points as any other pair of conics of the pencil.

2. (a) Let $\mathcal{C}$, $\mathcal{C}'$ each be a degenerate conic, with a line common to $\mathcal{C}$ and $\mathcal{C}'$. Show that every conic of the pencil determined by $\mathcal{C}$ and $\mathcal{C}'$ is degenerate.

(b) Let $\mathcal{D}$, $\mathcal{D}'$ be degenerate conics, each consisting of two lines intersecting in the same point. Show that every conic of the pencil determined by $\mathcal{D}$ and $\mathcal{D}'$ is degenerate.

(c) Show that (a) and (b) are the only types of pencils in which all conics are degenerate.

3. Fill in the algebraic details of the proof of Theorem 11–6.

4. Fill in the gaps in the proof of Theorem 11–7, especially the analysis of degenerate cases. (Theorem 10–9 may be helpful.)

11–3 CLASSIFICATION OF PENCILS

Types (i) and (ii). We can now describe the various types of pencils, corresponding to the five types of intersections of a pair of conics listed in Section 11–1. The numbering below will correspond with that used for those five cases.

CASE (i). *Four simple points: P_1, P_2, P_3, P_4.* There are three distinct degenerate conics in the pencil, as already described in Section 11–2. Any two of them may be used as base conics of the pencil. This observation furnishes a convenient method for finding the equation of a conic determined by five points.

If the five points actually determine a conic, no four of the five points are collinear; hence we can pick out some four of the five, such that no three of the four are collinear. Let $F = 0$, $G = 0$ be equations of two degenerate conics through these four points, and determine h, k, such that

$$hF + kG = 0$$

is the equation of a conic passing through the fifth given point (cf. the Example of Section 10–2.)

By a suitable change of coordinate frame, the equations of any two nondegenerate conics of this pencil can be simultaneously reduced to simple form. Let $\mathcal{C}$, $\mathcal{B}$ be two nondegenerate base conics of the pencil through P_1, P_2, P_3, P_4. Then, as we saw in Problem 5, Section 10–4, the diagonal triangle of the quadrangle $P_1P_2P_3P_4$ is self-polar with respect to both $\mathcal{C}$ and $\mathcal{B}$ (and also, indeed, to any nondegenerate conic of the pencil). If we choose this triangle as the fundamental triangle of our coordinate frame, each of the matrices of α and $\mathfrak{B}$ becomes diagonal (Problem 7, Section 10–4):

$$a_0' y_0^2 + a_1' y_1^2 + a_2' y_2^2 = 0, \qquad b_0' y_0^2 + b_1' y_1^2 + b_2' y_2^2 = 0,$$

where none of the coefficients is zero. By a further shift of coordinate frame:

$$\sqrt{a_i'}\, y_i = z_i \qquad i = 0, 1, 2,$$

we arrive at the equations:

$$\zeta^t A' \zeta \equiv z_0^2 + z_1^2 + z_2^2 = 0,$$
$$\zeta^t B' \zeta \equiv c_0 z_0^2 + c_1 z_1^2 + c_2 z_2^2 = 0. \tag{1}$$

It can be shown (Problem 3 below) that c_0, c_1, c_2 are equal, in some order, to the negatives of d_0, d_1, d_2, the values of the ratios $h:k$ corresponding to the three degenerate conics of the pencil (cf. proof of Theorem 11–6).

Thus, finally we have the canonical forms

$$z_0^2 + z_1^2 + z_2^2 = 0,$$
$$d_0 z_0^2 + d_1 z_1^2 + d_2 z_2^2 = 0. \tag{2}$$

We can summarize the results about Case (i) in the following theorem.

Theorem 11–8. By proper choice of coordinate frame, the equations of any two nondegenerate conics α, $\mathfrak{B}$ which intersect in four distinct points can be simultaneously reduced to the form of Eqs. (2). The pencil symbolized by $h\alpha + k\mathfrak{B}$ consists of all conics through the four points common to α and $\mathfrak{B}$. There are three distinct degenerate conics in this pencil, given by $h:k = d_0, d_1, d_2$.

CASE (ii). *One double point and two simple points:* P_1, P_1, P_3, P_4. If two conics, α and $\mathfrak{B}$, have this type of intersection, all the conics of the pencil determined by α and $\mathfrak{B}$ are tangent at P_1 (Theorem 11–3), with tangent line t, say, and pass through P_3 and P_4. Moreover, every conic tangent to t at P_1 and passing through P_3 and P_4 belongs to the pencil, for every such conic is determined by the condition that it pass through one further point (Problem 3(a), Section 10–3), and Theorem 11–5 assures us that there is such a conic in the pencil.

We are dealing with the case where the roots r_1, r_2, r_3, r_4 of Eq. (1) of Section 11–1 are not all distinct: $r_1 = r_2$, and r_3, r_4 are distinct from r_1 and from each other. If we were to express d_0, d_1, d_2, which determine the degenerate conics of the pencil, in terms of r_1, r_2, r_3, r_4, we would discover, in this case, that $d_0 = d_1 \neq d_2$. Thus there are only two *distinct* degenerate conics of this pencil: the line pair P_1P_3 and P_1P_4 (counted twice) and the line pair t and P_3P_4. We can conveniently use these degenerate conics as base conics of the pencil and determine constants of combination to make the resulting conic pass through any assigned point of the plane. Thus, we solve the following sort of problem: Find the equation of the conic tangent to line t at P_1, passing through P_3, P_4, and Q.

The problem of simultaneously reducing the equations of two arbitrary nondegenerate conics of a pencil of type (ii) to canonical form by coordinate transformation is not so "naturally" solved as the analogous problem for conics of type (i). The particular equations we will obtain are chosen because they fit into a general scheme for the simultaneous reduction of two matrices.

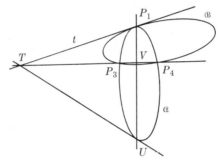

FIGURE 11-3

Suppose that α, $\mathcal{B}$ are nondegenerate conics tangent to line t at P_1, and passing through P_3 and P_4 (Fig. 11-3). Let P_3P_4 and t meet at T, and let the other tangent from T to α touch α at U. Let P_1U and P_3P_4 meet at V. Since the polars of P_1, U with respect to α are P_1T, UT, respectively, it is immediate that P_1U is the polar of T with respect to α. We shall show that P_1U is also the polar of T with respect to $\mathcal{B}$. We know that V is the harmonic conjugate of T with respect to P_3, P_4. Therefore V and T are conjugate points with respect to $\mathcal{B}$. Since T lies on the tangent to $\mathcal{B}$ at P_1, we conclude that P_1 and T are also conjugate points with respect to $\mathcal{B}$. Hence, PU is the polar of T with respect to $\mathcal{B}$.

Now choose P_1, U, T as vertices of the triangle of reference, with coordinates $(1, 0, 0)$, $(0, 1, 0)$, $(0, 0, 1)$ respectively, so that P_1U, UT, TP_1 have equations $x_2 = 0$, $x_0 = 0$, $x_1 = 0$, respectively. Suppose that α and $\mathcal{B}$ have equations

$$\xi^t A \, \xi = 0, \qquad \xi^t B \xi = 0,$$

where

$$A = [a_{ij}], \qquad B = [b_{ij}], \qquad i, j = 0, 1, 2,$$

relative to this coordinate frame. It can be verified that in order to satisfy the pole-polar relationships of the triangle of reference,

$$a_{00} = 0 = a_{02} = a_{11} = a_{12} \quad \text{and} \quad b_{00} = 0 = b_{02} = b_{12}.$$

Hence, equations of α and $\mathcal{B}$ are

$$2a_{01}x_0x_1 + a_{22}x_2^2 = 0,$$

and

$$2b_{01}x_0x_1 + b_{11}x_1^2 + b_{22}x_2^2 = 0. \tag{3}$$

The position of the unit point $(1, 1, 1)$ is still at our disposal; we can choose it so that $a_{01} = a_{22}$, making the equation of α

$$2x_0x_1 + x_2^2 = 0.$$

Now $b_{11} \neq 0$, for otherwise $\mathcal{B}$ would pass through U and hence coincide with α. The transformation

$$x_0 = \sqrt{-b_{11}}\, y_0,$$

$$x_1 = \frac{1}{\sqrt{-b_{11}}}\, y_1,$$

$$x_2 = y_2,$$

leads to the following equations for α and $\mathcal{B}$:

$$2y_0y_1 + y_2^2 = 0,$$

$$2b_{01}y_0y_1 - y_1^2 + b_{22}y_2^2 = 0. \tag{4}$$

Consider the pencil

$$h(2y_0y_1 + y_2^2) + k(2b_{01}y_0y_1 - y_1^2 + b_{22}y_2^2) = 0. \tag{5}$$

For $h{:}k = d_0$, Eq. (5) represents a pair of lines through $P_1(1, 0, 0)$; hence $b_{01} = -d_0$. For $h{:}k = d_2$, Eq. (5) represents a pair of lines through $T(0, 0, 1)$; hence $b_{22} = -d_2$.

We thus have the following canonical forms for α and $\mathcal{B}$:

$$2y_0y_1 + y_2^2 = 0,$$

$$2d_0y_0y_1 + y_1^2 + d_2y_2^2 = 0. \tag{6}$$

It is left to you to summarize the foregoing material in a theorem analogous to Theorem 11–8.

PROBLEM SET 11–3(A)

1. Use the method outlined in the discussion of Case (i) to solve Problem 10(a) and (b) of Section 10–2.

2. Use the method outlined in the discussion of Case (ii) to solve Problem 5(a) and (b) of Section 10–3.

3. With $\zeta^t A' \zeta$, $\zeta^t B' \zeta$ given as in Eqs. (1) of this section, express the fact that an appropriate linear combination of these conics is a line pair through $(1, 0, 0)$, and that other linear combinations are line pairs through $(0, 1, 0)$ and $(0, 0, 1)$. In this manner establish the fact that c_0, c_1, c_2 are the negatives of d_0, d_1, d_2, in some order.

4. Carry out the details of the algebra leading to Eqs. (3) of this section.

5. Carry out the details of the work to establish that $b_{01} = -d_0$, $b_{22} = -d_2$.

6. Summarize the material about Case (ii).

Types (iii), (iv), and (v). The remaining three cases are treated in much the same way as the first two. The discussion, then, will be abbreviated unless noteworthy points arise.

CASE (iii).   *Two double points: P_1, P_1, P_3, P_3.* Here any two conics of the pencil are tangent at P_1 and at P_3. Let the common tangent lines at P_1 and P_3 be t_1 and t_3. Then any conic tangent to these lines at P_1 and P_3 belongs to the pencil, for such a conic is determined by the condition that it pass through one further point, which condition will fix the ratio $h:k$ in Eq. (2) of Section 11–2. The roots r_1, r_2, r_3, r_4 of Eq. (1) of Section 11–1 are equal in pairs: $r_1 = r_2$, $r_3 = r_4$, $r_1 \neq r_3$. Hence it can be determined that $d_0 = d_1 \neq d_2$; i.e., there are two distinct degenerate conics of the pencil. One of these is the line pair t_1, t_3; the other is the repeated line $P_1 P_3$. These degenerate conics constitute a convenient pair of base conics for solving the following problem by a method which should be familiar by now: find the equation of the conic tangent to each of two given lines at assigned points on these lines, and passing through one further point.

In Fig. 11–4, the point T, common to t_1 and t_3, has the line $P_1 P_3$ as polar with respect to each of the nondegenerate conics $\mathfrak{C}$, $\mathfrak{B}$. Moreover,

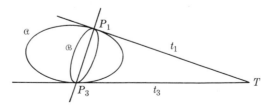

FIGURE 11–4

the points of any pair of the involution on P_1P_3 which has P_1 and P_3 as fixed points are conjugate with respect to each of the conics. Therefore, the triangle TXY, where X, Y are a pair of points of the above-mentioned involution, is self-polar with respect to each of $\mathcal{a}$, $\mathcal{B}$ (why?). This observation leads to a convenient method for finding canonical forms for the equations of any two nondegenerate conics of the pencil.

We use any one of the self-polar triangles TXY as the triangle of reference, with coordinates of T taken as $(0, 0, 1)$. Thus the equation of P_1P_3 takes the form $y_2 = 0$. Then, just as in the discussion of Case (i), we obtain Eqs. (1) as the equations of the two conics. To determine the coefficients c_0, c_1, c_2, we observe that if $h:k = d_0$, the linear combination symbolized by $h\mathcal{a} + k\mathcal{B}$ represents the repeated line, $z_2^2 = 0$; and if $h:k = d_2$, $h\mathcal{a} + k\mathcal{B}$ represents a line pair through $(0, 0, 1)$. Hence $c_0 = -d_0 = c_1$, and $c_2 = -d_2$. Thus we have the canonical forms

$$z_0^2 + z_1^2 + z_2^2 = 0,$$
$$d_0(z_0^2 + z_1^2) + d_2 z_2^2 = 0. \tag{7}$$

CASE (iv). *A triple point and a simple point:* P_1, P_1, P_1, P_4. If $\mathcal{a}$, $\mathcal{B}$ are two nondegenerate conics with this type of intersection, they have P_1 as a threefold point of intersection, and, *a fortiori*, they have the same tangent line t, at that point. Our previous work assures us that every pair of conics of the pencil determined by $\mathcal{a}$ and $\mathcal{B}$ will have P_1 as a threefold, and P_4 as a simple point of intersection. It is left as a problem (Problem 4 below) to establish the converse: that, if $\mathcal{a}$ is a conic of the pencil, and X is any conic having P_1 as a threefold, and P_4 as a simple point of intersection with $\mathcal{a}$, then X is a conic of the pencil.

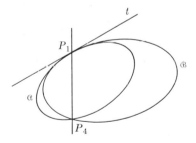

FIGURE 11-5

In this case, three of the roots of Eq. (1) of Section 11-1 are equal to each other, and the fourth root is distinct. It can be shown that $d_0 = d_1 = d_2$; i.e., there is just one degenerate conic in the pencil, consisting of the line pair t and P_1P_4.

If $\mathcal{C}$ is any nondegenerate conic of the pencil, we may write the typical member of the pencil symbolically as $h\mathcal{C} + k \cdot \tau \cdot P_1 P_4$.

The method of obtaining canonical forms for the equations of $\mathcal{C}$ and $\mathcal{B}$ will be omitted, and the result stated:

$$2y_0 y_2 + y_1^2 = 0,$$

$$d_0(2y_0 y_2 + y_1^2) + 2y_1 y_2 = 0. \tag{8}$$

CASE (v). *A quadruple point: P_1, P_1, P_1, P_1.* By an argument similar to that of the first paragraph of the discussion of Case (iv), we conclude that the pencil consists of all point conics which have P_1 as a fourfold point of intersection with a given nondegenerate conic through P_1.

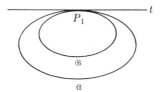

FIGURE 11–6

All four roots of Eq. (1) of Section 11–1 are identical, and $d_0 = d_1 = d_2$: the pencil contains one degenerate conic, viz., the common tangent at P_1, counted twice. The typical member of the pencil may be represented symbolically as

$$h\mathcal{C} + k\tau^2.$$

In this case, canonical forms for the equations of two nondegenerate conics of the pencil are

$$2y_0 y_1 + y_2^2 = 0,$$

$$d_0(2y_0 y_1 + y_2^2) + y_1^2 = 0. \tag{9}$$

PROBLEM SET 11–3(B)

1. Use the method sketched in the discussion of Case (iii) to solve Problem 6(a) and (b) of Section 10–3.

2. Complete the argument, in Case (iii), that TXY is a self-polar triangle with respect to each of $\mathcal{C}$, $\mathcal{B}$.

3. Fill in the omitted algebraic details leading to Eqs. (7) of this section.

4. Prove that if X is a conic having P_1 as a threefold, and P_4 as a simple, point of intersection with $\mathcal{C}$, then X is a member of the pencil $[P_1, P_1, P_1, P_4]$. [*Hint:* Choose another point Q on X. There is a conic of the pencil which passes through Q (why?). This conic coincides with X (why?).]

5. Prove the result contained in the first sentence of the discussion of Case (v).

6. Find the equation of the conic which has $(1, 1, 1)$ as a threefold, and $(2, 0, 1)$ as a simple, point of intersection with $x_0^2 + 3x_1^2 - 4x_2^2 = 0$, and which passes through the following points.

(a) $(1, -1, 1)$ (b) $(1, -1, 0)$ (c) $(4, 0, 1)$ (d) $(2, 8, 7)$

7. Find the equation of the conic which has $(1, 1, 1)$ as a fourfold point of intersection with $x_0^2 + 3x_1^2 - 4x_2^2 = 0$, and which passes through the following points.

(a) $(1, -1, 1)$ (b) $(4, 0, 1)$ (c) $(2, 8, 7)$

8. Summarize the results embodied in the discussions of each of Cases (iii), (iv), (v) in a theorem.

9. Define a pencil of line conics and state the duals of the results of Sections 11-2 and 11-3 as theorems about line conics.

11-4 SOME THEOREMS ON PAIRS AND PENCILS OF CONICS

This section is devoted to several theorems which have interesting ramifications.

Theorem 11-9. Suppose that conics $\mathfrak{A}$, $\mathfrak{B}$, $\mathfrak{C}$ all pass through P_1 and P_2, with at most one of the conics containing the entire line P_1P_2. Let the remaining intersections of $\mathfrak{A}$ and $\mathfrak{B}$ be P_3 and P_4; of $\mathfrak{B}$ and $\mathfrak{C}$ be Q_3 and Q_4; of $\mathfrak{B}$ and $\mathfrak{A}$ be R_3 and R_4. Then the lines P_3P_4, Q_3Q_4, R_3R_4 are concurrent.

Proof. Let equations of $\mathfrak{A}$, $\mathfrak{B}$, $\mathfrak{C}$ be respectively $a = 0, b = 0, c = 0$, and let equations of the lines P_1P_2, P_3P_4, Q_3Q_4, R_3R_4 be respectively $t = 0, u = 0, v = 0, w = 0$. Then, for some complex numbers h_1, k_1, h_2, k_2

$$h_1a + k_1b = t \cdot u, \quad \text{and} \quad h_2b + k_2c = t \cdot v.$$

Elimination of b between these equations gives

$$h_1h_2a - k_1k_2c = t(h_2u - k_1v).$$

The left side of this equation clearly represents a conic through P_1, P_2, R_3, R_4; the right-hand side represents a degenerate conic through P_1P_2. Hence $h_2u - k_1v = lw$, for some complex number, l. $\square$

Theorem 11-10 (*Desargues' Involution Theorem*). A line L which does not pass through a point common to all the conics of a pencil of point conics cuts those conics in pairs of points of an involution.

Proof. Choose a coordinate frame such that the equation of L is $x_2 = 0$. The points of intersection of L with a conic of the pencil

$$h \cdot \xi^t A \xi + k \cdot \xi^t B \xi = 0,$$

where $A = [a_{i,j}]$, $B = [b_{i,j}]$, $i, j = 0, 1, 2$, are determined by

$$h(a_{00}x_0^2 + 2a_{01}x_0x_1 + a_{11}x_1^2) + k(b_{00}x_0^2 + 2b_{01}x_0x_1 + b_{11}x_1^2) = 0.$$

By Theorem 8–24, these points are pairs of an involution.   □

There are two fixed points of the involution on L, corresponding to conics which are tangent to L at these points. (One or both of these conics may be degenerate, in which case we are dealing with a generalized concept of tangency.) We thus obtain a theorem extending our previous results on conics determined by points and lines (Corollary 2 of Theorem 10–4, and Problems 3 and 4, Section 10–3).

Theorem 11–11. There are two distinct point conics passing through four points, no three collinear, and tangent to a line not containing any of the four points.

PROBLEM SET 11–4

1. What does the statement of Theorem 11–9 become if $\mathcal{A}$, $\mathcal{B}$, $\mathcal{C}$ are circles? (Cf. Problem 26, Section 1–1.)

2. Why must the phrase "with at most one of the conics containing the entire line P_1P_2" be included in the statement of Theorem 11–9?

3. Prove the following theorem: A conic $\mathcal{C}$ which passes through exactly two of the points common to all the conics of a pencil of point conics cuts those conics in pairs of points of an involution on $\mathcal{C}$. How may this theorem be considered a sort of generalization of Theorem 11–10? Why is it not a true generalization?

4. Obtain Pascal's hexagon theorem as a corollary of Theorem 11–9.

5. State the dual of Theorem 11–10. (This is known as Sturm's theorem.)

6. State the dual of Theorem 11–11.

7. Prove that there are four distinct conics passing through three points, no three collinear, and tangent to two lines not passing through any of the points. [*Hint:* Choose the points as vertices of the triangle of reference; write the equation of a conic through these points; change to line coordinates and express the conditions that the two given lines, with coordinates (p_0, p_1, p_2) and (q_0, q_1, q_2), say, are lines of this conic.]

8. By considering the duals of results already obtained, state the results on the number of point conics (a) passing through 2 points and tangent to 3 lines; (b) passing through 1 point and tangent to 4 lines; (c) tangent to 5 lines.

9. Prove the following theorem: Let conics $\mathcal{A}$ and $\mathcal{B}$ have double contact at P_1 and P_3; and let conics $\mathcal{A}$ and $\mathcal{C}$ have double contact at Q_1 and Q_3, where P_1, P_3, Q_1, Q_3 are four distinct points. Then the lines P_1P_3 and Q_1Q_3 are separated harmonically by the lines constituting one of the degenerate conics of the pencil generated by $\mathcal{B}$ and $\mathcal{C}$.

11–5 POLES AND POLARS WITH RESPECT TO PENCILS OF CONICS

Suppose that we have two nondegenerate point conics $\mathfrak{A}$, $\mathfrak{B}$ with equations $\xi^t A \xi = 0$, $\xi^t B \xi = 0$. If point P has coordinate vector π, the polar of P with respect to $\mathfrak{A}$ is the line p_a with equation $\pi^t A \xi = 0$, and with respect to $\mathfrak{B}$ is the line p_b with equation $\pi^t B \xi = 0$. Now consider an arbitrary conic $\mathfrak{C}$ of the pencil generated by $\mathfrak{A}$ and $\mathfrak{B}$: $\mathfrak{C}$ has equation

$$h \xi^t A \xi + k \xi^t B \xi = 0.$$

The polar of P with respect to $\mathfrak{C}$ is the line p_c with equation

$$h \pi^t A \xi + k \pi^t B \xi = 0.$$

Since the equation of p_c is a linear combination of the equations of p_a and p_b, we conclude that the polars of a point, with respect to the conics of a pencil, are concurrent and thus form a pencil of lines. But there is one case in which this conclusion would not be justified: If p_a and p_b are the same line, then p_c would also be the same line. How can this occur? If $\pi^t A \xi = 0$, $\pi^t B \xi = 0$ are equations of the same line, then there are complex numbers c_1, c_2, not both zero, such that

$$c_1 \pi^t A \xi + c_2 \pi^t B \xi \equiv 0.$$

In other words, the polar of P with respect to the conic

$$c_1 \xi^t A \xi + c_2 \xi^t B \xi = 0$$

does not exist. From Theorem 10–9, we know that this happens when and only when the conic is degenerate and P is a singular point of the conic.

A bit more can be said in the general case. Since the equation of p_c is the *same* linear combination of the equations of p_a and p_b that the equation of $\mathfrak{C}$ is of the equations of $\mathfrak{A}$ and $\mathfrak{B}$, we conclude that there is a projective relation between the lines of the pencil of lines and the conics of the pencil of conics (both of which are known to be S_1's).

We can summarize the foregoing discussion as the following theorem.

Theorem 11–12.   The polars of a point P with respect to the conics of a pencil of point conics form a pencil of lines, projectively related to the pencil of conics, unless P is a singular point of one of the conics of the pencil, in which case the polars of P with respect to all the other conics of the pencil are the same line.

The point P^* which is the vertex of the pencil of polars of P, with respect to the conics of the pencil, is conjugate to P with respect to each

of the conics.   This relationship is abbreviated as *"P* is conjugate to P
with respect to the pencil of conics."* The relationship is a symmetrical one:
P is conjugate to P^* with respect to the pencil of conics, i.e., the polars
of P^* with respect to the conics of the pencil form a pencil of lines with
vertex at P.   In case P is a singular point of one of the degenerate conics
of the pencil, its conjugate point P^* is not determinate.

It is worthwhile to state the dual of Theorem 11–12 for contrast with
a subsequent theorem.

Theorem 11–13.   The poles of a line p with respect to the conics of a
pencil of *line* conics form a range of points projectively related to the
pencil of conics, unless p is a singular line of one of the conics of the
pencil, in which case the poles of p with respect to all the other conics
of the pencil are the same point.

Suppose, now, that we consider the poles of a line p with respect to
the conics of a pencil of *point* conics.   It must not be assumed that we
have here the situation described in Theorem 11–13.   Although the configuration consisting of a point conic and its tangent lines is the "same"
as that of a line conic and its contact points, a *pencil* of point conics is
not the "same" as a *pencil* of line conics.   To see this geometrically, consider two conics (points *and* lines) α, $\mathcal{B}$, as in Fig. 11–7, intersecting in
the points P_1, P_2, P_3, P_4, and having the four common tangents t_1, t_2
t_3, t_4.   The pencil of point conics generated by α and $\mathcal{B}$ consists of all
the conics through P_1, P_2, P_3, P_4, whereas the pencil of line conics generated by α and $\mathcal{B}$ consists of all the conics tangent to t_1, t_2, t_3, t_4—not
the same family at all.

Algebraically, the difference between the two types of pencils is seen
from the fact that if A and B are 3×3 matrices (Problem 1, Section
7–10),

$$(kA + lB)_{\text{adj}} \neq kA_{\text{adj}} + lB_{\text{adj}}.$$

We state, then, the result which *is* valid.

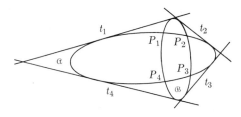

FIGURE 11–7

Theorem 11–14. If a pencil of point conics contains no repeated line, the poles of a line p with respect to the conics of the pencil constitute a point conic, which is nondegenerate unless p passes through a singular point of one of the conics of the pencil.

Proof. We choose to consider the pole of p with respect to a conic $\mathcal{C}$ as the point of intersection of the polars of two points on p. Let R, S be any two points on p. The polars of R, S, with respect to the conics of the pencil, are two pencils of lines with vertices R^*, S^*. By Theorem 11–12,

$$(r_a, r_b, r_c, \ldots) \wedge (\mathcal{C}, \mathcal{B}, \mathcal{C}, \ldots),$$

and

$$(s_a, s_b, s_c, \ldots) \wedge (\mathcal{C}, \mathcal{B}, \mathcal{C}, \ldots).$$

Hence the two pencils with vertices R^*, S^* are projectively related, and thus the points of intersection of corresponding lines of the two pencils (the desired poles) lie on a conic, $\mathcal{E}$.

The conic $\mathcal{E}$ will be degenerate if and only if (a) R^* and S^* are distinct and the line R^*S^* is self-corresponding in the projectivity, *or* (b) R^* and S^* coincide. In the first of these cases, there is some conic of the pencil, say $\mathcal{D}$, such that $r_d = s_d$. But by Problem 16, Section 10–4, this will occur if and only if the line p passes through a singular point of $\mathcal{D}$. In case (b), p is the polar of R^* with respect to each of the conics of the pencil; hence, by Theorem 11–12, R^* is a singular point of one of the conics of the pencil. Hence its polar passes through a singular point of one of the conics of the pencil (why?).   □

There is an alternative way of describing the conic $\mathcal{E}$ of Theorem 11–14. The proof of that theorem revealed that $\mathcal{E}$, which was found as the locus of the poles of p with respect to the conics of the pencil, passes through the point conjugate to any point on p. Hence we have the following result.

Theorem 11–15 (The same conic as in Theorem 11–14). If a pencil of point conics contains no repeated line, the conjugates of the points of a line p, with respect to the conics of the pencil, constitute a point conic, $\mathcal{E}$, which is nondegenerate unless p passes through a singular point of one of the conics of the pencil.

On the conic $\mathcal{E}$ of Theorem 11–14 (or 11–15) there are eleven distinguished points in case the pencil of conics is of type (i), with four distinct points P_1, P_2, P_3, P_4 common to all of them, and if p does not pass through any of the points P_i or through a singular point of one of the conics of the pencil:

(a) the *two* double points of the involution established on p by the pencil of conics;

(b) the *three* vertices of the diagonal triangle of the complete quadrangle $P_1P_2P_3P_4$;

(c) the *six* points which are harmonic conjugates with respect to P_i, P_j of the points A_{ij}, in which p meets the lines P_iP_j, $i, j = 1, 2, 3, 4, i \neq j$.

We shall prove that these eleven points lie on ε as follows.

(a) The double points of the involution on p are the points of tangency of the two conics of the pencil which are tangent to p. These points of tangency are the poles of p with respect to the two conics in question. Hence the double points lie on ε.

(b) The vertices of the diagonal triangle of the complete quadrangle $P_1P_2P_3P_4$ are the poles of p with respect to the degenerate conics of the pencil, and hence lie on ε.

(c) The harmonic conjugate of $A_{i,j}$ with respect to P_i and P_j is the conjugate of $A_{i,j}$ with respect to all the conics of the pencil, and hence lies on ε, for $i, j = 1, 2, 3, 4, i \neq j$.

The conic ε is known as the *eleven-point conic* of the line p with respect to the pencil of conics. The proof of the following theorem is left as a problem (Problem 5 below).

Theorem 11–16. The eleven-point conic of the ideal line, with respect to the pencil of conics which cut the ideal line in pairs of an involution whose double points are I and J, is a circle; i.e., the nine-point circle of each of the four triangles obtained by taking three of the four base points of the pencil of conics. The nine distinguished points associated with each of these triangles are the midpoints of the sides, the feet of the altitudes, and the points midway between the orthocenter and each of the vertices.

PROBLEM SET 11–5

1. State the duals of Theorems 11–14 and 11–15.

2. Justify the last sentence of the proof of Theorem 11–14.

3. In the discussion of the eleven-point conic above, the incidence of the two points (a) and of the three points (b) was established through the use of *poles*, by appealing to Theorem 11–14. Do the same thing, using *conjugates*, with appeal to Theorem 11–15.

4. Prove the following result about the existence of triangles which are self-polar with respect to each of the conics of a pencil.

There are no triangles which are self-polar with respect to all the conics of a pencil, unless the pencil is of type (i) or of type (iii).

For a pencil of type (i), there is just one such triangle: the diagonal triangle of the quadrangle formed by the base points of the pencil.

For a pencil of type (iii), there are infinitely many such triangles: one vertex is the pole of the line joining the two points of tangency of the conics, and the other two vertices are any pair of conjugate points on this line. [*Hint:* Use Theorem 11–12.]

5. Prove Theorem 11–16. [*Hint:* Use Problem 10(e), Section 10–8.]

6. Let conics $\mathcal{A}$ and $\mathcal{B}$ have double contact at P_1 and P_3. Let the tangents at P_1 and P_3 meet at Q and let the tangent to $\mathcal{A}$ at an arbitrary point T be t. Show that QT and t are conjugate lines with respect to $\mathcal{B}$. [*Hint:* Apply Theorem 11–12 to the polars of P with respect to $\mathcal{A}$, $\mathcal{B}$, and the degenerate conic, $(P_1P_3)^2$.]

11–6 INVARIANTS OF TERNARY QUADRATIC FORMS

We shall study the ternary quadratic form (and pairs of ternary quadratic forms) in much the same way that we analyzed binary quadratic forms in Section 8–9. Invariants of such forms will be interpreted geometrically in terms of properties of conics, which are the loci of the forms. Indeed, it is customary to speak of invariants of *conics* as synonymous with invariants of ternary quadratic forms.

Definitions of invariants of a ternary form and of simultaneous invariants of a pair of ternary forms are sufficiently like the corresponding definitions for binary forms in Section 8–9 as not to need explicit mention here (cf. Problem 7, Section 8–9). A complete study of the invariants of a conic and of pairs of conics is beyond the scope of this book; but we shall examine some invariants to give an idea of how the analysis can proceed.

Consider Eq. (3) of Section 11–2 in the light of Eq. (5) of Section 8–9. The latter equation, although it was developed in a discussion of *binary* forms, applies with equal force to quadratic forms in n variables, and so we can conclude that the determinant of a quadratic form in n variables is an invariant of weight two under linear transformations. Hence the left side of Eq. (3) of Section 11–2 is an invariant of weight two under linear transformations, for all values of h, k. Therefore, each of the coefficients of h^3, h^2k, hk^2, and k^3 is an invariant of weight two. We already knew of the invariance of the coefficients of h^3 and k^3, of course. We turn now to a consideration of Θ and Θ', which are simultaneous invariants of the forms with matrices A and B, under linear transformations.

Straightforward computation (Problem 1 below) shows that

$$\Theta = \sum_{i,j=0}^{2} A_{ij}B_{ij}, \qquad \Theta' = \sum_{i,j=0}^{2} A_{ij}B_{ij}. \qquad (1)$$

The following theorems explain the geometric significance of the vanishing of these invariants.

Theorem 11–17. If α and $\mathcal{B}$ are nondegenerate conics, there is a triangle self-polar with respect to α and inscribed in $\mathcal{B}$ if and only if $\Theta = 0$.

Proof. Because of the invariance of Θ, it will be sufficient to prove the result for a particular coordinate frame. Let P_1 be an arbitrary point on $\mathcal{B}$; let P_2 be one of the points in which the polar of P_1 with respect to α meets $\mathcal{B}$; and let P_3 be the pole of the line P_1P_2 with respect to α. Then $P_1P_2P_3$ is self-polar with respect to α and has two vertices on $\mathcal{B}$. Let $P_1P_2P_3$ be the fundamental triangle of the coordinate frame. The equation of α will reduce to (Problem 7, Section 10–4)

$$a_{00}x_0^2 + a_{11}x_1^2 + a_{22}x_2^2 = 0$$

with $a_{00} \cdot a_{11} \cdot a_{22} \neq 0$ because of the nondegeneracy of α; and $b_{00} = 0 = b_{11}$ because $P_1(1, 0, 0)$ and $P_2(0, 1, 0)$ lie on $\mathcal{B}$. We find that (Problem 2 below)

$$\Theta = a_{00} \cdot a_{11} \cdot b_{33}.$$

Hence $\Theta = 0$ if and only if $b_{33} = 0$, which is the condition that P_3 lie on $\mathcal{B}$. $\square$

By reversing the roles of α and $\mathcal{B}$, we immediately obtain the following result.

Theorem 11–18. If α and $\mathcal{B}$ are nondegenerate conics, there is a triangle self-polar with respect to $\mathcal{B}$ and inscribed in α if and only if $\Theta' = 0$.

It is interesting to compare Theorem 11–18 with the dual of Theorem 11–17.

Theorem 11–19 (*Dual of Theorem 11–17*). If α and $\mathcal{B}$ are nondegenerate conics, there is a triangle self-polar with respect to α and circumscribed about $\mathcal{B}$ if and only if $\Theta' = 0$.

From Theorems 11–18 and 11–19, we have an immediate corollary.

Theorem 11–20. If α and $\mathcal{B}$ are nondegenerate conics, there is a triangle inscribed in α and self-polar with respect to $\mathcal{B}$ if and only if there is a triangle self-polar with respect to α and circumscribed about $\mathcal{B}$.

Two binary quadratic forms were called *apolar* in case their simultaneous invariant Ψ vanishes (Section 8–9).

The ternary quadratic forms with matrices A and B_{adj} (or, the point conic α and the line conic $\mathcal{B}$) are said to be *apolar* if $\Theta' = 0$. Similarly, the line conic α and the point conic $\mathcal{B}$ are apolar if $\Theta = 0$. If both Θ and Θ' vanish, the conics are said to be *mutually apolar*, and enjoy interesting properties (see Todd, *op. cit.*, pp. 236–238).

PROBLEM SET 11-6

1. (a) Carry out the details of algebra leading to Eqs. (1).

(b) Show that Θ, Θ' can also be expressed as

$$\Theta = \text{tr} \{A_{\text{adj}} \cdot B\}, \qquad \Theta' = \text{tr} \{A \cdot B_{\text{adj}}\}.$$

Note that the invariance of Θ and Θ' follows immediately from this result and Problem 19, Section 8–5.

2. Verify the expression for Θ in the proof of Theorem 11–17.

CHAPTER 12

The Jordan Canonical Form

12-1 REVIEW OF OPERATIONS ON MATRICES

Depending upon the purpose in view, we have performed various operations on matrices in order to replace them by simpler matrices. The following table summarizes our results.

Purpose	Replace M by	Simplest Result	Name
(i) Solving systems of linear equations (Section 7–3)	EM, where E = product of elementary matrices	A Hermite matrix	
(ii) (Section 7–7)	PMQ, where P, Q are non-singular	$\begin{bmatrix} I_r & 0 \\ 0 & 0 \end{bmatrix}$	Rational equivalence
(iii) Simplifying equations of conics and quadrics by projectivity or co-ordinate transformation (Section 10–1)	$A^t M A$, where M is *symmetric* and A is nonsingular	$\begin{bmatrix} I_r & 0 \\ 0 & 0 \end{bmatrix}$	Congruence
(iv) Simplifying the equations of a collineation by coordinate transformation (Section 8–5)	$B^{-1}MB$, where B is nonsingular	$\begin{bmatrix} k_1 & 0 \\ 0 & k_2 \end{bmatrix}$ or $\begin{bmatrix} k_0 & 0 \\ 1 & k_0 \end{bmatrix}$ *for* 2×2 *matrices*	Similarity

As indicated in part (iv) of this table, we have found how to use a coordinate transformation to simplify the equations of a collineation in $S_1(C)$. In this chapter we shall study the corresponding problem for $S_n(C)$; we shall follow closely the elegant presentation of Seidenberg (see Bibliography).

12–2 THE CASE OF DISTINCT CHARACTERISTIC ROOTS; FIXED AND INVARIANT SUBSPACES

If the characteristic equation of the matrix of the collineation has distinct roots $k_1, k_2, \ldots, k_{n+1}$, say, we can show, by the same argument as was used to prove Theorem 8–7, that the matrix can be reduced by coordinate transformation to diagonal form,

$$
\begin{bmatrix}
k_1 & 0 & 0 & \ldots & 0 \\
0 & k_2 & 0 & \ldots & 0 \\
\vdots & & & & \\
0 & & \ldots & 0 & k_{n+1}
\end{bmatrix}.
$$

The case of multiple roots presents difficulties, and it is the analysis of this case to which we shall turn our attention. In S_1 the key to the situation was found in the consideration of *fixed points* of the collineation, and we must decide upon the proper analogue of this concept in higher dimensions.

Two possibilities present themselves. In a collineation of S_n, there may be a subspace of which *every point* is fixed. Such a subspace is called *invariant* under the collineation. A less stringent requirement is the following: The transform of each point of the subspace lies in that subspace, and such a subspace is called *self-corresponding* under the collineation. We state these definitions formally.

Definition 1. Let T be a collineation of S_n. Then, with respect to T, a subspace, S_k, is (a) *invariant*, if $P \in S_k$ implies that $T(P) = P$; (b) *self-corresponding*, if $P \in S_k$ implies that $T(P) \in S_k$.

We shall find that it is the concept of self-corresponding subspace which is fundamental to the solution of our problem.

Note that if S_k is a self-corresponding subspace of S_n with respect to the proper collineation T, then the mapping $P \to T(P)$, $P \in S_k$, describes a collineation in S_k which may be called the *restriction of T to S_k*, or the collineation *induced in S_k by T*. The phrase "collineation induced by T" is also used in another context. Suppose, for example, that S is a self-corresponding set of lines with respect to a collineation T in S_n—i.e., the points of a line of S are carried by T into the points of a line of S. Then we may say that T induces a collineation in S, the space whose elements are lines of S_n.

PROBLEM SET 12–2

1. State and prove a theorem similar to Theorem 8–7 for a collineation of S_n whose matrix has $n + 1$ distinct characteristic roots.

*2. Let T be a collineation of S_n, and let S_k, S_l be subspaces of S_n. Show that

   (a) $T(S_k)$ is a subspace of S_n;
   (b) $T(S_k \cap S_l) = T(S_k) \cap T(S_l)$;
   (c) $T([S_k, S_l]) = [T(S_k), T(S_l)]$.

[*Hint:* See Section 7–4.]

*3. Prove that if S_k, S_l are self-corresponding subspaces of S_n, with respect to a collineation T, then $S_k \cap S_l$ and $[S_k, S_l]$ are also self-corresponding with respect to T.

4. Prove that if S_k is an invariant subspace of S_n with respect to a collineation T, and if $S_l \subseteq S_k$, then S_l is also invariant.

5. Give an example to show that S_k, S_l may both be invariant subspaces without $[S_k, S_l]$ being invariant.

*6. Let T be defined in S_3 as follows: π is a certain plane, P is a certain point not in π. If X is not in π and if $X \neq P$, let PX meet π in $\tilde{X}$. Then $T(X)$ is the harmonic conjugate of X with respect to P and $\tilde{X}$.

   (a) For this T, what are reasonable definitions of $T(P)$ and of $T(Y)$ for Y in π?

   (b) For T, as extended in part (a), what are the self-corresponding and invariant subspaces of S_3?

12–3 REDUCIBLE AND IRREDUCIBLE SUBSPACES

Suppose that $S_n = [S_k, S_l]$, where S_k, S_l are skew to each other. Then by Theorem 5–7, $k + l = n - 1$. Let $A_0, A_1, \ldots, A_k$ be vertices of a simplex of reference in S_k, and $A_{k+1}, A_{k+2}, \ldots, A_n$ be vertices of a simplex of reference in S_l. Then $A_0, A_1, \ldots, A_n$ can be chosen as vertices of a simplex of reference in S_n; i.e., in S_n there is a coordinate system in which $A_0, A_1, \ldots, A_n$ have coordinate vectors $\epsilon_1, \epsilon_2, \ldots, \epsilon_{n+1}$, respectively. Relative to the chosen coordinate frame, the last $n - k$ components of the coordinate vector of each point of S_k are zeros, and the first $k + 1$ components of the coordinate vector of each point of S_l are zeros.

Now suppose that T is a collineation in S_n, with matrix M relative to the coordinate system just described. Suppose, moreover, that S_k, S_l are self-corresponding with respect to T. Then, since $T(A_i) \in S_k$, $i = 0$,

$1, \ldots, k$, and $T(A_i) \in S_l$, $i = k + 1, k + 2, \ldots, n$, the matrix M must have the following form (verify):

$$
\begin{array}{cc}
(k{+}1) & (n{-}k) \\
\text{columns} & \text{columns}
\end{array}
$$

$$
\begin{array}{c}
(k{+}1) \\
\text{rows} \\
(n{-}k) \\
\text{rows}
\end{array}
\left[
\begin{array}{c|c}
M_k & O \\
\hline
O & M_l
\end{array}
\right].
$$

Indeed, the restriction of T to the subspace S_k has the matrix M_k with respect to the simplex of reference $A_0, A_1, \ldots, A_k$; and the restriction of T to the subspace S_l has the matrix M_l with respect to the simplex of reference $A_{k+1}, A_{k+2}, \ldots, A_n$.

We now generalize to the case in which S_n is the join of more than two subspaces. It will be helpful to introduce terminology and symbolism slightly different from what we have used thus far.

Definition 2. If S is the join of spaces $S_p, S_q, \ldots, S_v$, in which each S_i is skew to the join of the remaining S_j's, we write

$$ S = S_p + S_q + \cdots + S_v, $$

and say that S is the *direct sum* of $S_p, S_q, \ldots, S_v$.

If $S_n = S_p + S_q + \cdots + S_v$, where each S_j is self-corresponding with respect to a collineation T, then, by proper choice of coordinate frame, the matrix M of T can be made to assume the form

$$
M = \begin{bmatrix}
M_p & O & & \cdots & O \\
O & M_q & O & \cdots & O \\
\vdots & & \ddots & \ddots & \\
O & & \cdots & O & M_v
\end{bmatrix}.
$$

We say that M "has the blocks $M_p, M_q, \ldots, M_v$ along the diagonal, and zeros elsewhere." Henceforth, when we refer to a "self-corresponding" space, it will be understood to mean a space that is self-corresponding with respect to the collineation of S_n being studied.

Definition 3. If a self-corresponding space S can be expressed as the direct sum of two self-corresponding spaces neither of which is empty, then S is called *reducible*; otherwise S is called *irreducible*.

We shall eventually solve our problem of finding a coordinate transformation to simplify M by expressing S_n as the direct sum of irreducible subspaces, and by finding a simple form for each of the blocks corresponding to an irreducible subspace.

12–4 SOME THEOREMS ON SELF-CORRESPONDENCE AND REDUCIBILITY

Since M is a matrix with complex numbers as elements, the characteristic equation of M has complex numbers as coefficients. Hence, by the Fundamental Theorem of Algebra, this characteristic equation has a root; therefore, the collineation determined by M has a fixed point. By appealing to duality in S_n, we conclude that the collineation has a self-corresponding hyperplane. The same argument can be applied to the restriction of the collineation to any self-corresponding subspace in S_n, leading to the following theorem.

Theorem 12–1. Every self-corresponding S_k contains a self-corresponding S_{k-1}.

Next comes a theorem about more than one fixed point.

Theorem 12–2. If a collineation has at least two fixed points, then it has at least two self-corresponding hyperplanes; and conversely.

Proof. We recall that if a collineation has matrix M as a point transformation, then it has matrix $(M^{-1})^t$ as a hyperplane transformation (Eq. (2) of Section 8–1); and that the characteristic roots of $(M^{-1})^t$ are the reciprocals of those of M (Problem 21 of Section 8–5). Thus, if M has two distinct characteristic roots (leading to two fixed points), then $(M^{-1})^t$ has two distinct characteristic roots (leading to two self-corresponding hyperplanes).

But if M has only *one* characteristic root k_0, say, leading to *two* fixed points, then the rank of $M - k_0 I$ must be $\leq n - 1$. Then, from the hint contained in Problem 21(c) of Section 8–5, and the theorem on the rank of the product of two matrices, we may conclude that the rank of $(M^{-1})^t - (1/k_0)I$ must be $\leq n - 1$. Hence, there must be at least two linearly independent solutions of $(M^{-1})^t \pi = (1/k_0)\pi$, i.e., at least two self-corresponding hyperplanes.

The converse follows by duality in S_n. $\square$

Theorem 12–3. If a collineation T in S has more than one fixed point, then S is reducible; and, if P is a fixed point, S can be written as the direct sum of self-corresponding subspaces, one of which contains P.

Proof. The proof falls naturally into several parts.

(1) If there are fixed points P_1, P_2, then there are self-corresponding hyperplanes π_1, π_2, by Theorem 12–2. If π_1 does not pass through P_1,

we see the reducibility of $S : S = \pi_1 + P_1$. Similarly with π_1 and P_2, with π_2 and P_1, and with π_2 and P_2. Thus the only case which presents difficulty is that in which both π_1 and π_2 pass through both P_1 and P_2.

(2) We consider the projective space $\widetilde{S}$ whose points are the lines of S through P_1. The one-dimensional spaces of $\widetilde{S}$ are the planes of S through P_1, the two-dimensional spaces of $\widetilde{S}$ are the three-dimensional subspaces of S containing P_1, etc. Hence, if S is n-dimensional, then $\widetilde{S}$ is $(n-1)$-dimensional. Note that hyperplanes of S through P_1 are hyperplanes of $\widetilde{S}$. Thus π_1 and π_2 are hyperplanes of $\widetilde{S}$, and the line P_1P_2 is a point of $\widetilde{S}$.

Our collineation T induces a collineation in $\widetilde{S}$ (verify), and π_1, π_2 are still self-corresponding. Hence, by Theorem 12–2, $\widetilde{S}$ has two fixed points, one of which is the self-corresponding line, P_1P_2.

(3) We complete the proof by induction on n.

(a) If $n = 1$, the theorem is clearly true (verify).

(b) We assume the validity of the theorem for dimension $<n$ and shall show that this assumption implies its validity for dimension n.

By our assumption, $\widetilde{S}$ is reducible: $\widetilde{S} = \widetilde{S}_p + \widetilde{S}_q$, where $\widetilde{S}_p$, $\widetilde{S}_q$ are self-corresponding subspaces of $\widetilde{S}$, and $\widetilde{S}_p$, say, contains the "fixed point" P_1P_2. In terms of the points of S, we can say that

$$S = [S_{p+1}, S_{q+1}]$$

where S_{p+1}, S_{q+1} are self-corresponding subspaces with P_1, P_2 in S_{p+1} and P_1 in S_{q+1}.

The restriction of T to S_{p+1} is a collineation having P_1, P_2 as fixed points. Hence, by the inductive hypothesis, $S_{p+1} = S_u + S_v$, say, with S_u, S_v self-corresponding, and P_1 in S_u. Thus S is the join of S_{q+1}, S_u, and S_v, or, what is the same thing, the join of $[S_{q+1}, S_u]$ and S_v. We shall show that $[S_{q+1}, S_u]$ and S_v are skew to each other by studying the dimensions of the various spaces. By use of Theorems 5–6 and 5–7, we find that (verify)

$$p + q + 2 = n,$$

$$u + v = p,$$

$$q + 1 + u + v \geq n + d([S_{q+1}, S_u] \cap S_v).$$

Hence,

$$d([S_{q+1}, S_u] \cap S_v) \leq -1.$$

Thus

$$S = [S_{q+1}, S_u] + S_v.$$

Since $[S_{q+1}, S_u]$ is self-corresponding (Problem 3 of Section 12–2) and since it contains P_1, we have established our result. $\square$

PROBLEM SET 12–4

The following problems refer to the proof of Theorem 12–3.

1. In part (1) of the proof check that a decomposition can be found such that any given fixed point is contained in one of the self-corresponding subspaces.

2. Show that T induces a collineation in S.

3. Show directly that the theorem is true for S_1.

4. Check the argument on dimensionality leading to the result that $[S_{q+1}, S_u]$ and S_v are skew to each other.

12–5 THE JORDAN FORM FOR AN IRREDUCIBLE SPACE

If S_r is irreducible with respect to the collineation T, there is only one fixed point P (Theorem 12–3) and hence only one self-corresponding hyperplane U_{r-1} (Theorem 12–2). The collineation induced in U_{r-1} by T has a fixed point; it must be P and this must be the *only* fixed point (why?). Hence, with respect to the space U_{r-1} there must be just one self-corresponding hyperplane, i.e., an $(r-2)$-dimensional space, U_{r-2}, etc. Thus, for each J, there must be just one self-corresponding J-dimensional space U_J; and, in this sequence, $U_{r-1} \supset U_{r-2} \supset \cdots \supset U_1 \supset P$.

Now choose vertices of the simplex of reference $A_0, A_1, \ldots, A_r$ as follows. Let $A_0 = P$; let A_1 be any other point of U_1; let A_2 be any point of U_2 not dependent on A_0 and A_1; etc. Let us analyze the matrix, $M = [m_{ij}]$ of the collineation T in this coordinate frame. Since $T(A_0) = A_0$, all elements of the first column of M, except for m_{11}, must be zero. Since $T(A_1) \in U_1$, a coordinate vector of $T(A_1)$ is a linear combination of $(1, 0, \ldots, 0)$ and $(0, 1, 0, \ldots, 0)$. Hence all elements of the second column of M below m_{22} must be zero. Proceeding in this way, we see that M is upper triangular. By Problem 22 of Section 8–5, we know that the diagonal elements of M are its characteristic roots. But M has only *one* characteristic root k_1, say. Hence, all diagonal elements of M are equal to k_1.

We shall now show that by appropriate choice of coordinate frame, we can make M assume the form

$$
J_{r+1} = \begin{bmatrix}
k_1 & 1 & & & & 0 \\
 & k_1 & 1 & & & \\
 & & & \cdot & \cdot & \\
 & & & & \cdot & \cdot \\
 & & & & & \cdot \\
 & & & & k_1 & 1 \\
0 & & & & & k_1
\end{bmatrix}; \tag{1}
$$

i.e., J_{r+1} has M's characteristic root k_1 along the principal diagonal,

1's along the diagonal immediately "above" the principal diagonal, and zeros elsewhere. [Note that, in the one-dimensional case which we studied earlier (Theorem 8–10), we obtained the 1 "below" the main diagonal to permit the use of intuitive geometric language ("translation"). We could just as easily have obtained the 1 "above" the main diagonal.] Let us attack the problem inductively, and illustrate its solution for $r = 3$; the general method will be clear from this special case. We assume, then, that the problem has been solved for $r = 2$, i.e., that we have found a coordinate frame within which the collineation in our irreducible S_2 has the form

$$J_2 = \begin{bmatrix} k_1 & 1 & 0 \\ 0 & k_1 & 1 \\ 0 & 0 & k_1 \end{bmatrix}.$$

Suppose that this involves the triangle of reference $A_0A_1A_2$ and unit point $\widetilde{D}$ of Fig. 12–1. Then the matrix of our collineation in S_3 will have the form

$$\begin{bmatrix} k_1 & 1 & 0 & ? \\ 0 & k_1 & 1 & ? \\ 0 & 0 & k_1 & ? \\ 0 & 0 & 0 & ? \end{bmatrix}.$$

We must show that the last column can be made to be 0, 0, 1, k_1. This will be done by an appropriate choice of unit point D in the three-dimensional coordinate frame.

Let $T(A_3) = A_3'$. Then $A_3' \neq A_3$ (why?). Suppose that the line A_3A_3' meets the plane U_2 in Q. The point Q cannot lie in U_1, for, if it did, the join of A_3 and U_1 would be a self-corresponding hyperplane, and we know that U_2 is the *only* self-corresponding hyperplane. Let us now move A_2 to coincide with Q. To do so is consistent with our original choice of simplex of reference ("let A_2 be any point of U_2 not dependent

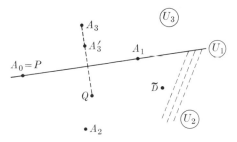

FIGURE 12–1

on A_0 and A_1"), and is also consistent with our inductive hypothesis, since we shall obtain the desired last column by appropriate selection of unit point, not of the vertices of the simplex of reference.

We decide on the location of D (1, 1, 1, 1) in the following roundabout

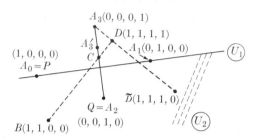

FIGURE 12–2

way. On line A_3A_3' locate C so that the cross ratio $(A_2A_3,\ A_3'C) = k_1$. Let B be the point with coordinate vector (1, 1, 0, 0). Then B lies in the plane $A_2A_3\widetilde{D}$ (verify). Hence BC meets $A_3\widetilde{D}$; let this point be the unit point D. Then C has coordinate vector (0, 0, 1, 1), and hence A_3' has coordinate vector (0, 0, 1, k_1). But this implies that the last column of our 4 × 4 matrix is also 0, 0, 1, k_1.

The matrix of Eq. (1) is called the *Jordan* matrix of a collineation T in a space S_p which is irreducible with respect to T.*

PROBLEM SET 12–5

1. Why is P the only fixed point of the collineation induced in U_{r-1} by T?

2. Modify the proof of Theorem 8–10 so as to obtain the canonical form

$$\begin{bmatrix} k_0 & 1 \\ 0 & k_0 \end{bmatrix}.$$

(This will give us the verification for $r = 1$ which is needed in our inductive argument.)

3. Why is it true that $A_3' \neq A_3$?

4. Why would the join of A_3 and U_1 be a self-corresponding hyperplane if Q lay in U_1?

5. Is it possible that $A_3' = A_2$?

6. Is it possible that $C = A_2$? A_3? A_3'? Are we then sure that $D \neq A_3$? $D \neq \widetilde{D}$?

7. Verify that B lies in the plane $A_2A_3\widetilde{D}$.

---

* Camille Jordan was a 19th century French mathematician.

8. Verify that C has coordinate vector $(0, 0, 1, 1)$.

9. Verify that A_3' has coordinate vector $(0, 0, 1, k_1)$.

10. Why is the last column of the matrix precisely $0, 0, 1, k_1$?

11. Carry through the argument of this section for general r.

12–6 THE JORDAN CANONICAL FORM OF A NONSINGULAR MATRIX

We now fuse the results of Sections 12–3 and 12–5. In Section 12–3, we found how to choose a coordinate frame so that the matrix of the collineation has blocks M_p, M_q, ..., M_r along the diagonal, and zeros elsewhere, each M_j being the matrix of the restriction of the collineation to an irreducible subspace. In Section 12–5, we learned how to choose yet another coordinate frame so that each M_j is replaced by a Jordan matrix. The final result is called the Jordan canonical form.

Definition 4. A matrix J is in Jordan canonical form if J consists of a number of blocks along the diagonal, each being the Jordan matrix of a collineation in an irreducible space, and zeros elsewhere.

We have established the following result.

Theorem 12–4. By change of coordinate frame, the matrix of a nonsingular collineation can be replaced by a matrix in Jordan canonical form.

We can interchange the order of the blocks by changing the subscripts of the A_i (the vertices of the simplex of reference). To have a more-or-less standard format, we agree on the following convention: all blocks associated with a given characteristic root are placed next to each other, the larger blocks before the smaller ones.

In terms of this convention, we define the *Segre symbol* (or *Segre characteristic*) as follows. If a characteristic root is associated with blocks of lengths a, b, ..., we write a, b, ... in parentheses; we do this for each characteristic root in turn, and we put square brackets around the whole thing.

It can be shown that the Jordan form is *canonical* in the sense that, for any matrix M, the blocks are uniquely determined except for order.

12–7 COLLINEATIONS IN S_2

We shall analyze the various types of collineations in a plane by examining their Jordan canonical forms.

CASE (i). The Segre symbol is $[(1)(1)(1)]$.

The equations are

$$rx_0' = k_1 x_0,$$

$$rx_1' = \quad k_2 x_1,$$

$$rx_2' = \quad\quad k_3 x_2,$$

where the three k's are all different. There are three fixed points (vertices of the triangle of reference) and three self-corresponding lines (sides of the triangle of reference).

CASE (ii).   The Segre symbol is $[(11)(1)]$.
The equations are

$$rx_0' = k_1 x_0,$$

$$rx_1' = \quad k_1 x_1,$$

$$rx_2' = \quad\quad k_2 x_2,$$

with $k_2 \neq k_1$. The fixed points are $(0, 0, 1)$ and all points of the line $x_2 = 0$; i.e., the line $x_2 = 0$ is invariant. Every line through $(0, 0, 1)$ is self-corresponding.

CASE (iii).   The Segre symbol is $[(111)]$.
The equations are

$$rx_0' = k_1 x_0,$$

$$rx_1' = \quad k_1 x_1,$$

$$rx_2' = \quad\quad k_1 x_2.$$

The collineation is the identity transformation.

CASE (iv).   The Segre symbol is $[(2)(1)]$.
The equations are

$$rx_0' = k_1 x_0 + x_1,$$

$$rx_1' = \quad k_1 x_1,$$

$$rx_2' = \quad\quad k_2 x_2,$$

where $k_2 \neq k_1$. There are two fixed points, $(1, 0, 0)$ and $(0, 0, 1)$, and two self-corresponding lines, $x_1 = 0$ and $x_2 = 0$.

CASE (v).   The Segre symbol is $[(21)]$.
The equations are

$$rx_0' = k_1 x_0 + x_1,$$

$$rx_1' = \quad k_1 x_1,$$

$$rx_2' = \quad\quad k_1 x_1.$$

The line $x_1 = 0$ is invariant, and there are no other fixed points.

CASE (vi). The Segre symbol is [(3)].

The equations are

$$rx_0' = k_1 x_0 + x_1,$$

$$rx_1' = k_1 x_1 + x_2,$$

$$rx_2' = k_1 x_2.$$

There is a single fixed point, $(1, 0, 0)$, and a single self-corresponding line, $x_2 = 0$. This is the irreducible case.

PROBLEM SET 12-7

1. In Case (i), what are the types of collineations induced on the self-corresponding lines? What is the transform of a pencil of lines whose vertex is a fixed point?

2. In Case (ii), what are the types of collineations induced on the self-corresponding lines? What is the transform of the pencil of lines with vertex $(0, 0, 1)$? Of a pencil with vertex on $x_2 = 0$?

3. In Case (iv), what are the types of collineations induced on the self-corresponding lines? What is the transform of the pencil with vertex $(1, 0, 0)$? Of the pencil with vertex $(0, 0, 1)$?

4. In Case (v), what are the self-corresponding lines, and what types of collineations are induced on them? What are the transforms of pencils with vertices on $x_1 = 0$?

5. In Case (vi), what type of collineation is induced on the self-corresponding line? What is the transform of a pencil with vertex $(1, 0, 0)$?

APPENDIX 1

Summary of Some Results of Three-Dimensional Analytic Geometry

1. (a) If P has coordinates (x, y, z), then the direction cosines of OP are x/r, y/r, z/r, where $r = \sqrt{x^2 + y^2 + z^2}$; direction numbers of OP are x, y, z.

(b) If P has coordinates (x_1, y_1, z_1) and Q has coordinates (x_2, y_2, z_2), then direction numbers of PQ are $x_2 - x_1$, $y_2 - y_1$, $z_2 - z_1$.

2. If the directed normal to plane π from O makes angles α, β, γ with the positive x-, y-, z-axes, and if the length of the segment of the normal from O to π is p, then an equation of π is

$$(\cos \alpha)x + (\cos \beta)y + (\cos \gamma)z = p.$$

3. If two lines have direction cosines l, m, n and l', m', n', then the angle θ between the lines is given by

$$\cos \theta = ll' + mm' + nn'.$$

4. The line through (x_1, y_1, z_1) with direction numbers p_1, p_2, p_3 has equations

$$\frac{x - x_1}{p_1} = \frac{y - y_1}{p_2} = \frac{z - z_1}{p_3}.$$

5. Consider

Plane (i): $ax + by + cz + d = 0,$

Plane (ii): $a'x + b'y + c'z + d' = 0,$

Line (iii): $\dfrac{x - x_1}{p_1} = \dfrac{y - y_1}{p_2} = \dfrac{z - z_1}{p_3},$

Line (iv): $\dfrac{x - x_2}{q_1} = \dfrac{y - y_2}{q_2} = \dfrac{z - z_2}{q_3}.$

328

(a) Planes (i) and (ii) are parallel $\Leftrightarrow a:a' = b:b' = c:c' \neq d:d'$.

(b) Planes (i) and (ii) are perpendicular $\Leftrightarrow aa' + bb' + cc' = 0$.

(c) Lines (iii) and (iv) are parallel $\Leftrightarrow p_1:q_1 = p_2:q_2 = p_3:q_3$.

(d) Lines (iii) and (iv) are perpendicular $\Leftrightarrow p_1q_1 + p_2q_2 + p_3q_3 = 0$.

(e) Plane (i) and line (iii) are parallel $\Leftrightarrow ap_1 + bp_2 + cp_3 = 0$.

(f) Plane (i) and line (iii) are perpendicular $\Leftrightarrow a:p_1 = b:p_2 = c:p_3$.

Most recent calculus books devote a chapter to three-dimensional analytic geometry in which the foregoing results are derived. More extended treatments are contained in the following references.

A. ALBERT, *Solid Analytic Geometry*. New York: McGraw-Hill (1949).

A. DRESDEN, *Solid Analytical Geometry and Determinants*. New York: Wiley (1930).

S. SCHUSTER, *Elementary Vector Geometry*. New York: Wiley (1962).

V. SNYDER, and C. H. SISAM, *Analytic Geometry of Space*. New York: Henry Holt (1914).

Summary of Results on Determinants

If $A = [a_{ij}]$ is an $n \times n$ matrix with complex numbers as elements, the determinant of A, written det A or $|A|$ or $|a_{ij}|$, is a complex number which can be defined recursively as follows.

For $n = 2$, if

$$A = \begin{bmatrix} a & b \\ c & d \end{bmatrix},$$

then det $A = |A| = ad - bc$.

For $n > 2$, if

$$A = [a_{ij}] \qquad i, j = 1, \ldots, n,$$

then

$$\det A = a_{11}A_{11} + a_{12}A_{12} + \cdots + a_{1n}A_{1n} = \sum_{j=1}^{n} a_{ij}A_{ij},$$

where A_{ij}, called the *cofactor of* a_{ij}, is defined as follows. Delete from A the ith row and the jth column, thus obtaining an $(n - 1) \times (n - 1)$ matrix whose determinant, called the *minor of* a_{ij}, is designated as M_{ij}; then

$$A_{ij} = (-1)^{i+j} M_{ij}.$$

It can be shown that for any i,

$$\det A = a_{i1}A_{i1} + a_{i2}A_{i2} + \cdots + a_{in}A_{in} = \sum_{j=1}^{n} a_{ij}A_{ij};$$

i.e., a determinant can be "expanded by *any* row."

Moreover, it can be shown that for any j,

$$\det A = a_{1j}A_{1j} + a_{2j}A_{2j} + \cdots + a_{nj}A_{nj} = \sum_{i=1}^{n} a_{ij}A_{ij};$$

330

i.e., a determinant can be "expanded by *any* column."

EXAMPLE

$$
\begin{vmatrix} 2 & 1 & 0 & -1 \\ 1 & 0 & -3 & 1 \\ 1 & 2 & -1 & 2 \\ 0 & 1 & 1 & -1 \end{vmatrix} = 2 \cdot \begin{vmatrix} 0 & -3 & 1 \\ 2 & -1 & 2 \\ 1 & 1 & -1 \end{vmatrix} - 1 \cdot \begin{vmatrix} 1 & -3 & 1 \\ 1 & -1 & 2 \\ 0 & 1 & -1 \end{vmatrix}
$$

$$
+ 0 \cdot \begin{vmatrix} 1 & 0 & 1 \\ 1 & 2 & 2 \\ 0 & 1 & -1 \end{vmatrix} + 1 \cdot \begin{vmatrix} 1 & 0 & -3 \\ 1 & 2 & -1 \\ 0 & 1 & 1 \end{vmatrix}
$$

$$
= 2 \left\{ 0 \cdot \begin{vmatrix} -1 & 2 \\ 1 & -1 \end{vmatrix} + 3 \cdot \begin{vmatrix} 2 & 2 \\ 1 & -1 \end{vmatrix} + 1 \cdot \begin{vmatrix} 2 & -1 \\ 1 & 1 \end{vmatrix} \right\}
$$

$$
- 1 \left\{ 1 \cdot \begin{vmatrix} -1 & 2 \\ 1 & -1 \end{vmatrix} + 3 \cdot \begin{vmatrix} 1 & 2 \\ 0 & -1 \end{vmatrix} + 1 \cdot \begin{vmatrix} 1 & -1 \\ 0 & 1 \end{vmatrix} \right\}
$$

$$
+ 1 \left\{ 1 \cdot \begin{vmatrix} 2 & -1 \\ 1 & 1 \end{vmatrix} - 0 \cdot \begin{vmatrix} 1 & -1 \\ 0 & 1 \end{vmatrix} - 3 \cdot \begin{vmatrix} 1 & 2 \\ 0 & 1 \end{vmatrix} \right\}
$$

$$
= 2\{3(-4) + 1(3)\} - 1\{-1 + 3(-1) + 1\} + 1\{1(3) - 3(1)\}
$$

$$
= -18 + 3 = -15.
$$

You should verify that the same result is obtained by "expansions" other than the one set out here in detail.

Expanding completely the determinant of a 3×3 matrix $A = [a_{ij}]$ by any row or column gives (verify):

$$
\det A = a_{11}a_{22}a_{33} + a_{21}a_{32}a_{13} + a_{31}a_{12}a_{23}
$$

$$
- a_{31}a_{22}a_{13} - a_{21}a_{12}a_{33} - a_{11}a_{32}a_{23}.
$$

Note that each term of this expansion is a product of elements of the matrix, one element from each row and column. Let us write each such product with the column indices in natural order, so that any term will be of the following type:

$$
a_{i_1 1} \cdot a_{i_2 2} \cdot a_{i_3 3}.
$$

If we take for i_1, i_2, i_3 all possible permutations of 1, 2, 3 we obtain all the terms of the expansion. The sign of any term is determined by the number of *transpositions* required to change the sequence i_1, i_2, i_3 into

1, 2, 3—plus if this number is even, minus if it is odd. For example, in $a_{21}a_{32}a_{13}$, we can transform 2, 3, 1 into 1, 2, 3 as follows: 2, 3, 1 $\rightarrow$ 2, 1, 3 $\rightarrow$ 1, 2, 3. Thus, the number of transpositions is *two* and the term $a_{21}a_{32}a_{13}$ has a plus sign. For the term $a_{31}a_{22}a_{13}$, we have 3, 2, 1 $\rightarrow$ 3, 1, 2 $\rightarrow$ 1, 3, 2 $\rightarrow$ 1, 2, 3. Since the number of transpositions is odd, this term is prefixed with a minus sign. Different sets of transpositions effect the same ultimate transformation. For example, we may take the following route: 2, 3, 1 $\rightarrow$ 3, 2, 1 $\rightarrow$ 3, 1, 2 $\rightarrow$ 1, 3, 2 $\rightarrow$ 1, 2, 3. Here the number of transpositions is *four*, rather than the *two* above. It can be shown that the *parity* (even or odd) will always be unchanged.

Furthermore it can be shown that the same sign will be determined for each term if the roles of the row and column indices are interchanged in this rule. It is clear from this that $|A| = |A^t|$.

We have here a result which holds for all n, not merely for $n = 3$.

If

$$A = [a_{ij}]$$

is an $n \times n$ matrix, then

$$\det A = \sum (-1)^m a_{i_1 1} \cdot a_{i_2 2} \cdots a_{i_n n},$$

where m is the number of transpositions required to transform i_1, $i_2, \ldots, i_n$ into 1, 2, $\ldots$, n, and the summation is extended over all permutations $i_1, i_2, \ldots, i_n$ of 1, 2, $\ldots$, n. The preceding sentence might have been chosen as the definition of $\det A$ in lieu of the definition given at the beginning of this appendix.

The determinant of a matrix can be thought of in terms of the row (or column) vectors of the matrix. If

$$A = [a_{ij}] = [\alpha_1 \alpha_2, \ldots, \alpha_n],$$

then

$$\det A = \Delta(\alpha_1, \alpha_2, \ldots, \alpha_n),$$

where Δ can be shown to have the following properties:

(i) $\Delta(\alpha_1, \ldots, k \cdot \alpha_j, \ldots, \alpha_n) = k\Delta(\alpha_1, \ldots, \alpha_j, \ldots, \alpha_n).$

(ii) $\Delta(\alpha_1, \ldots, \xi + \eta, \ldots, \alpha_n) = \Delta(\alpha_1, \ldots, \xi, \ldots, \alpha_n)$
$$+ \Delta(\alpha_1, \ldots, \eta, \ldots, \alpha_n).$$

(iii) $\Delta(\alpha_1, \ldots, \xi, \ldots, \eta, \ldots, \alpha_n) = -\Delta(\alpha_1, \ldots, \eta, \ldots, \xi, \ldots, \alpha_n).$

(iv) $\Delta(\epsilon_1, \epsilon_2, \ldots, \epsilon_n) = 1.$

The properties (i) through (iv) follow easily from the definition of a determinant. Moreover, it can be shown that these four properties characterize the determinant; i.e., a function of the column vectors of a matrix is the determinant function if it satisfies (i) through (iv).

Properties (i) through (iv) also hold for the determinant of a matrix if the vectors are the row, rather than the column, vectors of the matrix.

Several important theorems follow from Properties (i) through (iv).

(1) $\det (AB) = (\det A)(\det B)$.

(For a simple proof see S. N. Afriat, "On the definition of the determinant as a multilinear antisymmetric function," *Publicationes Mathematicae Debrecen* **5** (1957), pp. 38–39.)

(2) If A is an $n \times n$ matrix, (rank $A < n$) $\Leftrightarrow$ (det $A = 0$).

(3) $\sum_{j=1}^{n} a_{ij}A_{kj} = 0$ if $i \neq k$; i.e., the inner product of the elements of a row and the cofactors of a *different* row is zero. Hence,

$$\sum_{j=1}^{n} a_{ij}A_{kj} = (\det A) \cdot \delta_{ik},$$

where δ_{ik} is the Kronecker delta.

Similarly,

$$\sum_{i=1}^{n} a_{ij}A_{ik} = (\det A) \cdot \delta_{jk}.$$

(4) The value of $|A|$ is unchanged if α_i is replaced by $\alpha_i + k \cdot \alpha_j$.

The labor of computing the value of a determinant may be lessened by judicious use of (4). In the example above, for instance, replacing α_1 by $\alpha_1 + 2\alpha_4$ and α_2 by $\alpha_2 + \alpha_4$, then expanding by the fourth column, we have

$$\begin{vmatrix} 2 & 1 & 0 & -1 \\ 1 & 0 & -3 & 1 \\ 1 & 2 & -1 & 2 \\ 0 & 1 & 1 & -1 \end{vmatrix} = \begin{vmatrix} 0 & 0 & 0 & -1 \\ 3 & 1 & -3 & 1 \\ 5 & 4 & -1 & 2 \\ -2 & 0 & 1 & -1 \end{vmatrix} = -(-1) \cdot \begin{vmatrix} 3 & 1 & -3 \\ 5 & 4 & -1 \\ -2 & 0 & 1 \end{vmatrix} ;$$

then replacing α_1 by $\alpha_1 + 2\alpha_3$ in this third-order determinant, and expanding by the third row, gives

$$D = \begin{vmatrix} -3 & 1 & -3 \\ 3 & 4 & -1 \\ 0 & 0 & 1 \end{vmatrix} = 1 \cdot \begin{vmatrix} -3 & 1 \\ 3 & 4 \end{vmatrix} = -12 - 3 = -15.$$

Most of the properties of determinants mentioned in this appendix do not depend upon the elements of the matrix being complex numbers; they do not even have to be elements of a field. The existence of a multiplicative inverse for each nonzero element is not essential.

For a fuller discussion of determinants see the appropriate chapters of books on linear algebra listed in Section B of the Bibliography or one of the following:

A. C. AITKEN, *Determinants and Matrices*.   New York: Interscience (1954).

G. KOWALEWSKI, *Einführung in die Determinantentheorie*, 3rd ed. New York: Chelsea (1948).

Supplementary Problems and Suggestions for Projects

---

1. (a) Let $[a_{ij}]$ be a 4×4 matrix whose entries are complex numbers, and let $[A_{ij}]$ be its adjoint. Show that if $a_{ii} = 0$, $i = 1, 2, 3, 4$, and if three of the four elements $A_{11}, A_{22}, A_{33}, A_{44}$ are zero, then the fourth A_{ii} is also zero.

(b) Hence, or otherwise, establish the following result. Given two tetrahedra, $ABCD$ and $A'B'C'D'$, with the first inscribed in the second (i.e., A lies in plane $B'C'D'$, and similarly for B, for C, and for D); moreover, let A' lie in plane BCD, B' in plane CDA, and C' in plane DAB. Then D' lies in plane ABC.

Two such mutually inscribed tetrahedra are known as *Möbius tetrads* (see Baker, *An Introduction to Plane Geometry*).

2. Under "inversion in the circle with center O and radius r," any point P of the plane of the circle is transformed into the point P' on the line OP such that $OP \cdot OP' = r^{2}$.

(a) Is this a collineation of the plane? Is it a one-to-one transformation of the extended plane onto itself? Find equations for the transformation.

(b) Show that straight lines through O are carried into themselves; other straight lines into circles through O, and vice versa; circles not through O into circles (see Graustein, Bibliography; also F. Morley and F. V. Morley, *Inversive Geometry*, Chelsea).

3. Represent circles in two dimensions by points in three dimensions as follows. The circle with equation

$$a(x^2 + y^2) + bx + cy + d = 0 \tag{1}$$

is represented by (a, b, c, d), which may be thought of as homogeneous coordinates of a point in three dimensions.

(a) Show that point circles are represented by points on the paraboloid of revolution,

$$b^2 + c^2 - 4ad = 0, \tag{2}$$

and that every point on (2) corresponds to a point circle.

(b) Show that two circles are orthogonal if and only if the points representing them are conjugate with respect to the paraboloid with equation (2).

(c) Show that a point circle, P, is orthogonal to a given circle if and only if P lies on the circle. Hence, show that a point A on the paraboloid (2) is conjugate to another point B if and only if the line AB is tangent to the paraboloid. Hence, show that the points of a plane tangent to the paraboloid at A represent the circles passing through the point (circle) which is represented by A.

(d) Show that the circles of a coaxal system $(k_1 \mathcal{C}_1 + k_2 \mathcal{C}_2 = 0)$ are represented by the points of a line in three dimensions.

(e) Show that if l, m are two lines conjugate with respect to the paraboloid (2), then each circle of the coaxal system represented by l is orthogonal to each circle of the coaxal system represented by m.

4. A proof of Ceva's theorem and its converse. Let

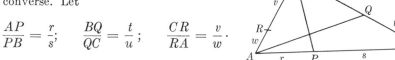

$$\frac{AP}{PB} = \frac{r}{s}; \qquad \frac{BQ}{QC} = \frac{t}{u}; \qquad \frac{CR}{RA} = \frac{v}{w}.$$

At A, B, C place masses s, r, tr/u, respectively. Then P is the centroid of $\{A, B\}$, and Q is the centroid of $\{B, C\}$. Hence, the centroid of $\{A, B, C\}$ lies on CP and also on AQ; i.e., O is the centroid of $\{A, B, C\}$. Now, BR passes through $O \Leftrightarrow R$ is the centroid of

$$\{C, A\} \Leftrightarrow \frac{tr}{u} \cdot v = sw \Leftrightarrow \frac{r}{s} \cdot \frac{t}{u} \cdot \frac{v}{w} = 1. \quad \square$$

Use this "method of masses" to solve Problem 21 of Section 1–1 (see "barycentric coordinates" in Graustein, Bibliography).

5. Let T be a collineation of line l. If P is a point of l, what is $\lim_{n \to \infty} T^n(P)$? Answer the question

(a) geometrically, by considering T as a perspectivity from l onto l' followed by a perspectivity from l' onto l; and

(b) algebraically, by considering T as determined, relative to a coordinate frame on l, by a 2×2 matrix. Use the method of Section 8–6 to obtain an expression for T^n.

6. Let G be the group of transformations which map proper Pythagorean triplets onto proper Pythagorean triplets and have determinant ± 1.

Theorem 1. G acts transitively on the proper Pythagorean triplets. Every triplet can be mapped onto any other by a transformation belonging to G.

Theorem 2. G is isomorphic to the group of all 2×2 matrices with integral coefficients and determinant ± 1. (J. Mariani, *Amer. Math. Monthly*, Feb. 1962.)

7. A field $\mathfrak{F}$ is said to be *orderable* if there is a subset P of $\mathfrak{F}$ with the following three properties:

(1) P does not contain the additive identity, z, of $\mathfrak{F}$;

(2) $x \in \mathfrak{F}$ and $x \neq z \Rightarrow x \in P$ or $x' \in P$;

(3) $x \in P$ and $y \in P \Rightarrow x + y \in P$ and $xy \in P$.

Show that the following set of three properties is equivalent to the above-mentioned set:

(1') P is not empty and $P \neq \mathfrak{F} - \{z\}$;

(2') $ab \in P \Rightarrow a \in P$ and $b \in P$, or $a \notin P$ and $b \notin P$;

(3') $a + b \in P \Rightarrow a \in P$ or $b \in P$.

8. Let P, Q be two points in the plane of a nonsingular conic $\mathcal{C}$. Prove that the locus of points X such that XP, XQ are conjugate lines with respect to $\mathcal{C}$ is a conic $\mathcal{C}'$, and that PQ has the same pole with respect to $\mathcal{C}'$ as with respect to $\mathcal{C}$ ($\mathcal{C}'$ is called the *director conic* of P, Q with respect to $\mathcal{C}$). What happens if P, Q are I, J? (See Baker, Bibliography.)

9. *The Cayley-Hamilton Theorem.* If matrix M has characteristic equation

$$a_0 k^n + a_1 k^{n-1} + \cdots + a_{n-1} k + a_n = 0,$$

then

$$a_0 M^n + a_1 M^{n-1} + \cdots + a_{n-1} M + a_n I = 0;$$

that is, "a matrix satisfies its own characteristic equation." See any of the books in part B of the Bibliography.

10. In Section 1–3 we referred to Poncelet's theorem on polygons inscribed in one conic and circumscribed about another. In Fig. 1.5 let P have nonhomogeneous coordinate x as a point of the one-dimensional space E_1. Show that the coordinate y of Q is a root of a quadratic equation whose coefficients depend upon x. Argue that this equation is symmetric in x and y. Show, further, that if z is the coordinate of R, then z is a root of a quadratic equation whose coefficients are quadratic expressions in x; and that this equation is symmetric in x and z. We have here examples of *two-to-two algebraic correspondences* (see Todd, Bibliography).

11. *A Theorem of Monge.* Given three circles, consider the points of intersection of pairs of tangents to pairs of the circles. The three pairs of external tangents intersect in collinear points; likewise, each pair of external tangents and two pairs of internal tangents intersect in collinear points. Alternatively phrased, the six centers of similitude of pairs of three circles are the vertices of a complete quadrilateral, whose diagonals meet in the centers of the circles.

Obtain other results by projection and by dualization.

12. Symmetric matrices are usually of interest only in the real domain; in the complex domain the analogous matrices are called *Hermitian:* a square matrix $H = [h_{ij}]$ is Hermitian if $h_{ij} = \bar{h}_{ji}$, where $\bar{h}_{ji}$ is the conjugate of h_{ji}.

Let $A = [a_{ij}]$ and $A^* = [\bar{a}_{ji}]$, that is, A^* is the "conjugate transpose of A." Then H is Hermitian $\Leftrightarrow H = H^*$.

Show that Theorem 10–32 is true for Hermitian, as well as for real symmetric, matrices.

Use the relationship between symmetric and Hermitian matrices as a clue to generalize (real) orthogonal matrices to what are called *unitary matrices* in the complex domain.

State and prove an analogue in the complex domain of Theorem 10–33.

For a discussion of unitary and Hermitian matrices see Schwerdtfeger (Bibliography).

Bibliography

A. Geometry

ARTIN, E., *Geometric Algebra.* Interscience (1957). Emphasizes the geometric interpretations of the properties of the algebraic systems through which coordinates can be defined.

BAER, R., *Linear Algebra and Projective Geometry.* Academic Press (1952). A sophisticated treatise.

BAKER, H. F., *Principles of Geometry*, 6 vols. Cambridge Univ. Press (1925–1934). A classic compendium.

———, *An Introduction to Plane Geometry.* Cambridge Univ. Press (1943).

BLUMENTHAL, L. M., *A Modern View of Geometry.* W. H. Freeman and Co. (1961). Similar to Artin, but more elementary.

BUSEMANN, H. and P. J. KELLY, *Projective Geometry and Projective Metrics.* Academic Press (1953).

COXETER, H. S. M., *Introduction to Geometry.* Wiley (1961). A remarkably complete treatment, in one volume, of many aspects of geometry.

———, *The Real Projective Plane*, 2nd ed. Cambridge Univ. Press (1955).

GRAUSTEIN, W. C., *Introduction to Higher Geometry.* Macmillan (1930). An excellent simple exposition.

HODGE, W. V. D. and D. PEDOE, *Methods of Algebraic Geometry*, 3 vols. Cambridge Univ. Press (1954).

SEIDENBERG, A., *Lectures in Projective Geometry.* D. van Nostrand (1962). A brief, elegant, clear introduction.

SEMPLE, J. G. and G. T. KNEEBONE, *Algebraic Projective Geometry.* Oxford Univ. Press (1952).

———, and L. ROTH, *Introduction to Algebraic Geometry.* Oxford Univ. Press (1949).

TODD, J. A., *Projective and Analytical Geometry.* Pitman and Sons (1947).

VEBLEN, O. and J. W. YOUNG, *Projective Geometry*, 2 vols. Ginn and Co. (1910 and 1918). Careful axiomatic introduction.

VAN DER WAERDEN, B. L., *Einführung in die algebraische Geometrie.* Springer (1939).

WALKER, R. J., *Algebraic Curves.* Princeton Univ. Press (1950).

WOODS, F. S., *Higher Geometry: An Introduction to Advanced Methods in Analytic Geometry.* Dover (1961). First published in 1922, this book is still a good introduction.

B. Linear Algebra, Matrices, Vector Spaces

FINKKEINER, D. T., *Introduction to Matrices and Linear Transformations.* W. H. Freeman and Co. (1960).

HALMOS, P. R., *Finite-Dimensional Vector Spaces*, 2nd ed. D. van Nostrand (1958). A masterful exposition.

HOFFMAN, K. and R. KUNZE, *Linear Algebra.* Prentice-Hall (1961).

HOHN, F. E., *Elementary Matrix Algebra.* Macmillan (1958).

MACDUFFEE, C. C., *Vectors and Matrices.* M. A. A. (1933). A simple introduction.

——, *The Theory of Matrices.* Chelsea (1946).

MIRSKY, L., *An Introduction to Linear Algebra.* Oxford Univ. Press (1955).

MURDOCH, D. C., *Linear Algebra for Undergraduates.* Wiley (1957).

SCHREIER, O. and E. SPERNER, *Introduction to Modern Algebra and Matrix Theory.* Chelsea (1951).

SCHWERDTFEGER, H., *Introduction to Linear Algebra and the Theory of Matrices.* Noordhoff (1950).

SMIRNOV, V. I., *Linear Algebra and Group Theory.* McGraw-Hill (1961).

STOLL, R. R., *Linear Algebra and Matrix Theory.* McGraw-Hill (1952).

THRALL, R. M. and L. TORNHEIM, *Vector Spaces and Matrices.* Wiley (1957).

TURNBULL, H. W. and A. C. AITKEN, *An Introduction to the Theory of Canonical Matrices.* Blackie (1952); republished by Dover (1961).

C. ABSTRACT ALGEBRA

BIRKHOFF, G. and S. MACLANE, *A Survey of Modern Algebra*, Rev. ed. Macmillan (1953). A modern classic.

DICKSON, L. E., *Modern Algebraic Theories.* Sanborn (1926).

JACOBSON, N., *Lectures in Abstract Algebra*, 2 vols. D. van Nostrand (1951, 1953).

JOHNSON, R. E., *First Course in Abstract Algebra.* Prentice-Hall (1953).

KELLEY, J. L., *Introduction to Modern Algebra.* D. van Nostrand (1960). The text for the Continental Classroom course.

MCCOY, N. H., *Introduction to Modern Algebra.* Allyn and Bacon (1960).

SAWYER, W. W., *A Concrete Approach to Abstract Algebra.* W. H. Freeman and Co. (1959).

VAN DER WAERDEN, B. L., *Modern Algebra*, 2 vols. 2nd rev. ed. Ungar (1949, 1950).

D. INVARIANTS

GRACE, J. H. and A. YOUNG, *The Algebra of Invariants.* Cambridge Univ. Press (1903).

TURNBULL, H. W., *The Theory of Determinants, Matrices, and Invariants*, 3rd ed. Dover (1960).

Index